STORIES OF MODERN AMERICA

STORIES

OF

MODERN

AMERICA

EDITED BY HERBERT GOLD

AND

DAVID L. STEVENSON

WESTERN RESERVE UNIVERSITY

ALTERNATE EDITION

ST MARTIN'S PRESS · NEW YORK

Contents

Introduction

The twenty-two short stories and the short novel in this collection are intensely alive in their concern with crucial issues, personal and social, of contemporary America. Beyond this, the ability of each writer to heighten our perceptions of an experience is a result of his artistic skill. The wide range of techniques and styles in these stories guided our selection.

Preceding each story is an introductory note in which we place each writer in his literary milieu, assess him as an artist, and relate the story in this collection to the main body of his work. In the brief analysis that follows each story, we give our sense of what is significant in it; the questions may provide a basis for discussion of both artistry and content.

Though we expect our comments to interest the reader, they are not intended to be definitive. The primary value of a collection such as this arises from the reader's own attempt to appraise an author's view of an experience, the particulars of his art, and his method of presentation. Taste and judgment develop in a reader, without the goading of an esthetic theory, when he discovers the pleasures to be derived from his own mind in action. For such a reader no set of critical hypothesis and no amount of literary information can substitute for the rewards of his own efforts.

This alternate edition of *Stories of Modern America* retains all the stories of the original hardcover edition; we omit only the three essays on the short story.

David L. Stevenson

Herbert Gold

1·

GROWING UP

"Boy in the Summer Sun," *by Mark Schorer*

"The Heart of the Artichoke," *by Herbert Gold*

"Winter Night," *by Kay Boyle*

Boy in the Summer Sun

by MARK SCHORER

Mark Schorer (1908-   ) is Professor of English at the University of California and a distinguished contemporary man of letters. Representative of his work as scholar and critic are *William Blake; The Politics of Vision* (1946) and his recently completed biography of Sinclair Lewis. His essay "Technique as Discovery" (*Hudson Review*, Spring 1948), is a major statement concerning the relationship of content to form in fiction. His two most recent novels, *The Hermit Place* (1941) and *The Wars of Love* (1953), are tense, psychological studies of men and women in love. *The State of Mind* (1947), is a collection of thirty-two of his short stories, astringent glimpses into moments of emotional crisis.

The story "Boy in the Summer Sun" is early work of Mr. Schorer's, and lacks the harsher ironies of his more recent fiction. It is a straightforward narrative of a late adolescent love affair which has moved excitingly and carelessly through midwestern summer days, and which ushers a young man and a young woman into sudden, adult knowledge of the expendable nature of early love.

Unalloyed, summer had lingered miraculously into late September without a suggestion that autumn was at hand. Leaves and grass were green still, smoke had not yet come into the air, and the lake was calm, almost sapphire blue. Mid-mornings were hot, like mornings in July. So they walked where the woods were thickest, where the air was always slightly damp and the cool of night never quite gone. They did not speak much but went silently along the path, almost shoulder to shoulder, their hands touching, or their arms, as they moved. Now and then the girl spoke, quietly, briefly pointed out a bird, a flower, once a green

Boy In the Summer Sun. Reprinted from *The State of Mind* (Houghton Mifflin Co.), by Mark Schorer. First printed in *Story Magazine*, 1937. Copyright 1937, by Mark Schorer. Reprinted with permission of Mark Schorer and Houghton Mifflin Co.

snake gliding through the grass, and the boy answered with a nod or a monosyllable, his face touched with abstraction and a slight worry. After they came to a place in the wood where they stretched out now with their arms about each other lightly as if the place and this gesture were habitual, they did not speak at all until at last the girl, Rachel, asked suddenly, 'Why are you so quiet? Is it Max? Are you angry because he's coming, Will?'

The boy started and looked into her face. 'Angry? No, I'm not angry . . . I was just thinking about that lousy job. When I'm out here it's hard to believe that a job like that can be waiting for me when I get back.'

The girl looked away into the depth of the wood. 'Is it, Will?' she asked. 'Or is it just that in college we never learn that for most people life finally comes down to work?'

'Maybe that's it.'

'Or is it foul, Will? Is it worse than most jobs in the city, in summer?'

'Maybe not. But it's still foul.'

They were quiet again, and it seemed a long time later, to him, when Rachel said, 'Anyway, I'm glad it isn't Max.'

His arms tightened around her shoulders. Then he sat up, his eyes narrowed in the shade, and he asked, 'Why should it be?'

She said, 'It shouldn't.'

He lay down beside her again. He stared up into the lacework of green leaves arched above them, and at the rare patches of blue sky that the leaves did not cover. Why should it be Max? Or why should she think it might be?

He had been awakened that morning by the ringing telephone, and lay sleepily in bed listening to Rachel's voice talking to someone in a way that did disturb him vaguely then, although now it seemed only mildly irritating that this week-end should be intruded upon. 'But darling!' her voice had cried over the telephone. 'What are you doing here? Come over at once! Mind? Of course not! We'll love it! In two hours? Good!'

When he came to breakfast, she smiled brightly and cried, 'Guess who's coming, Will! Max Garey! He got bored and started out early this morning, and just now called from the village. Isn't it grand? Mother's so fond of him—she'll take care of him.'

'Does your mother know him? I didn't know she did.'

'Oh, yes! I must have told you.'

'No, you didn't,' he said. And now he wondered why she had not told him.

Then Mrs. Harley came out on the porch. 'Good morning, Will,' she said brightly as she patted her white hair. 'Isn't it *nice* that Mr. Garey can come! I'm so fond of Mr. Garey!'

'Yes, isn't it?' Will said into his coffee, and looked across the table into Rachel's eyes, which, shining with pleasure, were heedless of the question in his.

'Did you have any work with Mr. Garey, Will? Rachel thought him such a splendid teacher.'

'No, I didn't,' Will said. 'His classes were always filled with girls.'

Rachel looked at him quickly. 'Now you're being unfair, Will. Everybody thinks he's a good teacher.'

'I'm sorry,' he said, and felt suddenly lonely in the bright morning with Rachel only across the table from him.

He was feeling that loneliness again now. 'Maybe it is more than the job,' he said. 'Everything's different since June. I don't know why.'

'What do you mean, Will?'

'Just a feeling that everything's breaking up.'

They were quiet then until Rachel said, 'I know. I'm different, too. Something's changed in me. There's something sad, some ache . . .'

Will knew that something had changed in her. She was older than she had been in June. There was something about her now that bewildered him, the feeling that she lived without him, an aloofness and self-sufficiency which was new. She was like a woman, sometimes, putting up with a boy. He had felt it almost every week-end, and this and the more general sadness of the summer had darkened otherwise bright hours. Yet her kisses, her sweet arms around him, her yielding body, all denied his feeling. With him, there still came from her throat a little moan of pain and passion which he knew no one else had ever heard. And yet, now in the deep cool wood as she lay in his arms, he felt that she had forgotten him beside her.

She spoke at last as with an effort, as if recalling herself from a dream. 'You know, Will, after you left college, in that week I stayed on, I saw Max rather often. Then mother met him. She invited him to come up. He was here earlier in the summer. Didn't I tell you?'

'No,' he said, his throat contracting. 'You must have forgotten.'

His sadness knotted in his throat intensely, and he remembered then very clearly, almost as if she were saying it again now, something she had said before he left her in June. 'Sometimes I wonder if this can last. We know each other as I think people almost never do. Now it begins to seem a little unreal, perhaps because it's been too lovely, part of this unreal life we're leaving. I wonder if that sometimes happens, Will.'

Then he had laughed; but now, as he remembered, his arms tightened around her suddenly, as if from fright, and he leaned down and kissed her. Her lips were quiet, without response. He saw that her eyes were fixed on some remote object in the arch of trees or beyond, some dream, something far from him. He stood up and moved away. 'Let's go back,' he said, and without waiting for her started quickly up the path, toward the house.

All the afternoon they lay on the raft, Rachel between them. Max talked, his voice reflective and lazy, mixing with the sun of that afternoon and the endless laziness in the sounds that insects made in the woods and in the long grass along the shore, his voice spinning itself out, pausing now and then to listen to itself, and going on again, with Rachel lying quiet between them, her eyes closed and the oil gleaming on her brown skin. Will's head was turned toward her, his eyes wandering back and forth from her parted lips and her gleaming lashes to the swell of her breasts under her white swimming suit, to her long browned legs and her crossed feet at the end of the raft.

All the time Max's voice went on, the lazy, professor's voice. Will could tell as he heard it that it was a voice that always talked and that always had listeners, and yet, now, it did not irritate him. He was almost content to lie in the sun with the sensation of burning on his skin, the soft warm glow of skin absorbing bright sun enough in the afternoon to allay for the moment the morning's inarticulate fears, even though it was Max who was lying stretched out beyond Rachel, who was talking, pausing, talking, sometimes falling silent and no word coming from Rachel or himself, and then starting up again, the voice spinning itself out softly in the afternoon sun, with all the laziness of the afternoon in his slow words.

'. . . and so in Donne the central factor is death . . . death, of course . . . he, more than any of the poets, built what he wrote upon what may be called a metaphysic of death . . . death as the great leveler on the one hand, the great destroyer of everything, beauty, love . . . and death as the figure at the gate of Heaven . . . these two, this one . . . the central factor, always present . . .'

His voice was slow, modulated, a little affected, quite soft, and in it, Will knew as he looked at Rachel's face, there was some magic of wisdom and experience that enthralled her.

Rachel's voice began, slow and soft as if infected by Max's voice, as warm as the sun, and speaking lines that Max first spoke to her, perhaps—only perhaps—in the classroom:

'When I died last, and, Dear, I die
    As often as from thee I go,
    Though it be but an hour ago,
And Lovers hours be full eternity,
    I can remember yet, that I
    Something did say, and something did bestow. . . .'

Max laughed. 'But darling,' he said, 'that's still another kind of death, not so serious.'

Rachel said nothing. And the sun wove around them its bright and golden web, and the whole world then as they lay there had slipped away and left the three of them stranded together in an unreality of sunlight on burning skin and closed eyelids, and nothing more. And Will, too, felt out of the world of fact, was empty of feeling, as if pure sensation had replaced it. And only slowly did a faint jangling come into his mind, the jangle of Max's word *darling*, like something shaken in a metal box, some harsh sound, or a feeling perhaps, shaking him abruptly from the web. He stirred. He turned. And in turning the web was broken, and he was free of it again, his hand plunged in the cold blue water of the lake and left to dangle there, his eyes turned from Rachel and Max for the moment but seeing nothing in the indeterminable depths of the blue water that gently lapped his hand.

'Not nearly so serious,' Max said. 'Only a metaphor, a way of speaking . . .'

Will turned toward them again and he saw in Rachel's face how serious it was, for she looked suddenly ill for all the glow of her skin, her face turned away from him and her lips fallen apart, and every line in her face and body taut suddenly, yearning, aching suddenly with sharp longing, sharp pain, she quite sick for love. Will's hands closed at his sides and opened again, turned empty to the sun.

'Poetry is full of such conventions, formalized short cuts to express familiar sentiments,' Max was saying. 'In Donne, of course, there's enough fire, usually, to vitalize them, but in others . . . mere metaphors . . .'

Something in Will's mind snapped, then seemed to shout, *Who cares? For God's sake, who cares?* He was enraged beyond endurance by the man's pompous classroom manner, his easy presence, his way of excluding Will, as if he were alone with Rachel and no one else existed. He hated him, and the very presence of Rachel there made his throat ache with something like the pressure of tears coming. The sun had lost its spell. The buzz of insects on the shore seemed for a moment unbearably loud, and the sun no longer warm, but hot, searing, parching his throat and mouth, blinding him. For now he hated Max, and he knew as he remembered Rachel's voice speaking those lines, that she was lost to him, that he had nothing more for her, that Max had all. And there Max lay, as if he belonged there, had every right to be there, talking and priding himself in his talk, delighting to hear his own words, lecturing as though he were in the classroom and Rachel in the front row looking up at him with wide eyes, lecturing as though Rachel and he were alone in the room and Will did not exist.

Will's eyes clouded in anger as he stared down into the water disturbed by his hand. He tried not to hear what their low voices said, and only when they were silent did he turn again suddenly on the raft to see how their bodies had moved together, so that their legs touched, and Max's hand lay quite near Rachel's hair. He stood abruptly, stirring the raft in the water, and then dived deep, swam quickly out and away from them, his arms beating the water in his anger, in a frantic effort to forget the hurt which came from Rachel's willing reception of the man's intolerable arrogance.

He struck out into the lake. The water was cold on his skin, and as he swam his anger cooled. But when his anger was gone, he felt sad and futile again, swam more slowly, felt helpless and wounded, felt almost weak in the water, so that he grew angry with himself instead and wished that he could hold that other anger. When he turned back and swam slowly toward the shore, only the hurt remained, and he did not go to the raft. There Max's words would still be spinning themselves out in the sunlight, catching Rachel's mind in their spell, catching her heart firmly and her whole mind and life, and holding them there, as if the words were really magic.

He walked up the beach and stretched out on the sand. He lay on his back and looked up into the blue sky, and as he lay there he felt suddenly that this was the last time in his life that he would be doing quite this. All summer he had been coming from the sweltering, grimy city, and in seeing Rachel in the country, in living in her mother's friendly house, in swimming and dancing and drinking and finding cool spots in the woods where the moss was thick and only the trees and birds made sound—in all of this it had seemed that nothing had changed or was ending. And this in spite of the fact that when they parted in June, when they walked for the last time along familiar walks between familiar buildings, they had vaguely felt that an end had come to a period, that a new life was waiting for both of them, and that (Rachel felt) somehow they were therefore ending for one another. But then Max was nothing to him, only a professor whom she liked; so for him nothing really ended.

Now the golden day was unbearable. He turned over on his stomach and put his face in his arms. Almost at once he could feel the sun burning his neck, his back. But it alleviated nothing. There was the dull ache in his chest and throat, the constant feeling that at any moment he would cry out like a child in sobs. It was a pressure in his body that he could not put into thoughts, only the feeling that something was ending, inevitably ending. He thought of his past and it was all gold, all brightness and gold, all magic landscape, all love, all an idyl, all a bright day, and all ending.

He thought he must cry. All his youth was gathered into a knot of pain that choked him, that, dull and heavy, pressed against his heart. He thought of going back to the city, to the hot office, to stupid work sweating over accounts, of the years he had ahead of him in which to slave there. And he knew as he lay in the sand, really *knew* for the first time, that all of that was no mere interlude.

He felt a touch on his shoulder, turned, and looked up. It was Rachel, brown in the sun, saying, 'Darling, don't be rude.'

He sat up. 'Am I being rude?'

'Does he bore you?'

'Yes. I don't like him much.'

'Well, I'm sorry he came, Will, but I couldn't help it. Come back and try to bear him. He's not bad, you know.'

'No?' Will asked as he got up.

She looked at him swiftly, then smiled. 'Don't be silly, darling.'

'No, *darling*.'

'Good.'

Then they went up the shore, back to the raft where Max still lay in the lessening glare of the sun.

Then finally he could put up with him no longer. The whole thing, suddenly, was impossible, too much for him. He sat at the table for a minute more and fought against the impulse to leave. But Mrs. Harley, cooing in a voice that almost made him ill ('But how *interesting*, Mr. Garey. *Do* go on! Do you *really* believe that?') and Max, toying with his fork and smiling with what Will supposed was great 'charm' before continuing his monologue, decided him. He looked quickly at Rachel. She sat at the end of the table, opposite her mother. She looked very cool in a white dress, brown throat and arms cool and lovely, her lips slightly parted, her eyes fixed—lost to him.

Then he rose quickly to his feet. 'Excuse me, please,' he said, and went to the porch, and then outside, down the steps, stumbled down toward the shore under the pines. He sat down in the grass. His fingers fumbled for a cigarette and a match in his pocket. Then he stared out at the water and the new moon hanging close over the opposite shore. In the reeds the frogs sang. From above came the ring of silver on china. He bit hard into his lower lip when he knew suddenly that the salt he tasted was of tears.

Then everything broke, collapsed in him like a sail when the wind dies. He wept as he had not wept since he was a small boy; and there, for a time in the night, he felt that he was a small boy still, alone in the dark and empty night. He lay on the grass and sobbed. And there was a violence in his weeping as of a body tortured. He smothered the sound in the grass.

But he could not smother the pain in his chest. It was like a live thing in his heart, heavy and pressing, torturing, not relieved by sobs. It came over him in waves of torment, and now it was no longer anything of the mind, but of the body alone, a physical pressure, wracking and violent, eruptive and convulsive, as if his very life, well-loved, were ending in the torment.

He did not feel Rachel's hand on his shoulder. It was her voice that recalled him: 'Will—darling—please!'

Even then he could not prevent his sobs from coming. It was as if they were something separate from him, separate from his will, as if they had their own life, must come to their own slow end. He felt no shame before her, had no feelings at all, no thoughts, was given over entirely to what seemed wholly a physical act. Then slowly, at last, his shoulders grew quieter. Slowly his breathing quieted. Slowly his eyes dried. And it was over at last. He felt empty, weak, desolate as he turned slowly over on his back to look at her.

The moon was almost in the water. He could see it, touching the opposite shore. The sky was dark, sprinkled with cold stars. These too he saw, blurred and faint, unsteady in the darkness. Beside him knelt Rachel, her white dress a vague lightness, her face above him a blur. She spoke again; 'Darling, what is it, what's *wrong?*'

He swallowed hard but could not speak. He lay on his back and looked at the blur of her face. His hand reached out and seized hers, held it tightly. Then she lay down beside him suddenly, put her arms around him, and her cheek to his mouth. He smelled the familiar perfume of her hair and moved away from her a little. Now he could see the stars more clearly; their light was brighter, harder, they were steadier in the sky, fixed and remote. Then, although Rachel's arms were around him and her face so close that he could feel her warm breath sweet on his face, he was alone, desolate, empty, alone on the shore under the stars. He did not say this then, nor did he even quite feel it, but he knew it, his body, empty and quiet, knew it—the cold loneliness of the stars even on a summer night. He lay still and looked up. Something momentous had happened.

'I felt sick,' he said at last, though Rachel had not spoken again.

She said nothing for a while, then whispered. 'I'm sorry.'

'It's all right now.'

As if startled by the deadly quiet of his voice, she sat up and looked closely into his face. '*Are* you all right now, Will?'

'Yes, it's all right now.' He said it clearly.

'What was it, though?' she asked.

'You know.'

'No.'

'Yes, you do.'

'Not *Max*, Will?'

'What else?'

'Oh, but *darling*——'

'It doesn't matter, Rachel.'

'What do you mean—doesn't matter? Do you think——'

'I know, Rachel. I knew it this morning. But only tonight suddenly at the table, when I saw your face while he was talking —it took that long until I really could believe it. But it doesn't matter now.'

'You think I love him?'

'You do love him.'

Then she did not answer.

'Yesterday I wouldn't have believed that things like this happen. For over a year . . .' He paused. Then, 'Nothing will ever be the same again—love, or anything.'

'Please, Will. Nothing's happened.'

'Everything's happened. Now it's over.'

She looked at him closely. Then she said, 'I've never heard you talk like that. You're different. Your voice—it's . . .'

'What?'

'You're different. Your voice frightens me. It's so quiet and cold and far away, so different—' She spoke jerkily. 'So dead!'

He sat up, leaned back on his elbows. The moon was gone, sunk under the water. The sky was darker, and the stars seemed brighter still, separate, and farther away. Then he lay down again and she beside him. They were both very quiet. Finally she said, 'Do you hate me?'

He turned to her. 'No,' he answered. He watched her face. He saw her eyes sparkling with tears. He said, 'What are you crying for?'

'I can't tell you why, I can't say, I don't know. I'm afraid. I do love you, Will. Only now I'm afraid, because I do love someone else—more. I don't want to. But I do. It frightens me!'

Now she was no longer older than he. She was a girl again, her woman's poise, given her briefly by this new love, taken from her again by that same love because, in the face of it, she was afraid. She was afraid of its swiftness, of what it might hold, of her own heart, turning. Now he felt older than she, felt that he could tell her something. He said, 'I know what it is. It isn't just that we've been in love. We've had such a fine time. I don't know if I can say this, but it's something like this anyway—you weren't just yourself for me, and I wasn't just myself for you. We were both in love with much more than each other. You were all of that life for me, and maybe I was that for you, too. We were that whole life for each other, and we didn't want to lose it, but we couldn't help ourselves, we couldn't keep it any longer.'

She was crying. She put her face on his shoulder and he felt her tears on his neck. Then he put his arms around her and held her close. But he felt no less alone. And he thought then that this aloneness would never entirely leave him again, but that when he got back to the city next day, after he had been there awhile, working in the office, after a week or two or perhaps a whole year, finally anyway, it would have left him somewhat less empty, less deadly calm. Then this day and this summer and all the golden days would have become the dream; and the other life would be real.

'How did your poem go, Rachel? "When I last died, and, dear, I die whenever you go from me. . . . ?"'

'Please—don't,' she said.

He began to stroke her hair. She was quiet now, no longer crying, held close in his arms. He said, 'Maybe it's always like this. Maybe the end of every love is a kind of little death, when you have to put behind more than just the love itself, but all the life, too, in which the love was wrapped. Maybe living is really a lot of little dyings.'

For a moment more they sat together and then she said, 'We must go back. They'll wonder . . .'

'All right,' he said.

Then, clinging together like children still under the stars, helping each other up the slope, they went back to the house, where the lights were and the sounds of voices.

EDITORS' ANALYSIS

"Boy in the Summer Sun" makes no urgent demands that we accept as valid and significant a rich outpouring of the details of American suburbia. As the title suggests, Schorer's story exists in the bright sunlight of its rural setting, its almost leafy atmosphere. The story depends for its effect upon the reader's sense of nostalgia, his own regretful recognition that a passionate but sentimental commitment to love is betrayed by time, by mere growing up. He identifies with the mutual grief of these young people which has brought them to an understanding, at the story's end, that certain kinds of love are evanescent and cannot, by the nature of things, be caught and held.

QUESTIONS

1. Is the country setting necessary to sustain the golden world of young love in "Boy in the Summer Sun"? If one were to change the setting would one lose some of the story's meaning?

2. How can Rachel be so disloyal with so little sense of guilt? And does the story make clear why the boy can be defeated so easily by his rival, why he does not try to fight back?

3. What attitudes in the English Instructor are suggested by the fact that he equates love and love-making with John Donne? Why does he seem more fascinating to the girl because of these attitudes?

4. Does one's reaction to this story depend, in part, upon one's age when reading it? Would it have a stronger impact on one of middle age, or on one in his early twenties?

The Heart of the Artichoke

by HERBERT GOLD

Herbert Gold (1924-   ) is one of the younger American writers who have made their reputations since World War II. He is the author of five novels, studies of men who attempt to discover the nature and the purpose of their lives in our competitive, romance-ridden society. His most recent novels are *The Man Who Was Not With It* (1956), *The Optimist* (1959), and *Therefore Be Bold* (1960). His short stories have reached the diverse audiences of *The New Yorker, Hudson Review, The Atlantic,* and *Playboy.* A collection of them was published in 1960 under the title *Love and Like.* He has also published literary criticism, represented by the essay "The Mystery of Personality in the Novel," in *The Living Novel,* edited by Granville Hicks (1957), and "Fiction of the Sixties" in *The Atlantic,* September, 1960.

"The Heart of the Artichoke" reflects a universal problem in growing up: how to resolve the quarrel between a young boy's ideal of the world he wants to have and the actual world that his father has created for him to exist in.

My father, his horny hands black with sulphur, lit a cigar with a brief, modest, but spectacular one-handed gesture, his thumbnail crr-racking across the blue-headed kitchen match; when he described his first job in America, selling water to the men building the skyscrapers, teetering across the girders for fifteen cents a pail, green flecks fumed and sailed in his yellowish Tartar eyes; he peeled an artichoke with both hands simultaneously, the leaves flying toward his mouth, crossing at the napkin politely tucked at the master juggler's collar, until with a groan that was the trumpet of all satisfaction he attained the heart; he—but he was a man of capabilities, such feats apart.

As my mother said of him before they married, "He's well-off. Lots of personality." Older than the other women of her family, she used the word *well-off* in a primitive sense, to signify a general relationship with the world, not substracting from the term all but its usual financial refrain: "Well-off very, he's a Buick . . ." But she took the word from Aunt Sarah and Aunt Ethel; it's important that the vocabulary derives from economic security, to be extended outward only by an exceptional act of vitality. We, my brothers and I, could never eat enough for her. "Don't aggravate me. Eat, Eat," she would say.

"We already ate," I pointed out.

"But look at your father!"

He was eating. He ate with silent respect for food, a great deal, and not out of gluttony but with appreciation for his own labor in it. He knew the cost. In each spoonful of soup carried with music to his mouth I heard the winds whistling through the branches of the *knaedloch* trees; I saw the farmers' trucks, laden with chopped liver, musing in his crocodile eyes. "Eat," he pronounced at intervals, assuaging his love for us, "eat, eat."

We ate with a hunger in our bellies or in a filial loyalty while his was in his heart. Wearing a sheepskin coat which came as a gift from Mother and Pitkin's with the no-overhead, a silvery-pronged crate hammer arming his back pocket, he climbed into the cab of his truck before dawn on market days, his wife's lips still parted against their single pillow while he checked off a list measured in gross over a breakfast of liver-and-onions with the other fruitmen in Solly's Market Tearoom. Perhaps at the earlier moment of supper, while we heedlessly digested, carloads of artichokes were coming in at the Food Terminal for the Thursday morning auction. He would get the best for Jack's Food & Vegetable: *The Best is the Best Buy.*

"Always," my mother piously breathed after him. She was proud of his slogan. "He made it up himself one day I remember it, he was by the cooler sorting asparagus. Lots of personality, loads," she informed Aunt Ethel and Aunt Sarah. "Eat," she said to me. "The nice ovenbaked potato."

I once asked the address of the poor hungry man in China who would be glad to finish my potato. "I'll send it to him with Mr. Kennedy the mailman," I suggested.

"I need your backtalk like I need my own brother Morton's agaragar oil for his constipation. A whole tablespoon," she said. "I need it." Repenting of my sarcasm, I never believed in the poor hungry man, although I had recently become convinced of China at least in Geography.

My father had the knowledge of things—how to hoist an orange crate in a movement like a dance, how to tell an honest farmer from one who will hide his bad Pascal or Iceberg under bravado and a show of good ones, whom to trust in the fleet meetings of money at a fruit auction; this is already a great deal. Only once was he famously tricked, and by Uncle Morton, a man who installed automatic sprinkling pipes in his lawn ("For show! for the neighbors!" my mother communicated, outraged) but spent his Sundays tightening the faucets and complaining that his daughters filled the bathtub too full. (How clean can you get?)

Well, this brother-in-law, exalted by cupidity in one federally sponsored moment, suggested a partnership in the property in order to eliminate my father's competition at an auction: Should brothers, or almost-brothers, bid each other up like cats and dogs? No, the answer.

Afterwards, the deal secured, my father approached, tendering a hand-rolled cigar fraternally-in-law and saying, "Nu Mort, now about the partnership I think well we should let Henry there in the Republic Building, not that Hank from 105th Street, Henry a reliable man Hazelton Hotels uses him, draw up the papers—"

"Partners! hah!" Villainous Uncle Morton, performing for some secret inner croak of applause, permitted himself laughter at such innocence. "I'm partners me only with my wife"—and they haven't spoken since, nor have his daughters and I, cousins all.

But this was real estate, not food, which was the true sphere of my father's power; besides, such an error brings scope and savor to a legend of paternal infallibilty. He could say, or let my mother say while above the broad cheekbones his eyes glittered like two long plump lima beams on sidewalk display in the sun: "The only time Jake got it but good, it was that time with the Woodward property, his own brother-in-law my brother, they run a house in the Heights and two cars—they need it?—a Buick sure and a Chevie for Yetta and the kids, may his breath turn sour in his old age—"

And his daughters' too. Amen.

As my mother talked my father measured us from under a vast biblical forehead which had sojourned in Kamenetz-Podolsk; it was a forehead that barely escaped the scars of reprisal for a tradesman's life given to a man who needed labor in the open air. He wrestled out this frozen compression, these knotty ravages, at the cost of an overquickening in the work of the store, wielding cases with a plunging violence and mounting trucks like a burly fruitstore tomcat. Overhappiness too is a threat, Zarathustra said. The yellow flecks of his long narrow eyes fumed in contemplation. His sons were strange animals, born in America.

Question-shaped, my belly in advance of my thoughts, I had unnoticed by all but myself become skinny, pimply, shrewd, and poetic. I trained myself to wake at dawn, not for work like my father or to drink formula like my youngest brother, but because of the possibility that Pattie Donahue might feel my presence and stir in response to it; I believed in telepathy, tuning in on no messages because no one sent me any. I searched her face during Miss Baxter's Reading and The Library How To Use It for a sign of complicity (received no answer); I never spoke to her, for reasons of shyness and reasons of magic. She had aquarium eyes, profoundly green, profoundly empty, and a mouth like a two-cent Bull's Eye candy, and pale transparent fingers busy as fins. She powdered her nose in public, no longer picking it; she touched her ears to make sure of their presence on the beach of her head; patiently she plucked the angora from her mittens off the front of her cardigan, with this gesture of pale-boned fingers exploring herself and me. Together only abstractly, we were linked by both imagining atrocious ways to wish her well.

I let her swim again in my memory. She considered the future by judging it with the deliberate active forgetfulness of a fish floating asleep under ice: power through patience. Pattie Donahue wanted more than love, more than strength; she wanted mastery in denial, divinity in refusal of her own blood. Up the ladder to godhood or down to fishliness? That was her one risk in life. Seaweed is good for you! Lots of iodine! She had a repertory of head-tuckings, wiggles, peeps, curtsies, suckings, winks, herself charmed by herself; she was crippled for eternity, condemned to increase by parthenogenesis. She could not laugh with her body because her body could never move to another's, sway as it might under the seas of her ambition. Bemused, pious, she granted herself an adoring hand, fingers straddling to squeeze her sweater at the root of milk and psychology. Recall that princess who could undress before a slave because she did not regard him as a human being? We are all sometimes slaves.

Slavishly I kneeled for her chamois penwiper where it fell behind her desk in Music and Singing.

"Oh thank you," she said.

"Never mind, never mind"—me melting like March ice in a spring pool of timidity and chagrin.

"Oh don't stop me, Daniel Berman. Thank you indeed. My mother says I need practice how to be gracious. Please let me do thank you. Oh thank you, Daniel Berman . . ."

This too is a sort of excess!—and I let her take me under the green grasp of her greedy eyes. The fishy princess pouted, ducked, abstractly reached; I worshiped this body shivering and glistening under bracelets like scale. I saw her as age. Age during that time signifies secret power, secret passion, and the death which follows age is known only as the death which follows love. Girls, born queens, are always older than boys, ten-thousand-eyed drones, living for love, empty-headed, precariously housebroken. "Oh thank you really," said Princess Pattie Donahue, her royal sardine, queen of the hive.

She was gracious on me.

One day, the talk of the Horace Greeley Junior High playground, a pride for events beyond me took her; she wore a shiny black brassiere which hung in lank splendor beneath the faintly distended yarn of her sweater and the morning's accretion of pink angora. She plucked, she pinched; in my poems I never found a rhyme for Donahue. Desire for a girl with nipples like tapioca spots! She went out, it was alleged, with high-school seniors.

It was at this era of sudden sweat and public rancor that the issue of working in the store afternoons or at least Saturdays became prominent. "To help out," my father said.

"To learn the value of a dollar," my mother said.

"To know what's what in life," my father said.

"To learn the value of a dollar," my mother said.

"To find out it's like something to be a man," my father said.

"To learn the value of a dollar," my mother said.

"To see how people—"

"To learn the value—"

"To help—"

"To learn—"

There always remained another word to propose on the subject. "I have homework to do?" I asked, making this a question because the whole world knew I did no homework.

"Your cousin Bernie works in his father's store," my mother said. "He's learning the value."

"Your cousin Irwin works in his father's store," my father said. "Very mature kit, grown-up. Knows what's what."

No fonder of my cousins, I began to work in the store. At first there were compensations besides learning the value and knowing what's what; for example, I quickly suspected the potentialities of stacking Jell-o. Its six delicious box colors made possible the development of a penchant toward baroque in counter displays. I gave over to fantasy in exercises of pure structure; I brought art to Dried Desserts (end of the first aisle), evolving from a gothic striving and simplicity to a rococo exuberance, raspberry mounting lemon in commercial embrace. The Jell-o man beamed and said I had talent. He promised me an autographed photograph of Jack Benny from his sample case, the signature printed as good as original, the *same identical thing*. I stood off, narrow-eyed, architectural, three loose boxes in each hand. While orange buttresses flew and lime vaulted over naves of cherry, my father grew impatient. "Is that all you got on your mind, the playboy?" It was not all, but he was right: there is a limit to what one can do with Jell-o. And what finally happened to my dream of a celestial engineering? Bananas were sliced into it.

I knew that my friends were playing touch football in the street or perhaps, if it were late afternoon, amorously lobbing rocks onto Pattie Donahue's front porch. Pity the man with an unemployed throwing arm! Aproned and earth-bound despite my Buster Brown aviator shoes, I stood in exile among the creak of shopping baskets and a cash register clang, such matters unmusical where a rumor of roller skates on a girl's sidewalk pledges passion eternal and a well-placed rock portends an invitation to Rosalie Fallon's second annual traditional Hallowe'en party; these are suburban verities which held even in the prehistory before Mayor Cassidy's first reign, when I began my studies of how to pee in an enameled pot. A marksman now, I turned sullen despite my skill, sour as a strawberry plucked too early; my father knew their need to ripen wild in the sun, unfingered by ambitious farmwives. I was a bad crop, green through, lazy for spite.

"Stop slouching," my mother said. "Stand up like a *mench*. Bernie *likes* the store. He stays and works even when Uncle Abe says go home, here's a quarter."

I learned contempt for my cousins, the submissive ones, who worked so that they could spend dimes like grownups instead of nickels in the Chippewa Lake slot machines. No amount of labor could harden their gluey hands. Irwin had flat feet, a mustache at fourteen because his mother did not tell him to shave, the habit of standing too close when he talked, and, as luck would have it, a talent for projecting his bad breath with such accuracy that any customer's sales resistance must have died in the first whiff. Later he learned to brush his tongue, shave his armpits, sprinkle himself with Johnson's Baby Powder, and rinse his mouth with spearmint mouthwash. Anything for a client. He gave up his soul, a pulpy one at that, which resided in the crevices of his teeth.

Bernie, Narcissus Gaynesbargh the Go-getter, developed an artist's pure love for illness, hospitals, and operations. He saved up enough—"All by his lonesome," bragged Aunt Sarah—for an operation which joined his ears more cunningly to his head. "Clark Gable can let himself go, he's a big man already, but not my Bernie," his mother proudly recounted. "Today he looks a million—stand frontways, Bernie! And how tall is your Daniel?"

Bernie had enough left over in his account to have his piles removed during the after-Christmas slow spell. *Carpe Diem*: he obeyed our junior high motto, constantly improving himself, a medically-made man, an expert on vitamin pills, eye exercises, and local anesthesia. He was also judicially made; let us not omit the subtle alterations in the orthography of his name. Imagine the legal nightmare in which a Ginsberg-into-Gaynesbargh signifies more rebirth than immolation! The suicide was a complete success. Neither his ears nor his ancestors stuck out, although the stitching showed.

"*They* will marry nice rich girls from New York City, you'll see," my mother threatened me. Later both took Marital Engineering courses, one at Miami University and the other at Cornell, and it paid, because Bernie married a nice rich shoe business from Hartford and Irwin married a wholesale Divan & Studio Couch, a steady thing.

"But," as my mother said, "you can't measure happiness in dollars and cents. There are things more important especially with taxes these days. A sweet little wife, a nice little family. . ."

"Have a piece Sanders." Aunt Sarah consoled her with the Continental assortment. "I got it by Sanders Chocolates when I went downtown to look for my new Person Lamb yesterday. Purse-and-lamb, I mean. Who knows maybe I'll settle for a Shirt Beaver, the season's almost over."

Not even Aunt Sarah can distract my mother when philosophy comes over her. "You could marry in a low element, maybe he wouldn't really be rich only pretending, living high, that kind of a click—"

"My Irwin hm hm, you should know he sent me a this year's pillow direct from the factory to me," Aunt Sarah might remark. "He don't have to put birds in his vest, my Irwin."

"Don't tell me, I know," Mother groaned. "Some people are real type bigshots, some people have to make look big to themselves with escalator heels and Scotch shoelaces, who ever heard?"

"My Irwin—"

"What, you crazy? He's a nice steady boy your Irwin, clean-cut, a neat dresser. I'm mentioning it so happens one of those fast clicks, oh, oh."

"Ho," breathed Aunt Sarah.

They communed in silence over the family shame. They clopped the bitter memory from their outraged palates. They drew the lesson from what befell poor Cousin Bessie, who returned from a vacation—she had a nice job with the government, too—with pierced ears and coral earrings, a pair of chartreuse silk slacks, and a new man to replace the one who broke his head. "My new husband," she announced, indicating a plump individual with oily sunburned pouches under his eyes, Novelty-style shoelaces, and a sky-blue Kalifornia Kravate with a silver-lightning pin, the tie tucked into a Hickock Kowboy type belt: "Roland, he's in the wholesale business in Los Angeles."

"Wholesale what?" Mother had asked, suspicious already.

"Just wholesale," Cousin Bessie said equably. Roland smiled to show the gap in his teeth bridged by invisible platinum. His little woman spoke for him: "He has the biggest outlet in Los Angeles."

"Ellay," he corrected her.

Later, after Uncle Moish from Indian River Drive discovered that this Roland was a bad-type thief off the legit, not a dealer in factory-to-you eliminate-the-middleman low-costs, they helped Bessie out again. She promised to be more careful next season. She was pushing thirty-five, although the family loyally counted only the last twenty-seven of them; she had combed the summer-time mountains and the winter-time seaside since she buried Lester. Mother took three deep breaths and announced, addressing her in the ceremonial third person while Bessie wept whole-sale tears: "Next time she should vacate a week ten days in Atlantic City on the Atlantic, the sun, the salt water taffy, she should meet a nice steady New York type fella, she still got her health why not? Knock on wood. Just he shouldn't have the biggest outlet in Ellay."

Still my cousins were generally nice, steady, and successful even at that early time. I was recalcitrant, a failure in affairs.

"The whole world knows. Aunt Ethel and Aunt Sarah know, it should happen to me I try to be a good mamma to you. The whole city knows."

Aunt Sarah encouraged my mother in her own way. " '*Mama*,' my Bernie tell me,"—and her eyes moistened over such devotion—" 'Mama,' he says, 'you look like sugar in the urine again. What did I tell you about those two-dollar Sanders assortments?' . . . So thoughtful," she concluded, folding her arms across a high stalwart bone of her *garment*, leaning back, and waiting for my mother to tell something good about me. I couldn't even read an oral thermometer. After a while she sighed for pity, yawned for contentment, and added soothingly, "Your Danny working nice in the store these days maybe? Just tell him about my Bernie, he'll learn, you got to encourage."

"I look in the looking glass I ask myself why, I got no answer. A son of mine, why? A thirteen-years-old lump," she encouraged.

It wasn't laziness. That's a maternal answer. I would have worked in other ways, and did; if I could have remained at some comprehensible task, delivering orders perhaps, building shelves, loading the truck, or manipulating the stock in the basement, I might have attained a fulfillment equal in its way to Cousin Bernie's avarice for operations. The constant pouring of commands from a triumphant father shivered and shattered my sense for work; he wanted me by his side, proud of an eldest son, any eldest son. For good reasons of his own—he had been poor, he wanted me to see what he had done for himself and for us all —he urged me to learn the pleasure of a direct delicious manipulation of money, its worn old touch of cloth, its warmth of hands and pockets, its smell of sex and work, its color of economy or death in our world, signed in those days by Andrew W. Mellon. "Here! it says right here. Read it yourself. That's the secretary of the treasurer of the United States of America, U.S.A., his own autograph."

"Oh for God's sake. Jake, you can notice such things?"—my mother discovering new depths, she a modest economist, my father not.

"Notice notice," he admitted virtuously. Money was poetry, a symbol of life and power on one side, economy and death for him with the White House on the other, but only a symbol— how could I understand such metaphysics, undergraduate-schooled in that epoch of despair with girls and ambitions of purity? My agile Tartar-eyed father made the distinction by enjoying both the earning and the spending, finding his truth higgledy-piggledy in an exploit of strapping a load-and-a-healthy-half on his 1928 White Motors truck or in giving himself to a snack of artichoke with Kraft's dressing, the heart his end but the money-colored leaves loved for what they were.

He wanted me to clerk, to *wait on trade*, then, to be an aproned catalyst toward the final term. How could I take money from Mrs. Donahue, whose daughter no one but Tom Moss knew I loved, while Pattie herself teased her mouth with an end of lipstick without glancing at me in my feminizing wraparound? My languishing yip should have betrayed me: "That'll be just three sixty-five, please," recited as I had been taught. It did not; no one saw me. The money joined money in the new Serv-a-slip cash register. *O love me, Pattie! look!*—and I feared that she would. I gave the cash to Hannah, the cashier, my father's deputy while he bargained with the Wheaties jobber for bonus Eversharps and an electric fan-flame wood-glow fireplace.

"Okay, Little Jack, you're picking up now. I'll tell your pa. Just keep the hands out of the pockets when you're making a sale. Say thank you to the customer." Hannah had a tongue cracked and ridged, mounds at the meaty sides and fissures among the yellowish scale, betrothed to dyspepsia. These wounds came of a continual talking confused with a continual eating. No one knew a remedy. She suffered unsilently, chewing Baseball Gum. "I said take hands out of pockets that's a boy. I said say thank you to the nice customer."

"Thank you, Mrs. Donahue," I mumbled miserably.

I carried Mrs. Donahue's order to her Hudson. Pattie moved ahead, her rump twitching like a snapdragon delicately pinched. I fled as she fumbled with her purse for a tip. The next Monday, inspecting my approach from her station at the side entrance to Horace Greeley Junior High, without taking her eyes off mine she bent significantly to whisper into her friend Rosalie Fallon's ear. To stifle their laughter the two of them made paws of their silly adored hands at their mouths. This gesture insured politeness and (reward for a suburban virtue) the secret renewal of laughter when the grocery boy has passed. Sober and unblinking, Pattie nonchalantly rubbed her edible kneecap.

"Don't call me Little Jack," I told Hannah once more without hope. "Call me my name."

"Okay . . . Little Jack," she said, humorously chewing.

Sometimes I carried a book to work, wearing it piously between my shirt and my chest, and then hid with it and a cigarette in the basement among the cases of Libby's Whole Sliced Pineapple and Hinz-zuzz Pork and Beans with Tomato Sauce. The white-washed walls sweated; the storeroom smelled of dampness, rat poison, cardboard packing cases, and a broken bottle of soy sauce. Here I was happy, the complicated atmosphere making me dizzy as I perched corrupt with one of Andy's Wing butts on a peak of pineapple under the dusty 40-watt bulb. Sometimes I put down the Poe (I had memorized *Ulalume* without being able to pronounce it) and moodily considered my childhood, before Pattie Donahue and before my parents had decided I was a man, when I had sometimes visited this range of cans and bottles to leap like a goat among it in my innocence. I practiced a tragic sigh, inhaling soy.

Always my father roared down the stairway to discover me. "YOU THINK YOU CAN KID ME, HAH? The A & P can't even kid me, I got a list of your tricks—"

I stood up with no answer, understanding that he would forever find me, silent in my wished chagrin. I could not explain to him the disgrace of working in a store in a neighborhood where boys had important unexplainable things to do, secret clubs and fatal loafing, while their fathers managed offices for Standard Machines or handled law cases for insurance companies downtown. I wanted him to commute instead of work, like the others; I could not tell either of us the reason for my stubborn reluctance to follow him to the market, racy and challenging though it was. I felt a justice in his despair with me. A coward, I hid each time.

"Your mother says today you'll be good, I say I'll find you sneaking off with a book."

I studied his boots on the cement and deeply assented. He had looked in the backroom to see if I were filling orders, giving me the benefit of a doubt and profligate hope which is still my debt.

"*Nu,* what do you say for yourself? I'm going crazy upstairs, it's a big one-cent-sale, the Saturday help's no good these days . . . Hah?"

I said nothing.

"Why not tell me another lie, you'll be good like you promised I should be happy?"

I stared, Poe sweaty in my hands.

"So why don't you at least say you had to go the toilet, the mensroom"—a treble note of exasperation hidden in his bass, wanting an excuse for me, loving his oldest.

I refused this. I was overmoral for a moment, going on thirteen, as he was overhappy; I despised anything but extreme commitments, surrender to his world or defiance of it.

"What's the matter, you constipated? You got stomach trouble?"—pretending that I had given us this excuse, unable to bear our misery together.

He watched the tears silently fill my eyes.

He relented; he appealed to me, trying to preserve his anger by shouting; he betrayed his helplessness by heavily sitting down beside me on the canned pineapple. "What's the matter, you hungry, you want your mother should make you a tomato and balonny sandwich with Kraft's Miracle Whip dressing?"

"I want to go upstairs and help out," I whispered at last.

Reconciled, unable to preserve animus, he bumped against me up the narrow steps. Instead of letting me sink into the crowd of customers reaching with their lists and their clippings of advertisements at the counters, he ordered me to go to lunch with him, knowing that I liked this. To have the Business Men's special with Dad in a restaurant was one of the compensations; choosing food is the act of a god—only gods and businessmen don't have mothers to tell them what to eat, filling their plates with it. It was a pure joy although a bad restaurant; we had to go there because Guy Mallin owed my father two hundred dollars, which he never paid and we couldn't eat through by the time he left his wife and ran off to Montreal with Stella, the waitress, and a week's receipts. (When this happened Dad tried, although he knew little about the restaurant business, to help out poor Mrs. Mallin, who had no children but only a thyroid condition to give her an interest in life.) Both of us would have preferred an egg roll and hamburger steak at Louie's, the Chinaman across the street, and our unity on this—winking across the table as fast-talking Guy Mallin approached—cleared the hatred of civilizations between father and son. I should insist on this: the storm confined itself to its direct object, my laziness, rising like an east wind to its peak on the busy day, Saturday or before holidays, then falling away. "You learn with meet people," he only said. "You learn with know their ways."

After we finished our lunch I hid in the basement of the store to read Edgar Allan Poe.

II

As the months went by, the ruses deepened and the anger swam like some exiled bull carp in the deepest pools of the natures of my mother, my father, and me. Pattie Donahue had definitively given up roller skating in the street, and not only on bricked Pittsburg Road but also on the mellifluous asphalt of Chesterton Avenue. We were freshmen in junior high, seventh graders learning dignity from a Social Dancing teacher added to the curriculum by the Board of Education which decided that Grace and Poise (formerly Comportment) were as essential as geography and algebra to the Young Men & Women of Tomorrow, be they bond salesmen like their fathers or *homemakers* like their mothers. The Real Estate Taxpayers League issued a protest against educational frills; pioneering virtues that made our country great, assessment already excessive, it argued. Artichokes, bulky and hard to handle, were coming into season again.

Shamefully I pretended to be sleeping Saturday mornings when my father had gotten up at three or earlier. Mother was more violent, my father more deeply hurt—the denial, after all, was of him. She nagged constantly; yet on Saturdays when I stayed motionless slugabed, her pride in sleep—"It's very healthy" —protected me there. Later, my father telephoning to ask if I had arisen yet, he fell silent before her report, pressing the receiver to his ear amid the mob of shoppers importunate about fork-tongued Hannah's dais, and he darkly said nothing while Mother repeated, infuriated with me but stubborn in her alle-, giance to health: "Let the kid sleep just one more morning, kids need sleep. It's good for them."

Having vacuumed, she herself got ready to go to the store for *relief*. Out of some relic of pride I could not bring myself to feign until she would safely leave me among my angry bed-clothes in the occult reproach of a house. "I'm up," I fatally admitted. I reached for a paltry revenge in wearing yesterday's socks. She edified me in a steady torrent on the streetcar to the store:

"No good! big lump! lazy good-for-nothing! You're thirteen already and look at you!"

"Twelve," I corrected her.

" 'Please Daddy I want to work in the store like a big man,' Bernie always says. Aunt Sarah says. Such a go-getter! But what do you say?—look ma the dog wet the rug I'm twelve years old.

Aunt Sarah says I should stop aggravating myself. Please give
a look my waricose weins from standing up." She had forgotten
that the effect of threatening to telephone Aunt Sarah when I
was *bad* had been dissipated years ago with the advent of Unlim-
ited Calls. Sometimes I had even offered to dial the number for
her.

"A big lump like you he should give me a rest, take the load
off your feet Ma like Bernie, not trouble trouble all the time."

"Why is it you always say I'm thirteen when it's something you
want me to do and you know I'm twelve?" I asked, a savant without rimless glasses. "And when I want to do something I can't
because I'm not old enough, I'm only eleven? My birthday is
July twentieth at six o'clock in the morning."

"I remember," she said morosely. "And a fine night I had with
you in Mount Sinai all night too, they almost had to use force-its.
Dr. Shapiro said my bones were so delicate close together . . .
Thirteen, going on now. Even Uncle Morton knows about you,
I'm so ashamed in the family why I told Aunt Ethel I'll never
hold my head high again, at least Morton he got daughters they
keep themselves clean at least not so much aggravation, all right
so worry a tiny bit they should marry nice, but not heartache a
no-good like you day in day out—"

Outside the streetcar the first autumn leaves were burning in
piles on the street, sending up an odor redolent of freedom in
the open air. My friends flamboyantly loitered on the Saturday
streets, chalk in their mouths, their hearts unfettered. Pattie Donahue was perhaps walking alone in Rocky River Park, just waiting
for me telepathically to find her.

The store opened about us with the intense plushy smell of
old vegetables. Hannah was comforting old Mrs. Simmons, a
childless widow whose husband had been manager of the Guar-
antee Trust, Rocky River branch; she generally admitted herself
among us with the distant face of someone who disliked the smell
of the inside of her own nose, but now she claimed to have seen
a spider in a hand of bananas. "It probably wasn't a deadly poisonous banana spider," Hannah said. "Did it have a lot of legs?
Furry ones from Costo Rico?"

"A South American banana spider! oh!" Mrs. Simmons, realizing
that it was a foreign element, rolled her eyes in search of a
pleasant place to faint.

"Probably not deadly poisonous, though. Probably just a sleepy
little old banana spider from the deadly jungles of Hatey." Mrs.

Simmons fainted. That is, considering her dignity and the aristo-
cratic unpaid bills in the drawer with Hannah's sandwiches, she
swooned. "Anyway no one else saw it, the thousand-legger bug,
the horrible deadly spider," Hannah mused on, rubbing Mrs.
Simmons' wrists without taking off her Ovaltine Birthstone &
Goodluck Ring.

"Ouch, you're scratching," said Mrs. Simmons.

My father, harried but always expecting the best, greeted me
with an order. Stack the oranges, wait on Mrs. Simmons, put on
your apron, what's the matter with you? . . . Could I confess the
chief reason for my tardiness, a hope that telepathic pressure
concentrated among my bedclothes might compel Mrs. Donahue
to buy her Ohio State hothouse tomatoes and Swansdown ready-
mix no-sift cake flour before my surrender to penance in a wraparound? *Develop Your Will Increase Your Power. Sample Booklet
Fool Your Friends. 25c Coin or Stamps.* No, I could not. My
father's will developed, he spoke a language in which existed no
vocabulary to explain that, among the people with whom he
chose to bring me up, it was more important to run end in a
pick-up touch football game, spinning craftily about the young
trees planted by the Our Street Beautiful committee, than to
fill orders in sour old orange crates on Saturday afternoons. We
all paid, in our various ways, a price for those trees and for
the privilege of overhead doors on our garages and colonial-
style magazine racks for our Saturday Evening Posts. He did
not draw the consequences of his ambition for me; if he judged
our neighborhood to be better than that of his childhood, then
our neighborhood would judge his world. In a develop-your-will
(Fool Your Friends) like my father's the only lack was the will
to find my will-less longing. He worked! Mother worked! Like
dogs!—They were right, but they could not see through to my
rightness, forgetting a child's hunger to belong. Ulalume might
have been for the ages, but Rosalie Fallon and Pattie tongued
their malicious pencils and wrote my fate in their Slam Books.
He knew he was a foreigner, my father did; I had to discover it
in pain, shame before my parents, and self-judging. "I earned
my own living when I was thirteen, and proud of it," he had said.

"Your father earned his own living when he was twelve,"
Mother remarked contentedly in explanation, "and he is proud of
it. *Proud* of it."

"Thirteen he said," I said.

"Proud he said," she said.

He studied me in sorrow and silence, figuring with his short black-nailed thick-knuckled hands reaching for the silvery crating hammer in his back pocket. I was just a kid. I even looked like him. Hannah said so. Even Guy Mallin said I was a chip off the. Hey kid? You want a Business Men's plate with chocolate ice cream instead of the green peas with butter sauce? It should be easy to figure . . . "Gravy on that there ice cream haw-haw yessir, hey kid? Gravy!" Guy Mallin roared. "A real chip if I ever saw one, Jake. I'm telling you listen to me now. Your eyes. Your chin. His mother's, a sweet little woman you got there, nose. Yessir. Your hair. Off the old block there, Jake. Good material, hey? It won't be long before it's *Jake & Son,* what-do-you-say? I'm telling you now Jake you heard what I said."

"Maybe things are different these days," he told me. "You ain't the way I was."

My father had the gift of listening to the artichokes at the top of a load in such a way—they informed him in a language which only he and the artichokes spoke—that he always knew when their brothers at the bottom were defective, defeated, edged with rust or shriveled from a stingy soil. Silent in their hampers, they communicated by the violence of love, all knowing their role on this occasion as opportunities, each thick-leafed one, for a sociable debating between farmer and merchant, green, crisp, candid, and nutritive after a pleasant journeying into the hands of women. They accepted the gift of himself which my father made, their shoots curly for him, their unbaked hearts shy in a bra of ticklish felt. Buy us! sell us!—they asked nothing more. Artichokes understood my father, and his sympathy for vegetables arose to meet theirs for him. Devotion—he gave this freely. He accepted, too, being stuck with thorns.

Unfortunately I, even in those days, was not an artichoke—perhaps not so rewarding, my heart not luscious with a dab of Miracle-Whip, stunted in fact, even hornier, full of bad character and a brooding plant rust. "Lots of personality," my mother had said, feebly defending me when as a child I had refused to shell lima beans for the store with the rest of the family on Friday nights. "Everyone says he takes after your side, Jake. Ethel says, Sarah says."

"Since I was thirteen! I got scars on my back, the bucket cut me, the greenhorn I didn't get a pad cloth. Look at Irwin, look at Bernie born the same week like you in Mount Sinai, you was the first so I got your mother a semi-private. A healthy kid like you, he sleeps all morning Saturday."

"Since he was twelve years old a greenhorn," Mother mournfully intoned. "Who ever heard of it?"

Pattie Donahue plucked at her sweater and pouted with kiss-proof lipstick (maybe) over teeth lucky to serve her. Lewis Snyder, the sheik, told stories about Rosalie Fallon and Pattie. Tom Moss told me. "The liar," we agreed, ferociously believing him.

Such matters flowed in time; the store remained outside time, its claim ripening through the spines but as incredible to me as a heartless artichoke to my father. The store gulped me down. I evaded, I squirmed, I stubbornly bent, receded, and persisted like heartburn, taking all shapes but in fact knowing only itself, which has no shape and a mysterious matter.

"You don't want, what kind of a reason is that?" my mother demanded, fertile as Hera in argument. "No reason, that's what kind."

I couldn't explain to myself or to them, much less to Aunt Sarah or to Aunt Ethel, to Hannah, Guy Mallin, or Cousin Bernie the Smarty. Let him marry a nice rich girl from New York Queens in the clothing business, I don't care, I sacrilegiously insisted. My single purpose was love for Pattie Donahue, whose father carried a portfolio to work in his hairless pink little hands; she would love only the elaborate loungers, the conspicuous consumers—a little Veblenite she was! You Americans all long for the useless, the hymen no proper end; it feathers no beds, it fleshes no bellies—this Mother and Dad might have pointed out if they had argued their philosophy. I sensed, too, that my father's agility and strength and love moving among the objects all his in the store were a threat to me, the more dangerous because— one of his few fatal thoughts outside the moment—he was beginning to see Jack's Fruit & Vegetable in terms of immortality for both of us. He asked only a sign of recognition for this gift to me.

I refused his gift daily now. Even the Jell-o counter fell into ruins. My ultimate denial lay outside morality, essential to character. My father was overhappy, overmoral. I crouched like a troll under a mushroom in the cellar, a troll who read *Ulalume* and murmured, "Pattie Donahue!" with dilated eyes in the shadow of a shipment from Procter & Gamble. Poor Dad!

We can measure his desolation. He left his struggle and joyous head-on combat with farmers, jobbers, salesmen, Saturday help, policemen, wilting lettuce and pears which remained green until they rotted, competitors, the chain stores, the landlord, debtors, creditors, the delivery truck, the account books, the government, insects, rodents, spoilage, wastage, heat, cold, the margin of profit, draw items, push merchandise, merchandise which he could not get, premiums, samplers,one-cent giveaways, Christmas trees on January second and Easter candy in May, children who skated through a display of jars of olives (the olives lined up one by one in bottles shaped like a straw, optically illusive, expensive all the same), Mr. Jenkins who insisted on Aunt Mary's pancake mix and would not be content with Aunt Jemimah's or any other Aunt's because he wanted to honor in this way his poor dead old Aunt Mary his mother's sister, Mrs. Rawlings the klepto whose chauffeur dropped her off at the store every morning to slip a bottle of vanilla extract into her pink muff (her daughter paid, but we had to keep score), the charity ladies and the lottery girls, the kids selling advertisements in their parochial school bulletins, the beggars who claimed to have had a store just like his in Phoenix, Arizona, until they hit a run of bad luck back in '29 (he was unanimously elected to a directory circulated by a syndicate of beggars, Phoenix & Miami Beach Chapter), the faithful customers who tried to convert him to their religions, Mrs. Colonel Greenough who came with tears to tell him that her husband forbade her to shop at Jack's Fruit & Vegetable any longer because the colonel himself had given him three months to read a book on technocracy and he had not yet complied (she bought a farewell bouquet of cauliflower before she left), the high-school teacher who wanted to pay an overdue bill in the privacy of her chamber, the judges asking support both moral and ah financial in the coming primaries, the tax collectors, the bill collectors, the garbage collectors, the health inspectors, the housing inspectors, the zoning inspectors, electricians, refrigerator repair men, insurance which only covered fires begun by safety matches when his fire had resulted from a cigar butt, illness among his clerks, jealousies, rivalries, romances, extended lunch hours, female troubles which (a gentleman) he could not publicly doubt, inventories, lentil soup in cans labeled liver pâté, children who descended like locusts to remove all the tops from the Ralston boxes to send away as a mark of esteem for Tom Mix, the electric cash register playing Chopin in a short circuit, Hannah who had B.O., Andy who left his hair among the macaroons, Myrna who showed too much of her bosom in order to encourage Mr. Tramme to take an extra cantaloupe, and other problems which I'll not mention because I want to avoid making a list.

My father abandoned his direct response to these issues in order to *use psychology* on me. He appealed in subtle ways. He tried to get *me interested*. His Tartar eyes were made to squint for laughter and appetite, not cunning. My heart contracts with sadness for him now, sadness and regret. He came to me on the porch one Sunday afternoon, his great arms slack at his sides, saying, "Say!" in the way of a good fellow, and asked me to write a paragraph for his weekly advertisement in the neighborhood throwaway. I responded, too, working hard at a composition modeled on "The Raven," sharpening three pencils into oblivion before I finished. Proudly I announced to Tom Moss the prospect of publication in the West Side Advertiser.

The work never appeared. Trochees had no place next to bargains in Crisco. The Crisco people paid half and supplied the engraving; the Spry people, not caught napping at the shortening, offered to pay sixty per cent and sent my mother a portable sun lamp for her sinuses. I wasn't even impregnated with Vitamin D or Viosterol from Wisconsin, living by Poe and Pattie. Psychology failed; my father came as an alien to such maneuvers. Nevermore!

One day I sneaked out of the store at four-thirty, made my own dinner of Laub's rye, Blue Moon pimento cheese with those taste-delightful little chopped-up pieces of real pimento, Krunchy peanut butter (kan't remember the brand), and Thursday's spoiled milk; then I went to an Edward G. Robinson with Tom Moss. The three of us stood off the coppers for a reel and a half, and when they finally got Edward G. the camera noticed a paper boat which sailed down the gutter in the symbolic rain. "Just like The Strange Case of Monsieur Whatsizname," I pedantically reminded Tom. We fought back our tears, magnificent to THE END, ate a dime's worth of evergreen mints, and went divvies on a Spicy Detective to read under the Jantzen's Swimsuit for That Lee-*uscious* Look billboard on the way home. I told him about Pattie and he told me about Rosalie Fallon. Our patient listening to each other was more than politesse; we learned through it although the histories remained classically similar, unmodified in months except for the time Rosalie kicked Tom in the shins when he complimented her by rubbing one of the last March snowballs in her face. He rolled up his pantleg to show me the wound once more. I accused him of preserving it with salt. He denied this. He accused me of envy. I lowered my eyes. Tom was a lady-killer, he was; I'll never understand how he did it.

"Well, good night Tom. Good luck with Rosalie."

"Well, good night Dan. I'll ask Lewis Snyder about Pattie. He took Virginia Thompson out on a date and maybe she knows something. He'll tell me if I ask him because I know something on him."

Good night . . . Good night . . . In that midworld of childish seriousness and the first adult frivolity of passion Tom and I needed the sense of banding together, our sufferings held in common while our sense of them remained untouchable, pariahs of glandular enthusiasm in a structure built of economy. He gave me the Spicy to hide in the garage. I had often dreamed of moving through an atmosphere of glue, invisibly held from my family's home in an empty night. Empty?—full of unknown excess. Now I whistled, leaving Tom Moss an hour before midnight, forgetting that I had last seen my parents seven hours earlier when my father had said, "Wait on trade!" and I had crept out the back door where Andy was boxing strawberries and beet greens were blackening in the sun.

The door to our house was locked. The windows were dark. There was no key under the mat. The crickets suddenly deafened me, like in the movies. I thought I knew, then, how Edward G. felt when the boys went over to the South Side mob, but found a basement window open, crawled through the coal chute, and significantly murmured Pattie's name out of the side of my mouth. Ulalume Donahue, Killer Berman's moll . . . I'd have flipped a quarter with disdain except that it was too dark and I had no quarter. *Dad!* I thought. I worried about the gas stove upstairs. Maybe they were all dead and so I should bang on the door until they let me in to sleep in my own bed. What if there were rats in the basement? Big ones like in the Paris sewers with Gene Valgene? The washing machine opened its mouth at me in the darkness. *Mother!* I thought. If the water pipes broke and I got drowned they'd be sorry. They'd be sorry someday when I spit blood into my monogrammed handkerchief from sleeping all alone in a damp basement. They would be sorry. I was sorry. *Mother and Dad!* I thought.

Without taking off my shoes I slept on the extra kitchen table in the basement, amid dirty laundry (my pillow) and old hatreds (my dreams).

III

Even this passed. The next Saturday I was as faithful as Irwin, as true as Bernie with his eyes like spoiled oysters. I tasted during one evening the delights of approval, staying up with Mother and Dad while we discussed the day's business, counted the receipts, and discussed the pros and cons of tangle displays against neat pyramids of cans or fruit. I spoke for tangle displays, Mother for order; Dad listened to us both, sipping his tea with little Ahs through his lump of sugar, and reserved decision. He tried to lasso my head as he used to in a ring of cigar smoke. "It's too big," he complained. "Just like mine, a size seven seven-eights. So look who needs a hat! You want a Stetson?"

We had a long late supper, and before going to bed he slipped me three dollar bills in a secret conspiratorial gesture while Mother stacked the dishes.

"I saw! I saw!" she cried out, her eyes peeping bright in the mirror over the sink. We all giggled together.

Dad slapped her rump, yawned, and said, "Nothing like a good day's work, hey?" in his imitation of Guy Mallin.

"Jake, you crazy?" At peace with each other we parted. "And don't forget whose birthday is next month," my mother said: "Yours. You'll be thirteen, kiddel."

She had it right this time. It was a real truce; I knew its joys. But had anything been altered? As aphoristic Aunt Ethel might say, "A leopard coat can't change its spots."

A few days afterward I received a letter. The envelope carried my name on the outside, together with the smart-alecky title *Master,* all printed in green ink. I studied it, marveling, my first mail since the revolutionary discovery of INCREASE YOUR WILL POWER FOOL YOUR FRIENDS, and for that I had sent away a coupon and a quarter. I sniffed it. I licked the ink and made a smear of what our art teacher called *graded area.* I tasted my name in green, finding it more subtle than black but just as lucid. At last I decided to open the letter.

It was an invitation from Mr. B. Franklyn Wilkerson to go on a Nature Walk a week from Saturday. Mr. Wilkerson, who taught General Science to the seventh grade, had worked out a plan to augment his income during the summer vacation by conveying flower names and leaf shapes to suburban scholars. Small, swarthy, with three daughters and thin black hair artfully spaced and glued into place to cover his scalp, Mr. Wilkerson recited

Science (general) with his neck petrified for fear a sudden breeze
or emotion might betray his baldness. Zealous, he devoted himself to general science textbooks, turning the pages slowly to
avoid drafts. A real scientist would have perforated the pages.
He was but a general scientist, however, combining, as he
thought, the virtues of the practical and the theoretical in Elevating the Young, an intellectual sort whose pink resentful mouth
and clenched neck gave him the expression of someone who had
swallowed a banana sideways.

The first walk, a free trial, would take place on a Saturday,
and the Saturday before the Fourth, the third-busiest day of the
year in the store. I decided not to go.

Tom Moss was going. Lewis Snyder, who had dates alone with
girls, was going. I learned that several of them, including Rosalie
Fallon and Pattie Donahue, would be botanically present. I
decided to go.

We met, everyone carrying lunch but me, at eleven-thirty.
Mother didn't know about it; I had run away from the store,
taking my cap from under the cash register and, for some last
scruple, telling Hannah to tell my father that I had gone.
"Where?"—but I disappeared without answering, subtle as a
hungry tomcat unable to hide its rut, sneaking around corners
with its yellow eyes scheming. Lewis Snyder had a scout can-
teen filled with near-beer left over after repeal. I suspected him
of planning to offer Pattie some.

Pedantic, amorous, shifty-eyed general scientists, we followed
Mr. Wilkerson into the Rocky River reservation. He wore a
checkered golf cap, its band black with Sta-Neet, and showed
how he had taught his wife to wrap his lunch—cellophane insu-
lated the deviled eggs each from each. "Practical. Sanitary germ-
free. Vitamins spoil in the open air," he advised us.

Tom Moss, my friend the skeptic, whispered to me that he
thought it was supposed to be *good* for you to be out in the fresh
air, and then went to step on Rosalie Fallon's heels.

We penetrated the woods, already hungry. "Now right here
on your left children we find an interesting phenomenon page
one hundred and forty-eight in Brenner's figure sixteen that
orange growth over there with the black spots now that's a wild
spermaphore," Mr. Wilkerson remarked. "Ess. Pee. Ee. Arrh—"

"Looks like a toadstool to me," I said.

"Spermaphore. Silver spoons unreliable poor quality silver
these days no workmanship. Damp places. Twenty-four on a

picnic without a general scientist. Could have told them. Whole party dead in eight to ten hours. Horrible. Too bad. Ess, pee, ee—"

A voice occurred behind me, whispering, "Hello, Daniel Berman." It was Pattie. "Toadstools are very poisonous"—she leaned sociably. "Do you like are you fond of mushrooms?"

I soared into paradise at her feet. "My mother cooks spermaphores with meat loaf," I said, "and stuffed peppers."

"Oh!"—a gasp of scandal. "She does not! You'll all be dead . . . Does she?"

"Yes," I lied, death-defying—what could be a better beginning between lovers? All lies come true in a world of such supple twelve-year-old facts. I was cool here across the city from the store. Birds soon to be falsely named cocked their heads in the trees and lectured us. Some place customers swarmed amid the imperatives of telephones and the distance between my father and me widened past even the nine-month doubt separating an instant of giving from the birth of a son. Fatherhood, a metaphysical idea, was being taken from Dad as Mrs. Rawlings slipped her daily bottle of vanilla extract into her bosom, no one to distract her, and as Mr. Wilkerson bravely broke the perfidious spermaphore with a five-foot stick, no academician he, a man of general action in science. Rosalie Fallon gave her pressed-lip assent and moral outrage against hypocritical silver spoons while my thoughts fled back from the store to recall prepared speeches of passion for Miss Donahue, known by Killer Berman and Edward G. as Ulalume or The Lost Lenore.

"Oh-h-h," she was saying.

"Look the bug," I replied.

She pretended to be scared, not. I knew. Death and complicity —love is not a biological gesture in suburban children, O Mr. Wilkerson! I had forgotten my speeches and Ulalume.

Despite this meeting I again felt deserted, lunchless at lunchtime. Tom Moss pretended not to notice: excuse him his hunger. "Where's yours?" Pattie asked, her mouth full.

"Don't have any. My mother didn't. Not hungry anyway."

Girls always have enough to give. Suburban girls (economical) always have enough to invest. Sweetly she murmured, "You can have one of my bacon and tomato-motto sandwiches and a bite of cottage cheese with the canopy, please do." Smiling, licking her lipstick, her eyes calculating under the modest fluttering venereal lids, she whispered intimately: "And a cookie the one with the candied cherry in the middle, please do, really."

"Oh!" I protested.

Take, take, my mother would have said.

"Really, I don't mind, please do," said dainty Miss Patricia Donahue.

I did.

Later, when we bid farewell to sporting, big-toothed, intellectual (generally scientific) Mr. Wilkerson, and thanked him for a lovely nice afternoon, and promised to ask our parents to fork over five smackeroos for a Program of Nature Walks, Pattie Donahue allowed it to be know that I was walking her home. Under the circumstances even Lewis Snyder had to count it a date with a girl alone; the evidence whelmed, overwhelmed. I obeyed the protocol. We had a coke and then an ice cream stick. That Snyder must have been eating his heart out, at least aggravated. All right then—I soliloquied with Tom Moss *qua* Conscience & Scorekeeper—half-credit then for a daytime date.

"Did you get a free one?" I asked.

She read her ice cream stick. "No." she said.

"Neither did I. Don't believe in luck anyway"—and I expounded my philosophy of will power concentrate your way to fame and/or fortune. I tried to recite *Ulalume* but forgot it.

My mother's arches were hurting in her Enna Jetticks, but she avoided my father so that he would not order her home. Andy was making off to the vegetable cooler with a bagful of macaroons. Basketwood splintered under orders; customers fidgeted untended; my father wiped his forehead with a paper towel from the pine forests of Maine, leaving crumbs of lint, and mourned me.

"I never knew you were so smart," said Pattie Donahue.

We had fallen silent, sitting on the front steps of her house in the shadow of a bush where her mother could not see us. Up the street someone was hosing his car, an incontinent sound, in preparation for a Fourth of July trip. The afternoon was over. Pattie Donahue, an economical creature, an Indian giver, took back her gift in a way which expressed her genius. Business acumen. Operating costs and turnover. Appraising me with her turtle-round eyes, shrewd to calculate the value of an investment, she first created a bear market by sighing Ohh, rustling her dress, and accidentally touching my arm with her transparent turquoise-veined hands. Cologned and dusted with powder, she breathed on me.

"Yes!" I spilled out, naked in summer smells. "Do you like me, Pattie? I like you."

"Sure I like you"—disappointment and a pout that it had been so easy. Even economy becomes sport with such a housekeeper. "Sure I like you but you're too fat."

"Fat?" I repeated stupidly.

Her laughter twinkled in the July calm by the watered bush. "Fat I mean skinny. I mean you're just a *grocery* boy, you. You just grub around a certain store I could name all the Saturdays *I* ever heard about, except I suppose today—"

She was a sly old creature, that Pattie Donahue. The lips: *grocery boy.* The frozen iris: the same. Her laughter caroled forth, free, enterprising, resolute, the investment paying off in a Saturday afternoon dividend of power. Not all men are men, her laughter told her. This is a profit forever, my face told her.

"Oh but—oh but—oh but—" I said.

She put her little hand to her mouth and delicately closed it. Tee-hee. She looked at me, unblinking. My father, knowing he was a foreigner, could have accepted this in the perspective of history. I had to discover a fact without a past; it leapt out at me like some fierce fish from the glittering shale of Pattie Donahue's economical eyes.

I stood up. "Thank you for the sandwich and the cookie," I said. (The cookie with a preserved cherry on it.)

"Oh me no," she said.

"I was hungry."

"Oh you're welcome really," she said. "Thank you for the coke. Thank you for the ice cream."

"Good-by, Pattie."

"It was nice, Daniel Berman," she said, "truly very nice."

IV

I prowled, growing up fast that afternoon. I climbed a fat hump of a mailbox for packages and, my hands hanging in front, or my elbows on my knees and my fists in my cheeks, I watched the traffic on Parkside Boulevard. I did not choose the sentimental places, the tree by the lake, the woods where the river on which we skated in winter spread out like a sheet. I began to understand how the lost Lenore really got mislaid, without a dark conversational bird, without a tomb, without even a long metrical sigh. A heavy July sky lowered and thickened above me. I perched on the box like an animal in a dream.

But I was no animal in no dream. I was wide-awake, me, itchy, straddling a mailbox. Once someone mailed a book between my legs. I did not stop to wonder whether it were some quaint and curious volume, this being already forgotten lore. I studied the houses squatting like fat-necked bullfrogs along the boulevard, puzzled over the nay-saying mouths and step of the emerging strollers, celebrated and grieved for the crystallizing structure of my judgment (my *complexes*), no longer contained by sad and pretty words—grieved but did not cry.

Long after dark I finally went home. My parents were in the kitchen, talking in low voices, the relieved hawing of Saturday nights absent today. Entering at the street, I went directly to my room and lay down on the bed. I made none of the dramatic flourishes of locking the door or pushing the footstool in front of it.

"Daniel!"

Doltish, I wondered if this were what it felt like to be an adult. It was true that for weeks I had been awakening mornings with my bite clamped, my jaw aching, and tongue plunged against my teeth. Was that the seeding for Pattie Donahue's educational crop? her economy predicted by my extravagance in sleep?

"Daniel!"—Mother's voice. I went. Mother stood by the kitchen table. Dad sat without looking at me, his head lowered, his hands about a bowl of soup. "You should come when I called you," she said.

"I did come."

"When I called you I said. Not whenever you please." She looked at my father and waited for him to speak. He did not. We all waited for him, the challenged one, amid the summer smell of flypaper in the kitchen and the buzzing of the wily flies.

Resentfully I broke the stillness: "I went on a nature walk."

"What?—what?"

"I learned what's a toadstool and the names of birds. A naturewalk. Mr. Wilkerson general science from junior high, he—"

"And what about Mr. and Mrs. Slave-their-heads-off, I suppose your parents by the store?" my mother asked. The sarcasm gave me hope; it was, after all, only dialectic again. How soon hope returns! We dwell in it even after the exile to which Pattie Donahue's laughter and nibbling teeth send us.

Turning to my father, whose head bent over the table in a way I only remembered afterward—his brother had died and Mother said he was crying because he was sad and I didn't believe her because daddies don't cry—I appealed to him with a manly challenge: "Almost everyone I know went on the naturewalk."

He did not yet look up.

"It's educational. Mr. Wilkerson says. Tom Moss was there. Almost everyone in our grade Seven-B Seven-A was there—"

"Lookit my waricose from standing up all day working like a horse eating my heart out," Mother said. "You should take a load off my feet, not I should carry you like a baby you're going on fourteen."

"Thirteen," I said.

"Going on anyway," she insisted, "*going* on. That's what it means. Big lummox. Look at my waricose go on look lookit."

She could not know—my cruelty at twelve years, soon thirteen!—that my only concern was for surgery on the distended veins, as other woman had, instead of wearing the lumpy corset that bulged about her calves under webbed brown stockings. My garment, she called it. Like taxes, Jake says. Teeth too, O! Sarah had the same trouble after Bernie and she took calcium. You ask me I think better injections in the arm, injections.

Dad listened watchfully over the soup in the evening heat. He hunched and studied vegetables in the bowl.

See how I admit the two of them to paper. Put my refusal of their world, which was their deepest gift to me, beside a son's longed-for and imagined love for his parents. Let me call myself a liar, but don't you be quick to do it. "Want to playboy around all your life dreaming smoke in the head?" my father used to ask me, and yet he loved me despite the law that we cannot love someone who refuses our gifts. I did not see the power and light of his world, in which the four causes were felt in action with my mother, vegetables and the Saturday specials; I had looked for light and power in Pattie and Poe while all the Aristotelian potencies and more lay waiting for me with the combustible garbage swept into the backyard at closing time each evening. The backroom, emptied and cleaned, was filled and emptied of carrot tops, beet greens, and the furry blue glow of spoiled oranges. I stalled; my father waited. I looked; my father watched.

A week earlier I had overheard Mother murmuring into the telephone, "So how's your Bernie? My Daniel shouldn't be better, he got a all-A report card and with a B plus in gymnistics, he gained two pounds by the scale but he's full of complexes, still a heart-ache in the store. . . Yah. . . I read in the paper it's complexes, Jake says he'll grow out. . ."

But only the complexes kept growing out. It's because I really like my parents that it costs me so much to speak kindly of them.

I remember how my father offered me his entire world and I threw it in his face like a rotten orange because he left out one little lump of an Atlantis, my own world.

"Listen to your father he's talking," my mother said. He had not yet spoken, but she knew him well and knew he now would. "You take his fifteen cents for a movie, don't you? Listen to your father."

Still sitting in his washed-out shirt crusted with salt under the armpits, in his old blue serge work pants, once dress-up with the sharpy stripe down the legs, more generous than fathers have a right to be, he tried to help me expiate my sin in a ritual of reprimand. No ceremony could heal him this time, but he waited. This came before the beginning: "At your age I was a man," he said.

He was right.

He swayed over the soup, food breathing back into his body the prayers he had forgotten in leaving his own father. His swaying shoulders heavily sloped and remembered. His father had forbidden him to go to godless America, better to die than to be unfaithful. This too he had forgotten, his father struck down by a Cossack's rifle, but the chant in his voice and the dance of his shoulders remembered.

"Look at you"—he could not. "Are you a man?"

No. Right again.

"A playboy. A naturewalker. A eater of ice cream."

All true. I still like ice cream, especially with Hershey's chocolate syrup. He taught me quality in food, my father. I waited for him to force me to make myself what we both agreed I should be; no ceremony could compel it though only ceremony could confirm it. Still I had to choose. Untheological, without brand names, we improvised ritual.

"A lollypop!" my mother shrilled, thinking she was on her husband's side. Here she was wrong. I was not a lollypop.

"Let me tell it, Rose," my father said softly, as if this were an incident on their trip to South Haven. "It's my turn to tell it, Rose."

"I don't care"—me turning in my pointed shoes perforated for ventilation and sweet beauty's sake under the eyes of Pattie. I mourned her now, blaming my birth. "I don't care about you." I lowered my gaze to my father's stubby foreign feet in steel-backed boots. "None of the kids have to do it. I don't care about you and your store."

He needed an instant for this. I gave it to him overflowing. "And—your—store."

His hand floated up like a speck fuming on the eyes; his fist crashed down on the enameled table like the plunging claw of a crate hammer. "Oh! Oh!"—Mother. Soup splashed out on his pants and ran weeping with little red carrot eyes.

His gaze was prophetic in mine. "*Some kits help out in the store,*" he said.

"We were practically supposed to go," I said, neither retreating nor regretting, gaining time and learning patience. "Mr. Wilkerson is a teacher."

"*Some kits remember their father and mother.*"

Everyone knows where it hurts when you begin to cry—that place at the back of the throat. Pins jabbed under my eyelids. My palate ached. The tears hurt most in that instant before they break out. . . And then I imagined cologned Pattie's cool laughter at my father's pronunciation of the *d* in *kits* ("—remember their father and mother"), and then drunk with the idea of the murder of someone I loved, my belly awash at the thought, I screamed him to his feet: "I won't, I *won't* work in your store. I don't want it. It's not my life. I hate it. I hate it!"

He stood huge over me, smelling of leafy vegetables and sweat, smelling of his strength and his terror because he would have to beat me. This is the reek of power, what the men at the Food Terminal understood when Ollie the Agent tried to shake down him first of the West Side men. . . The opponents were uneven. He had wise muscles, protected by years of work and good eating, the skills of use, the satisfactions of his time of life. He had three sons, only one of those baby brothers of mine lying awake to listen. His swaying body knew it loved me as his father had loved him, the woman carrying her child on a belly or breast, the man taking his son only at the eye or the fist. There must have been a great satisfaction in his fear and love at that moment.

My sole weapon was exactly my dissatisfaction. My father's arms swam with veins among the curled oily hairs on his light bluish freckled flesh. No bow-straight shoulders like Atlas the World's Most Perfect Develop It! No Culver Academy athlete calling for Pattie Donahue in his uniform at Christmastime! It was a body which had worked well and been used with pleasure, a happy body, soup on the pants, making its own purpose and content with this.

Mine, as I have said: discontented. I looked for a use for it. I said: "And you and your grocery boys and everyone! *I hate you!*"

Mother was crying and stacking the dishes in the sink when his open hand—generous! open!—struck my shoulder. I flew back and then up at him, slipping past his collar rough as a dog's tongue. Mother screamed. I climbed him, flailing; he was planted on the floor and he rocked under my weight for a moment, both of us silently straining toward each other and apart, our sweat pouring together while Mother screamed on and on—the malignant smell of hate and fear becoming the myrrh of two men fighting, the sweet cunning of love and death. I clung to his great neck to strangle it. His beard scratched my arm. He hugged my ribs, forcing them up—cracking!—pushing my hair out, lengthening my bones, driving my voice deep. Savagely he told me his life, wringing my childhood from me. I took this after his long day and had nothing to give in return but my unfleshed arms roped about his neck. We embraced like this.

The broken blood fled for a window into my mouth. I felt myself fainting.

Abruptly I lunged down, perhaps permitted to beg free. His weighty old-country strength: my agile sporting slyness: as he glanced for pity at my mother I threw myself like a pole against his knees in a playground stunt performed without thinking. The trick uprooted his legs; he crashed; his forehead above the unsurprised Tartar eyes hit my mother's foot when he fell.

He sat up and started to his feet as she held him. I could not breathe, my chest frozen. I turned from his sprawling. I let him hear me choke and then ran to my room. Yes, I had wanted to win, but now, fatalistic, in an instant guessing ahead, I made the highest demand on a father: that he know he had beaten me too, only because he had let it happen.

"What's happening to us all?"—those first tears of old age. "What's happening to us?" Dad was crying in the bathroom with the door shut and the water running in the sink so that no one would hear an old man with an ingrate son. He had locked Mother out, who was dry-eyed now, figuring.

If I am bereaved of my sons, the first Jacob said, *then am I bereaved.* To fight back was all I needed: he had given too much. Economy in Pattie! my father a spendthrift—such knowledge comes late to me now.

EDITORS' ANALYSIS

"The Heart of the Artichoke" involves the reader with its characters and its actions in a fairly complex way. It uses intellectual judgment and analysis (sometimes playfully), and depends for its effects, in part, upon the reader's responsiveness to the verbal paraphernalia of American life—to slogans, brandnames, and suburban clichés. The story exists in the cumulative immediacy of the successive scenes, as it explores the blocked resentments of childhood, contrasting adolescent romance with adolescent rebellion against parents. In the anger and the violence of the final episode is a suggestion of reconciliation between the hopes of the two generations, between the son and his father.

QUESTIONS

1. What does the father's attack on the artichoke, in the opening scene, symbolize for the whole story? What are the characteristics of an artichoke which the author intends to apply to the father?

2. Can you name the boy's resentment, or is it deeper than the incidents of the story which illustrate it? Is it a cluster of resentments? How are they linked with hopes and ambitions?

3. What is the effect of the final comment of the story: "such knowledge comes late to me now"? Does it alter an earlier point of view of the reader toward the boy?

4. How much of your own self do you find in this story? How much resistance does the story generate in you against the point of view of the teller of the story and in favor of the reactions of the other characters?

5. Do you as reader respond to the devices of the story-telling, as described in the "Editors' Analysis," above?

6. Do you prefer Schorer's simple narrative style to Gold's more intensely dramatized one? What are the gains of each style? The losses?

Winter Night

by KAY BOYLE

Kay Boyle (1903-   ) created her reputation between the two wars as a writer of subtle fiction, somewhat elusive in tone and atmosphere. Although born in America, she has lived much of her life in Europe, and many of her novels and short stories have European settings. The importance of her fiction lies in her skillful, evocative use of language by which she makes the characters and the events of her stories take on a social or political implication in excess of their surface meaning. Her novel *His Human Majesty* (1949), for example, portrayed a ski troop made up of men from European countries, in training in Colorado to go back one day to seize their pre-Nazi heritage. Her most famous short story, "The White Horses of Vienna" (*Harper's*, April 1936), is a study in conflicting political and cultural elements in Austria on the eve of its conquest by Hitler.

The short story "Winter Night" has a New York setting, and exploits the reader's awareness of the terrifying vulnerability of a child in her need for love and reassurance. At a certain moment in growing up, the world can seem hostile merely because the day is ending and a parent has not come home for dinner. But this story has a larger, more insistent meaning.

There is a time of apprehension which begins with the beginning of darkness, and to which only the speech of love can lend security. It is there, in abeyance, at the end of every day, not urgent enough to be given the name of fear but rather of concern for how the hours are to be reprieved from fear, and those who have forgotten how it was when they were children can remember nothing of this. It may begin around five o'clock on a winter afternoon when the light outside is dying in the windows. At that hour the New York apartment in which Felicia lived was filled with shadows, and the little girl would wait alone

Winter Night. Reprinted from *Thirty Stories*, by Kay Boyle. First printed in *The New Yorker*, January 19, 1946. Copyright 1946 by Kay Boyle.

in the living room, looking out at the winter-stripped trees that stood black in the park against the isolated ovals of unclean snow. Now it was January, and the day had been a cold one; the water of the artificial lake was frozen fast, but because of the cold and the coming darkness, the skaters had ceased to move across its surface. The street that lay between the park and the apartment house was wide, and the two-way streams of cars and busses, some with their headlamps already shining, advanced and halted and poured swiftly on to the tempo of the traffic signals' altering lights. The time of apprehension had set in, and Felicia, who was seven, stood at the window in the evening and waited before she asked the question. When the signals below would change from red to green again, or when the double-decker bus would turn the corner below, she would ask it. The words of it were already there, tentative in her mouth, when the answer came from the far end of the hall.

"Your mother," said the voice among the sound of kitchen things, "she telephoned up before you came in from nursery school. She won't be back in time for supper. I was to tell you a sitter was coming in from the sitting parents' place."

Felicia turned back from the window into the obscurity of the living room, and she looked toward the open door, and into the hall beyond it where the light from the kitchen fell in a clear yellow angle across the wall and onto the strip of carpet. Her hands were cold, and she put them in her jacket pockets as she walked carefully across the living-room rug and stopped at the edge of light.

"Will she be home late?" she said.

For a moment there was the sound of water running in the kitchen, a long way away, and then the sound of the water ceased, and the high, Southern voice went on:

"She'll come home when she gets ready to come home. That's all I have to say. If she wants to spend two dollars and fifty cents and ten cents' carfare on top of that three or four nights out of the week for a sitting parent to come in here and sit, it's her own business. It certainly ain't nothing to do with you or me. She makes her money, just like the rest of us does. She works all day down there in the office, or whatever it is, just like the rest of us works, and she's entitled to spend her money like she wants to spend it. There's no law in the world against buying your own freedom, that's all we're doing. And we're not doing nobody no harm."

"Do you know who she's having supper with?" said Felicia from the edge of dark. There was one more step to take, and then she would be standing in the light that fell on the strip of carpet, but she did not take the step.

"Do I know who she's having supper with?" the voice cried out in what might have been derision, and there was the sound of dishes striking the metal ribs of the drainboard by the sink. "Maybe it's Mr. Van Johnson, or Mr. Frank Sinatra, or maybe it's just the Duke of Wincers for the evening. All I know is you're having softboiled egg and spinach and applesauce for supper, and you're going to have it quick now because the time is getting away."

The voice from the kitchen had no name. It was as variable as the faces and figures of the women who came and sat in the evenings. Month by month the voice in the kitchen altered to another voice, and the sitting parents were no more than lonely aunts of an evening or two who sometimes returned and sometimes did not to this apartment in which they had sat before. Nobody stayed anywhere very long any more, Felicia's mother told her. It was part of the time in which you lived, and part of the life of the city, but when the fathers came back, all this would be miraculously changed. Perhaps you would live in a house again, a small one, with fir trees on either side of the short brick walk, and Father would drive up every night from the station just after darkness set in. When Felicia thought of this, she stepped quickly into the clear angle of light, and she left the dark of the living room behind her and ran softly down the hall.

The drop-leaf table stood in the kitchen between the refrigerator and the sink, and Felicia sat down at the place that was set. The voice at the sink was speaking still, and while Felicia ate it did not cease to speak until the bell of the front door rang abruptly. The girl walked around the table and went down the hall, wiping her dark palms in her apron, and, from the drop-leaf table, Felicia watched her step from the angle of light into darkness and open the door.

"You put in an early appearance," the girl said, and the woman who had rung the bell came into the hall. The door closed behind her, and the girl showed her into the living room, and lit the lamp on the bookcase, and the shadows were suddenly bleached away. But when the girl turned, the woman turned from the living room too and followed her, humbly and in silence,

to the threshold of the kitchen. "Sometimes they keep me standing around waiting after it's time for me to be getting on home,
the sitting parents do," the girl said, and she picked up the last
two dishes from the table and put them in the sink. The woman
who stood in the doorway was a small woman, and when she
undid the white silk scarf from around her head, Felicia saw that
her hair was black. She wore it parted in the middle, and it had
not been cut, but was drawn back loosely into a knot behind her
head. She had very clean white gloves on, and her face was pale,
and there was a look of sorrow in her soft black eyes. "Sometimes
I have to stand out there in the hall with my hat and coat on,
waiting for the sitting parents to turn up," the girl said, and, as
she turned on the water in the sink, the contempt she had for
them hung on the kitchen air. "But you're ahead of time," she
said, and she held the dishes, first one and then the other, under
the flow of steaming water.

The woman in the doorway wore a neat black coat, not a new-
looking coat, and it had no fur on it, but it had a smooth velvet
collar and velvet lapels. She did not move, or smile, and she
gave no sign that she had heard the girl speaking above the
sound of water at the sink. She simply stood looking at Felicia,
who sat at the table with the milk in her glass not finished yet.

"Are you the child?" she said at last, and her voice was low,
and the pronunciation of the words a little strange.

"Yes, this here's Felicia," the girl said, and the dark hands
dried the dishes and put them away. "You drink up your milk
quick now, Felicia, so's I can rinse your glass."

"I will wash the glass," said the woman. "I would like to wash
the glass for her," and Felicia sat looking across the table at the
face in the doorway that was filled with such unspoken grief. "I
will wash the glass for her and clean off the table," the woman
was saying quietly. "When the child is finished, she will show
me where her night things are."

"The others, they wouldn't do anything like that," the girl said,
and she hung the dishcloth over the rack. "They wouldn't put
their hand to housework, the sitting parents. That's where they
got the name for them," she said.

Whenever the front door closed behind the girl in the evening,
it would usually be that the sitting parent who was there would
take up a book of fairy stories and read aloud for a while to
Felicia; or else would settle herself in the big chair in the living
room and begin to tell the words of a story in drowsiness to her,

while Felicia took off her clothes in the bedroom, and folded them, and put her pajamas on, and brushed her teeth, and did her hair. But this time, that was not the way it happened. Instead, the woman sat down on the other chair at the kitchen table, and she began at once to speak, not of good fairies or bad, or of animals endowed with human speech, but to speak quietly, in spite of the eagerness behind her words, of a thing that seemed of singular importance to her.

"It is strange that I should have been sent here tonight," she said, her eyes moving slowly from feature to feature of Felicia's face, "for you look like a child that I knew once, and this is the anniversary of that child."

"Did she have hair like mine?" Felicia asked quickly, and she did not keep her eyes fixed on the unfinished glass of milk in shyness any more.

"Yes, she did. She had hair like yours," said the woman, and her glance paused for a moment on the locks which fell straight and thick on the shoulders of Felicia's dress. It may have been that she thought to stretch out her hand and touch the ends of Felicia's hair, for her fingers stirred as they lay clasped together on the table, and then they relapsed into passivity again. "But it is not the hair alone, it is the delicacy of your face, too, and your eyes the same, filled with the same spring lilac color," the woman said, pronouncing the words carefully. "She had little coats of golden fur on her arms and legs," she said, "and when we were closed up there, the lot of us in the cold, I used to make her laugh when I told her that the fur was so pretty, like a little fawn's skin on her arms, would always help to keep her warm."

"And did it keep her warm?" asked Felicia, and she gave a little jerk of laughter as she looked down at her own legs hanging under the table, with the bare calves thin and covered with a down of hair.

"It did not keep her warm enough," the woman said, and now the mask of grief had come back upon her face. "So we used to take everything we could spare from ourselves, and we would sew them into cloaks and other kinds of garments for her and for the other children. . . ."

"Was it a school?" said Felicia when the woman's voice had ceased to speak.

"No," said the woman softly, "it was not a school, but still there were a lot of children there. It was a camp—that was the name the place had; it was a camp. It was a place where they put

people until they could decide what was to be done with them."
She sat with her hands clasped, silent a moment, looking at
Felicia. "That little dress you have on," she said, not saying the
words to anybody, scarcely saying them aloud. "Oh, she would
have liked that little dress, the little buttons shaped like hearts,
and the white collar——"

"I have four school dresses," Felicia said. "I'll show them to
you. How many dresses did she have?"

"Well, there, you see, there in the camp," said the woman, "she
did not have any dresses except the little skirt and the pullover.
That was all she had. She had brought just a handkerchief of her
belongings with her, like everybody else—just enough for three
days away from home was what they told us, so she did not have
enough to last the winter. But she had her ballet slippers," the
woman said, and her clasped fingers did not move. "She had
brought them because she thought during her three days away
from home she would have the time to practice her ballet."

"I've been to the ballet," Felicia said suddenly, and she said it
so eagerly that she stuttered a little as the words came out of her
mouth. She slipped quickly down from the chair and went around
the table to where the woman sat. Then she took one of the
woman's hands away from the other that held it fast, and she
pulled her toward the door. "Come into the living room and I'll
do a pirouette for you," she said, and then she stopped speaking,
her eyes halted on the woman's face. "Did she—did the little
girl—could she do a pirouette very well?" she said.

"Yes, she could. At first she could," said the woman, and Felicia
felt uneasy now at the sound of sorrow in her words. "But after
that she was hungry. She was hungry all winter," she said in a
low voice. "We were all hungry, but the children were the hun-
griest. Even now," she said, and her voice went suddenly savage,
"when I see milk like that, clean, fresh milk standing in a glass, I
want to cry out loud, I want to beat my hands on the table, because it did not have to be . . ." She had drawn her fingers
abruptly away from Felicia now, and Felicia stood before her,
cast off, forlorn, alone again in the time of apprehension. "That
was three years ago," the woman was saying, and one hand was
lifted, as in weariness, to shade her face. "It was somewhere
else, it was in another country," she said, and behind her hand
her eyes were turned upon the substance of a world in which
Felicia had played no part.

"Did—did the little girl cry when she was hungry?" Felicia
asked, and the woman shook her head.

"Sometimes she cried," she said, "but not very much. She was very quiet. One night when she heard the other children crying, she said to me, 'You know, they are not crying because they want something to eat. They are crying because their mothers have gone away.'"

"Did the mothers have to go out to supper?" Felicia asked, and she watched the woman's face for the answer.

"No," said the woman. She stood up from her chair, and now that she put her hand on the little girl's shoulder, Felicia was taken into the sphere of love and intimacy again. "Shall we go into the other room, and you will do your pirouette for me?" the woman said, and they went from the kitchen and down the strip of carpet on which the clear light fell. In the front room, they paused hand in hand in the glow of the shaded lamp, and the woman looked about her, at the books, the low tables with the magazines and ash trays on them, the vase of roses on the piano, looking with dark, scarcely seeing eyes at these things that had no reality at all. It was only when she saw the little white clock on the mantelpiece that she gave any sign, and then she said quickly: "What time does your mother put you to bed?"

Felicia waited a moment, and in the interval of waiting the woman lifted one hand and, as if in reverence, touched Felicia's hair.

"What time did the little girl you knew in the other place go to bed?" Felicia asked.

"Ah, God, I do not know, I do not remember," the woman said.

"Was she your little girl?" said Felicia softly, stubbornly.

"No," said the woman. "She was not mine. At least, at first she was not mine. She had a mother, a real mother, but the mother had to go away."

"Did she come back late?" asked Felicia.

"No, ah, no, she could not come back, she never came back," the woman said, and now she turned, her arm around Felicia's shoulders, and she sat down in the low soft chair. "Why am I saying all this to you, why am I doing it?" she cried out in grief, and she held Felicia close against her. "I had thought to speak of the anniversary to you, and that was all, and now I am saying these other things to you. Three years ago today, exactly, the little girl became my little girl because her mother went away. That is all there is to it. There is nothing more."

Felicia waited another moment, held close against the woman, and listening to the swift, strong heartbeats in the woman's breast.

"But the mother," she said then in a small, persistent voice, "did she take a taxi when she went?"

"This is the way it used to happen," said the woman, speaking in hopelessness and bitterness in the softly lighted room. "Every week they used to come into the place where we were and they would read a list of names out. Sometimes it would be the names of children they would read out, and then a little later they would have to go away. And sometimes it would be the grown people's names, the names of the mothers or big sisters, or other women's names. The men were not with us. The fathers were somewhere else, in another place."

"Yes," Felicia said. "I know."

"We had been there only a little while, maybe ten days or maybe not so long," the woman went on, holding Felicia against her still, "when they read the name of the little girl's mother out, and that afternoon they took her away."

"What did the little girl do?" Felicia said.

"She wanted to think up the best way of getting out so that she could go find her mother," said the woman, "but she could not think of anything good enough until the third or fourth day. And then she tied her ballet slippers up in the handkerchief again, and she went up to the guard standing at the door." The woman's voice was gentle, controlled now. "She asked the guard please to open the door so that she could go out. 'This is Thursday,' she said, 'and every Tuesday and Thursday I have my ballet lessons. If I miss a ballet lesson, they do not count the money off, so my mother would be just paying for nothing, and she cannot afford to pay for nothing. I missed my ballet lesson on Tuesday,' she said to the guard, 'and I must not miss it again today.'"

Felicia lifted her head from the woman's shoulder, and she shook her hair back and looked in question and wonder at the woman's face.

"And did the man let her go?" she said.

"No, he did not. He could not do that," said the woman. "He was a soldier and he had to do what he was told. So every evening after her mother went, I used to brush the little girl's hair for her," the woman went on saying. "And while I brushed it, I used to tell her the stories of the ballets. Sometimes I would begin with *Narcissus*," the woman said, and she parted Felicia's locks with her fingers, "so if you go and get your brush now, I will tell it while I brush your hair."

"Oh, yes," said Felicia, and she made two whirls as she went quickly to the bedroom. On the way back, she stopped and held on to the piano with the fingers of one hand while she went up on her toes. "Did you see me? Did you see me standing on my toes?" she called to the woman, and the woman sat smiling in love and contentment at her.

"Yes, wonderful, really wonderful," she said. "I am sure I have never seen anyone do it so well." Felicia came spinning toward her, whirling in pirouette after pirouette, and she flung herself down in the chair close to her, with her thin bones pressed against the woman's soft, wide hip. The woman took the silver-backed, monogrammed brush and the tortoise-shell comb in her hands, and now she began to brush Felicia's hair. "We did not have any soap at all and not very much water to wash in, so I never could fix her as nicely and prettily as I wanted to," she said, and the brush stroked regularly, carefully down, caressing the shape of Felicia's head.

"If there wasn't very much water, then how did she do her teeth?" Felicia said.

"She did not do her teeth," said the woman, and she drew the comb through Felicia's hair. "There were not any toothbrushes or tooth paste, or anything like that."

Felicia waited a moment, constructing the unfamiliar scene of it in silence, and then she asked the tentative question.

"Do I have to do my teeth tonight?" she said.

"No," said the woman, and she was thinking of something else, "you do not have to do your teeth."

"If I am your little girl tonight, can I pretend there isn't enough water to wash?" said Felicia.

"Yes," said the woman, "you can pretend that if you like. You do not have to wash," she said, and the comb passed lightly through Felicia's hair.

"Will you tell me the story of the ballet?" said Felicia, and the rhythm of the brushing was like the soft, slow rocking of sleep.

"Yes," said the woman. "In the first one, the place is a forest glade with little pale birches growing in it, and they have green veils over their faces and green veils drifting from their fingers, because it is the springtime. There is the music of a flute," said the woman's voice softly, softly, "and creatures of the wood are dancing——"

"But the mother," Felicia said as suddenly as if she had been awaked from sleep. "What did the little girl's mother say when she didn't do her teeth and didn't wash at night?"

"The mother was not there, you remember," said the woman, and the brush moved steadily in her hand. "But she did send one little letter back. Sometimes the people who went away were able to do that. The mother wrote it in a train, standing up in a car that had no seats," she said, and she might have been telling the story of the ballet still, for her voice was gentle and the brush did not falter on Felicia's hair. "There were perhaps a great many other people standing up in the train with her, perhaps all trying to write their little letters on the bits of paper they had managed to hide on them, or that they had found in forgotten corners as they traveled. When they had written their letters, then they must try to slip them out through the boards of the car in which they journeyed, standing up," said the woman, "and these letters fell down on the tracks under the train, or they were blown into the fields or onto the country roads, and if it was a kind person who picked them up, he would seal them in envelopes and send them to where they were addressed to go. So a letter came back like this from the little girl's mother," the woman said, and the brush followed the comb, the comb the brush in steady pursuit through Felicia's hair. "It said good-by to the little girl, and it said please to take care of her. It said: 'Whoever reads this letter in the camp, please take good care of my little girl for me, and please have her tonsils looked at by a doctor if this is possible to do.'"

"And then," said Felicia softly, persistently, "what happened to the little girl?"

"I do not know. I cannot say," the woman said. But now the brush and comb had ceased to move, and in the silence Felicia turned her thin, small body on the chair, and she and the woman suddenly put their arms around each other. "They must all be asleep now, all of them," the woman said, and in the silence that fell on them again, they held each other closer. "They must be quietly asleep somewhere, and not crying all night because they are hungry and because they are cold. For three years I have been saying 'They must all be asleep, and the cold and the hunger and the seasons or night or day or nothing matters to them——'"

It was after midnight when Felicia's mother put her key in the lock of the front door, and pushed it open, and stepped into the hallway. She walked quickly to the living room, and just across the threshold she slipped the three blue foxskins from her shoulders and dropped them, with her little velvet bag, upon the chair. The room was quiet, so quiet that she could hear the sound of breathing in it, and no one spoke to her in greeting as she crossed toward the bedroom door. And then, as startling as a slap across her delicately tinted face, she saw the woman lying sleeping on the divan, and Felicia, in her school dress still, asleep within the woman's arms.

EDITORS' ANALYSIS

Unlike either "The Heart of the Artichoke" or "Boy in the Summer Sun," Kay Boyle's "Winter Night" attains its effect by being almost wholly static. It is a conversation piece between the child and the "sitting parent," with a delicate, omniscient author's assertion at the beginning, and the mother's brief entrance at the end, to solidify its meaning. "Winter Night" involves the reader with the vulnerability not just of the Felicia of the story, but with that of all children. The title and the sitter's reactions also suggest the awful night of civilization itself, where other Felicias have felt the normal terror of growing up, but not in a New York apartment—in a concentration camp.

QUESTIONS

1. The emotions conveyed by this story are really not stated in the story at all, or so understated as to make it difficult to describe them in lines taken from the story. How does Kay Boyle manage this feat? By what kinds of implication?

2. Are Felicia's anxious moments meant to be any less terrible for her because they take place in a relatively safe environment?

3. Does the story, by implication, indict the mother for leaving her child with the sitter? If not, what is the intended effect of the brief, last scene, in which the child and the paid sitter are asleep in each others' arms?

4. To what degree does this story intend to suggest the general anxiety of the postwar period? What are the implications of the sitter's memories of the war years?

5. Do all three stories of this section have a common emotional denominator in that they all present aspects of the fear of the loss of love, the fear of not belonging?

2.

EDUCATION

"Of This Time, Of That Place," *by Lionel Trilling*

"The Unvexed Isles," *by Robert Penn Warren*

Of This Time, of That Place

by LIONEL TRILLING

Lionel Trilling (1905-   ) is Professor of English at Columbia University, literary critic and scholar, and occasional writer of fiction. His two book-length critical studies, *Matthew Arnold* (1939) and *E. M. Forster* (1943), and three collections of shorter essays, *The Liberal Imagination* (1950), *The Opposing Self* (1955), and *A Gathering of Fugitives* (1956), have been as widely discussed in England as in America. He is the author of one novel, *The Middle of the Journey* (1947), a fictional study of conflicting political philosophies in America in the post-depression years.

"Of This Time, Of That Place" has no special relationship to the main body of Trilling's published work except that, as a study of college life and its problems, it is a fictional product of the environment in which he works. The story itself, however, has become a minor classic of our time as an exploration of a student caught up in a severe psychological crisis and his instructor's vain wish to respond adequately to it.

It was a fine September day. By noon it would be summer again, but now it was true autumn with a touch of chill in the air. As Joseph Howe stood on the porch of the house in which he lodged, ready to leave for his first class of the year, he thought with pleasure of the long indoor days that were coming. It was a moment when he could feel glad of his profession.

On the lawn the peach tree was still in fruit and young Hilda Aiken was taking a picture of it. She held the camera tight against her chest. She wanted the sun behind her, but she did not want her own long morning shadow in the foreground. She raised the camera, but that did not help, and she lowered it, but that made things worse. She twisted her body to the left, then to the right. In the end she had to step out of the direct line of the sun. At last she snapped the shutter and wound the film with intense care.

Howe, watching her from the porch, waited for her to finish and called good morning. She turned, startled, and almost sullenly lowered her glance. In the year Howe had lived at the Aikens', Hilda had accepted him as one of her family, but since his absence of the summer she had grown shy. Then suddenly she lifted her head and smiled at him, and the humorous smile confirmed his pleasure in the day. She picked up her bookbag and set off for school.

The handsome houses on the streets to the college were not yet fully awake, but they looked very friendly. Howe went by the Bradby house where he would be a guest this evening at the first dinner party of the year. When he had gone the length of the picket fence, the whitest in town, he turned back. Along the path there was a fine row of asters and he went through the gate and picked one for his buttonhole. The Bradbys would be pleased if they happened to see him invading their lawn and the knowledge of this made him even more comfortable.

He reached the campus as the hour was striking. The students were hurrying to their classes. He himself was in no hurry. He stopped at his dim cubicle of an office and lit a cigarette. The prospect of facing his class had suddenly presented itself to him and his hands were cold; the lawful seizure of power he was about to make seemed momentous. Waiting did not help. He put out his cigarette, picked up a pad of theme paper, and went to his classroom.

As he entered, the rattle of voices ceased, and the twenty-odd freshmen settled themselves and looked at him appraisingly. Their faces seemed gross, his heart sank at their massed impassivity, but he spoke briskly.

'My name is Howe,' he said, and turned and wrote it on the blackboard. The carelessness of the scrawl confirmed his authority. He went on, 'My office is 412 Slemp Hall, and my office-hours are Monday, Wednesday and Friday from eleven-thirty to twelve-thirty.'

He wrote, 'M., W., F., 11:30—12:30.' He said, 'I'll be very glad to see any of you at that time. Or if you can't come then, you can arrange with me for some other time.'

He turned again to the blackboard and spoke over his shoulder. 'The text for the course is Jarman's *Modern Plays*, revised edition. The Co-op has it in stock.' He wrote the name, underlined 'revised edition' and waited for it to be taken down in the new notebooks.

When the bent heads were raised again he began his speech of prospectus. 'It is hard to explain—' he said, and paused as they composed themselves. 'It is hard to explain what a course like this is intended to do. We are going to try to learn something about modern literature and something about prose composition.'

As he spoke, his hands warmed and he was able to look directly at the class. Last year on the first day the faces had seemed just as cloddish, but as the term wore on they became gradually alive and quite likable. It did not seem possible that the same thing could happen again.

'I shall not lecture in this course,' he continued. 'Our work will be carried on by discussion and we will try to learn by an exchange of opinion. But you will soon recognize that my opinion is worth more than anyone else's here.'

He remained grave as he said it, but two boys understood and laughed. The rest took permission from them and laughed too. All Howe's private ironies protested the vulgarity of the joke, but the laughter made him feel benign and powerful.

When the little speech was finished, Howe picked up the pad of paper he had brought. He announced that they would write an extemporaneous theme. Its subject was traditional, 'Who I am and why I came to Dwight College.' By now the class was more at ease and it gave a ritualistic groan of protest. Then there was a stir as fountain pens were brought out and the writing-arms of the chairs were cleared, and the paper was passed about. At last, all the heads bent to work, and the room became still.

Howe sat idly at his desk. The sun shone through the tall clumsy windows. The cool of the morning was already passing. There was a scent of autumn and of varnish and the stillness of the room was deep and oddly touching. Now and then a student's head was raised and scratched in the old, elaborate students' pantomime that calls the teacher to witness honest intellectual effort.

Suddenly a tall boy stood within the frame of the open door. 'Is this,' he said, and thrust a large nose into a college catalogue, 'is this the meeting place of English 1A? The section instructed by Dr. Joseph Howe?'

He stood on the very sill of the door, as if refusing to enter until he was perfectly sure of all his rights. The class looked up from work, found him absurd and gave a low mocking cheer.

The teacher and the new student, with equal pointedness, ignored the disturbance. Howe nodded to the boy, who pushed his head forward and then jerked it back in a wide elaborate arc to clear his brow of a heavy lock of hair. He advanced into the room and halted before Howe, almost at attention. In a loud, clear voice he announced, 'I am Tertan, Ferdinand R., reporting at the direction of Head of Department Vincent.'

The heraldic formality of this statement brought forth another cheer. Howe looked at the class with a sternness he could not really feel, for there was indeed something ridiculous about this boy. Under his displeased regard the rows of heads dropped to work again. Then he touched Tertan's elbow, led him up to the desk and stood so as to shield their conversation from the class.

'We are writing an extemporaneous theme,' he said. 'The subject is, "Who I am and why I came to Dwight College."'

He stripped a few sheets from the pad and offered them to the boy. Tertan hesitated and then took the paper, but he held it only tentatively. As if with the effort of making something clear, he gulped, and a slow smile fixed itself on his face. It was at once knowing and shy.

'Professor,' he said, 'to be perfectly fair to my classmates'—he made a large gesture over the room—'and to you'—he inclined his head to Howe—'this would not be for me an extemporaneous subject.'

Howe tried to understand. 'You mean you've already thought about it—you've heard we always give the same subject? That doesn't matter.'

Again the boy ducked his head and gulped. It was the gesture of one who wishes to make a difficult explanation with perfect candor. 'Sir,' he said, and made the distinction with great care, 'the topic I did not expect, but I have given much ratiocination to the subject.'

Howe smiled and said, 'I don't thing that's an unfair advantage. Just go ahead and write.'

Tertan narrowed his eyes and glanced sidewise at Howe. His strange mouth smiled. Then in quizzical acceptance, he ducked his head, threw back the heavy, dank lock, dropped into a seat with a great loose noise and began to write rapidly.

The room fell silent again and Howe resumed his idleness. When the bell rang, the students who had groaned when the task had been set now groaned again because they had not finished. Howe took up the papers, and held the class while he made the first assignment. When he dismissed it, Tertan bore down on him, his slack mouth held ready for speech.

'Some professors,' he said, 'are pedants. They are Dryasdusts.

However, some professors are free souls and creative spirits. Kant, Hegel and Nietzsche were all professors.' With this pronouncement he paused. 'It is my opinion,' he continued, 'that you occupy the second category.'

Howe looked at the boy in surprise and said with good-natured irony, 'With Kant, Hegel and Nietzsche?'

Not only Tertan's hand and head but his whole awkward body waved away the stupidity. 'It is the kind and not the quantity of the kind,' he said sternly.

Rebuked, Howe said as simply and seriously as he could, 'It would be nice to think so.' He added, 'Of course I am not a professor.'

This was clearly a disappointment but Tertan met it. 'In the French sense,' he said with composure. 'Generically, a teacher.'

Suddenly he bowed. It was such a bow, Howe fancied, as a stage-director might teach an actor playing a medieval student who takes leave of Abelard—stiff, solemn, with elbows close to the body and feet together. Then, quite as suddenly, he turned and left.

A queer fish, and as soon as Howe reached his office, he sifted through the batch of themes and drew out Tertan's. The boy had filled many sheets with his unformed headlong scrawl. 'Who am I?' he had begun. 'Here, in a mundane, not to say commercialized academe, is asked the question which from time long immemorably out of mind has accreted doubts and thoughts in the psyche of man to pester him as a nuisance. Whether in St. Augustine (or Austin as sometimes called) or Miss Bashkirtsieff or Frederic Amiel or Empedocles, or in less lights of the intellect than these, this posed question has been ineluctable.'

Howe took out his pencil. He circled 'academe' and wrote 'vocab.' in the margin. He underlined 'time long immemorably out of mind' and wrote 'Diction!' But this seemed inadequate for what was wrong. He put down his pencil and read ahead to discover the principle of error in the theme. 'Today as ever, in spite of gloomy prophets of the dismal science (economics) the question is uninvalidated. Out of the starry depths of heaven hurtles this spear of query demanding to be caught on the shield of the mind ere it pierces the skull and the limbs be unstrung.'

Baffled but quite caught, Howe read on. 'Materialism, by which is meant the philosophic concept and not the moral idea, provides no aegis against the question which lies beyond the tangible (metaphysics). Existence without alloy is the question presented.

Environment and heredity relegated aside, the rags and old clothes of practical life discarded, the name and the instrumentality of livelihood do not, as the prophets of the dismal science insist on in this connection, give solution to the interrogation which not from the professor merely but veritably from the cosmos is given. I think, therefore I am (cogito etc.) but who am I? Tertan I am, but what is Tertan? Of this time, of that place, of some parentage, what does it matter?'

Existence without alloy: the phrase established itself. Howe put aside Tertan's paper and at random picked up another. 'I am Arthur J. Casebeer, Jr.,' he read. 'My father is Arthur J. Casebeer and my grandfather was Arthur J. Casebeer before him. My mother is Nina Wimble Casebeer. Both of them are college graduates and my father is in insurance. I was born in St. Louis eighteen years ago and we still make our residence there.'

Arthur J. Casebeer, who knew who he was, was less interesting than Tertan, but more coherent. Howe picked up Tertan's paper again. It was clear that none of the routine marginal comments, no 'sent. str.' or 'punct.' or 'vocab.' could cope with this torrential rhetoric. He read ahead, contenting himself with underscoring the errors against the time when he should have the necessary 'conference' with Tertan.

It was a busy and official day of cards and sheets, arrangements and small decisions, and it gave Howe pleasure. Even when it was time to attend the first of the weekly Convocations he felt the charm of the beginning of things when intention is still innocent and uncorrupted by effort. He sat among the young instructors on the platform, and joined in their humorous complaints at having to assist at the ceremony, but actually he got a clear satisfaction from the ritual of prayer and prosy speech, and even from wearing his academic gown. And when the Convocation was over the pleasure continued as he crossed the campus, exchanging greetings with men he had not seen since the spring. They were people who did not yet, and perhaps never would, mean much to him, but in a year they had grown amiably to be part of his life. They were his fellow-townsmen.

The day had cooled again at sunset, and there was a bright chill in the September twilight. Howe carried his voluminous gown over his arm, he swung his doctoral hood by its purple neckpiece, and on his head he wore his mortarboard with its heavy gold tassel bobbing just over his eye. These were the weighty and absurd symbols of his new profession and they pleased him. At twenty-six Joseph Howe had discovered that he was neither so well off nor so bohemian as he had once thought. A small income, adequate when supplemented by a sizable cash legacy, was genteel poverty when the cash was all spent. And the literary life—the room at the Lafayette, or the small apartment without a lease, the long summers on the Cape, the long afternoons and the social evenings—began to weary him. His writing filled his mornings and should perhaps have filled his life, yet it did not. To the amusement of his friends, and with a certain sense that he was betraying his own freedom, he had used the last of his legacy for a year at Harvard. The small but respectable reputation of his two volumes of verse had proved useful—he continued at Harvard on a fellowship and when he emerged as Doctor Howe he received an excellent appointment, with prospects, at Dwight.

He had his moments of fear when all that had ever been said of the dangers of the academic life had occurred to him. But after a year in which he had tested every possibility of corruption and seduction he was ready to rest easy. His third volume of verse, most of it written in his first years of teaching, was not only ampler but, he thought, better than its predecessors.

There was a clear hour before the Bradby dinner party, and Howe looked forward to it. But he was not to enjoy it, for lying with his mail on the hall table was a copy of this quarter's issue of *Life and Letters*, to which his landlord subscribed. Its severe cover announced that its editor, Frederic Woolley, had this month contributed an essay called 'Two Poets,' and Howe, picking it up, curious to see who the two poets might be, felt his own name start out at him with cabalistic power—Joseph Howe. As he continued to turn the pages his hand trembled.

Standing in the dark hall, holding the neat little magazine, Howe knew that his literary contempt for Frederic Woolley meant nothing, for he suddenly understood how he respected Woolley in the way of the world. He knew this by the trembling of his hand. And of the little world as well as the great, for although the literary groups of New York might dismiss Woolley, his name carried high authority in the academic world. At Dwight it was even a revered name, for it had been here at the college that Frederic Woolley had made the distinguished scholarly career from which he had gone on to literary journalism. In middle life he had been induced to take the editorship of *Life and Letters*, a literary monthly not widely read but heavily endowed, and in its pages he had carried on the defense of what he sometimes called the older values. He was not without wit, he had great knowledge and considerable taste, and even in the full movement of the 'new' literature he had won a certain respect for his refusal to accept it. In France, even in England, he would have been connected with a more robust tradition of conservatism, but America gave him an audience not much better than genteel. It was known in the college that to the subsidy of *Life and Letters* the Bradbys contributed a great part.

As Howe read, he saw that he was involved in nothing less than an event. When the Fifth Series of *Studies in Order and Value* came to be collected, this latest of Frederic Woolley's essays would not be merely another step in the old direction. Clearly and unmistakably, it was a turning point. All his literary life Woolley had been concerned with the relation of literature to mortality, religion, and the private and delicate pieties, and he had been unalterably opposed to all that he had called 'inhuman humanitarianism.' But here, suddenly, dramatically late, he had made an about-face, turning to the public life and to the humanitarian politics he had so long despised. This was the kind of incident the histories of literature make much of. Frederic Woolley was opening for himself a new career and winning a kind of new youth. He contrasted the two poets, Thomas Wormser, who was admirable, Joseph Howe, who was almost dangerous. He spoke of the 'precious subjectivism' of Howe's verse. 'In times like ours,' he wrote, 'with millions facing penury and want, one feels that the qualities of the *tour d'ivoire* are well-nigh inhuman, nearly insulting. The *tour d'ivoire* becomes the *tour d'ivresse,* and it is not self-intoxicated poets that our people need.' The essay said more: 'The problem is one of meaning. I am not ignorant that the creed of the esoteric poets declares that a poem does not and should not *mean* anything, that it *is* something. But poetry is what the poet makes it, and if he is a true poet he makes what his society needs. And what is needed now is the tradition in which Mr. Wormser writes, the true tradition of poetry. The Howes do no harm, but they do no good when positive good is demanded of all responsible men. Or do the Howes indeed do no harm? Perhaps Plato would have said they do, that in some ways theirs is the Phrygian music that turns men's minds from the struggle. Certainly it is true that Thomas Wormser writes in the lucid Dorian mode which sends men into battle with evil.'

It was easy to understand why Woolley had chosen to praise

Thomas Wormser. The long, lilting lines of *Corn Under Willows* hymned, as Woolley put it, the struggle for wheat in the Iowa fields, and expressed the real lives of real people. But why out of the dozen more notable examples he had chosen Howe's little volume as the example of 'precious subjectivism' was hard to guess. In a way it was funny, this multiplication of himself into 'the Howes.' And yet this becoming the multiform political symbol by whose creation Frederic Woolley gave the sign of a sudden new life, this use of him as a sacrifice whose blood was necessary for the rites of rejuvenation, made him feel oddly unclean.

Nor could Howe get rid of a certain practical resentment. As a poet he had a special and respectable place in the college life. But it might be another thing to be marked as the poet of a wilful and selfish obscurity.

As he walked to the Bradbys', Howe was a little tense and defensive. It seemed to him that all the world knew of the 'attack' and agreed with it. And, indeed, the Bradbys had read the essay but Professor Bradby, a kind and pretentious man, said, 'I see my old friend knocked you about a bit, my boy,' and his wife Eugenia looked at Howe with her childlike blue eyes and said, 'I shall *scold* Frederic for the untrue things he wrote about you. You aren't the least obscure.' They beamed at him. In their genial snobbery they seemed to feel that he had distinguished himself. He was the leader of Howeism. He enjoyed the dinner party as much as he had thought he would.

And in the following days, as he was more preoccupied with his duties, the incident was forgotten. His classes had ceased to be mere groups. Student after student detached himself from the mass and required or claimed a place in Howe's awareness. Of them all it was Tertan who first and most violently signaled his separate existence. A week after classes had begun Howe saw his silhouette on the frosted glass of his office door. It was motionless for a long time, perhaps stopped by the problem of whether or not to knock before entering. Howe called, 'Come in!' and Tertan entered with his shambling stride.

He stood beside the desk, silent and at attention. When Howe asked him to sit down, he responded with a gesture of head and hand, as if to say that such amenities were beside the point. Nevertheless, he did take the chair. He put his ragged, crammed briefcase between his legs. His face, which Howe now observed fully for the first time, was confusing, for it was made up of florid curves, the nose arched in the bone and voluted in the nostril, the mouth loose and soft and rather moist. Yet the face was so thin and narrow as to seem the very type of asceticism. Lashes of unusual length veiled the eyes and, indeed, it seemed as if there were a veil over the whole countenance. Before the words actually came, the face screwed itself into an attitude of preparation for them.

'You can confer with me now?' Tertan said.

'Yes, I'd be glad to. There are several things in your two themes I want to talk to you about.' Howe reached for the packet of themes on his desk and sought for Tertan's. But the boy was waving them away.

'These are done perforce,' he said. 'Under the pressure of your requirement. They are not significant; mere duties.' Again his great hand flapped vaguely to dismiss his themes. He leaned forward and gazed at his teacher.

'You are,' he said, 'a man of letters? You are a poet?' It was more declaration than question.

'I should like to think so,' Howe said.

At first Tertan accepted the answer with a show of appreciation, as though the understatement made a secret between himself and Howe. Then he chose to misunderstand. With his shrewd and disconcerting control of expression, he presented to Howe a puzzled grimace. 'What does that mean?' he said.

Howe retracted the irony. 'Yes. I am a poet.' It sounded strange to say.

'That,' Tertan said, 'is a wonder.' He corrected himself with his ducking head. 'I mean that is wonderful.'

Suddenly, he dived at the miserable briefcase between his legs, put it on his knees, and began to fumble with the catch, all intent on the difficulty it presented. Howe noted that his suit was worn thin, his shirt almost unclean. He became aware, even, of a vague and musty odor of garments worn too long in unaired rooms. Tertan conquered the lock and began to concentrate upon a search into the interior. At last he held in his hand what he was after, a torn and crumpled copy of *Life and Letters*.

'I learned it from here,' he said, holding it out.

Howe looked at him sharply, his hackles a little up. But the boy's face was not only perfectly innocent, it even shone with a conscious admiration. Apparently nothing of the import of the essay had touched him except the wonderful fact that his teacher was a 'man of letters.' Yet this seemed too stupid, and Howe, to test it, said, 'The man who wrote that doesn't think it's wonderful.'

Tertain made a moist hissing sound as he cleared his mouth of saliva. His head, oddly loose on his neck, wove a pattern of contempt in the air. 'A critic,' he said, 'who admits *prima facie* that he does not understand.' Then he said grandly, 'It is the inevitable fate.'

It was absurd, yet Howe was not only aware of the absurdity but of a tension suddenly and wonderfully relaxed. Now that the 'attack' was on the table between himself and this strange boy, and subject to the boy's funny and absolutely certain contempt, the hidden force of his feeling was revealed to him in the very moment that it vanished. All unsuspected, there had been a film over the world, a transparent but discoloring haze of danger. But he had no time to stop over the brightened aspect of things. Tertan was going on. 'I also am a man of letters. Putative.'

'You have written a good deal?' Howe meant to be no more than polite, and he was surprised at the tenderness he heard in his words.

Solemnly the boy nodded, threw back the dank lock, and sucked in a deep, anticipatory breath. 'First, a work of homiletics, which is a defense of the principles of religious optimism against the pessimism of Schopenhauer and the humanism of Nietzsche.'

'Humanism? Why do you call it humanism?'

'It is my nomenclature for making a deity of man,' Tertan replied negligently. 'Then three fictional works, novels. And numerous essays in science, combating materialism. Is it your duty to read these if I bring them to you?'

Howe answered simply, 'No, it isn't exactly my duty, but I shall be happy to read them.'

Tertan stood up and remained silent. He rested his bag on the chair. With a certain compunction—for it did not seem entirely proper that, of two men of letters, one should have the right to blue-pencil the other, to grade him or to question the quality of his 'sentence structure'—Howe reached for Tertan's papers. But before he could take them up, the boy suddenly made his bow-to-Abelard, the stiff inclination of the body with the hands seeming to emerge from the scholar's gown. Then he was gone.

But after his departure something was still left of him. The timbre of his curious sentences, the downright finality of so quaint a phrase as 'It is the inevitable fate' still rang in the air. Howe gave the warmth of his feeling to the new visitor who stood at the door announcing himself with a genteel clearing of the throat.

'Doctor Howe, I believe?' the student said. A large hand advanced into the room and grasped Howe's hand. 'Blackburn, sir, Theodore Blackburn, vice-president of the Student Council. A great pleasure, sir.'

Out of a pair of ruddy cheeks a pair of small eyes twinkled good-naturedly. The large face, the large body were not so much fat as beefy and suggested something 'typical'—monk, politician, or innkeeper.

Blackburn took the seat beside Howe's desk. 'I may have seemed to introduce myself in my public capacity, sir,' he said. 'But it is really as an individual that I came to see you. That is to say, as one of your students to be.'

He spoke with an English intonation and he went on, 'I was once an English major, sir.'

For a moment Howe was startled, for the roast-beef look of the boy and the manner of his speech gave a second's credibility to one sense of his statement. Then the collegiate meaning of the phrase asserted itself, but some perversity made Howe say what was not really in good taste even with so forward a student, 'Indeed? What regiment?'

Blackburn stared and then gave a little pouf-pouf of laughter. He waved the misapprehension away. '*Very* good, sir. It certainly is an ambiguous term.' He chuckled in appreciation of Howe's joke, then cleared his throat to put it aside. 'I look forward to taking your course in the romantic poets, sir,' he said earnestly. 'To me the romantic poets are the very crown of English literature.'

Howe made a dry sound, and the boy, catching some meaning in it, said, 'Little as I know them, of course. But even Shakespeare who is so dear to us of the Anglo-Saxon tradition is in a sense but the preparation for Shelley, Keats and Byron. And Wadsworth.'

Almost sorry for him, Howe dropped his eyes. With some embarrassment, for the boy was not actually his student, he said softly 'Wordsworth.'

'Sir?'

'Wordsworth, not Wadsworth. You said Wadsworth.'

'Did I, sir?' Gravely he shook his head to rebuke himself for the error. 'Wordsworth, of course—slip of the tongue.' Then, quite in command again, he went on. 'I have a favor to ask of you, Doctor Howe. You see, I began my college course as an English major,'—he smiled—'as I said.'

'Yes?'

'But after my first year I shifted. I shifted to the social sciences. Sociology and government—I find them stimulating and very *real*.' He paused, out of respect for reality. 'But now I find that perhaps I have neglected the other side.'

'The other side?' Howe said.

'Imagination, fancy, culture. A well-rounded man.' He trailed off as if there were perfect understanding between them. 'And so, sir, I have decided to end my senior year with your course in the romantic poets.'

His voice was filled with an indulgence which Howe ignored as he said flatly and gravely, 'But that course isn't given until the spring term.'

'Yes, sir, and that is where the favor comes in. Would you let me take your romantic prose course? I can't take it for credit, sir, my program is full, but just for background it seems to me that I ought to take it. I do hope,' he concluded in a manly way, 'that you will consent.'

'Well, it's no great favor, Mr. Blackburn. You can come if you wish, though there's not much point in it if you don't do the reading.'

The bell rang for the hour and Howe got up.

'May I begin with this class, sir?' Blackburn's smile was candid and boyish.

Howe nodded carelessly and together, silently, they walked to the classroom down the hall. When they reached the door Howe stood back to let his student enter, but Blackburn moved adroitly behind him and grasped him by the arm to urge him over the threshold. They entered together with Blackburn's hand firmly on Howe's biceps, the student inducting the teacher into his own room. Howe felt a surge of temper rise in him and almost violently he disengaged his arm and walked to the desk, while Blackburn found a seat in the front row and smiled at him.

II

The question was, At whose door must the tragedy be laid?

All night the snow had fallen heavily and only now was abating in sparse little flurries. The windows were valanced high with white. It was very quiet; something of the quiet of the world had reached the class, and Howe found that everyone was glad to talk or listen. In the room there was a comfortable sense of pleasure in being human.

Casebeer believed that the blame for the tragedy rested with heredity. Picking up the book he read, 'The sins of the fathers are visited on their children.' This opinion was received with general favor. Nevertheless, Johnson ventured to say that the fault was all Pastor Manders' because the Pastor had made Mrs. Alving go back to her husband and was always hiding the truth. To this Hibbard objected with logic enough, 'Well then, it was really all her husband's fault. He *did* all the bad things.' De Witt, his face bright with an impatient idea, said that the fault was all society's. 'By society I don't mean upper-crust society,' he said. He looked around a little defiantly, taking in any members of the class who might be members of upper-crust society. 'Not in that sense. I mean the social unit.'

Howe nodded and said, 'Yes, of course.'

'If the society of the time had progressed far enough in science,' De Witt went on, 'then there would be no problem for Mr. Ibsen to write about. Captain Alving plays around a little, gives way to perfectly natural biological urges, and he gets a social disease, a venereal disease. If the disease is cured, no problem. Invent salvarsan and the disease is cured. The problem of heredity disappears and li'l Oswald just doesn't get paresis. No paresis, no problem—no problem, no play.'

This was carrying the ark into battle, and the class looked at De Witt with respectful curiosity. It was his usual way and on the whole they were sympathetic with his struggle to prove to Howe that science was better than literature. Still, there was something in his reckless manner that alienated them a little.

'Or take birth-control, for instance,' De Witt went on. 'If Mrs. Alving had some knowledge of contraception, she wouldn't have had to have li'l Oswald at all. No li'l Oswald, no play.'

The class was suddenly quieter. In the back row Stettenhover swung his great football shoulders in a righteous sulking gesture, first to the right, then to the left. He puckered his mouth ostentatiously. Intellect was always ending up by talking dirty.

Tertan's hand went up, and Howe said, 'Mr. Tertan.' The boy shambled to his feet and began his long characteristic gulp. Howe made a motion with his fingers, as small as possible, and Tertan ducked his head and smiled in apology. He sat down. The class laughed. With more than half the term gone, Tertan had not been able to remember that one did not rise to speak. He seemed unable to carry on the life of the intellect without this mark of respect for it. To Howe the boy's habit of rising seemed to accord with the formal shabbiness of his dress. He never wore the casual sweaters and jackets of his classmates. Into the free and comfortable air of the college classroom he brought the stuffy sordid strictness of some crowded, metropolitan high school.

'Speaking from one sense,' Tertan began slowly, 'there is no blame ascribable. From the sense of determinism, who can say where the blame lies? The preordained is the preordained and it cannot be said without rebellion against the universe, a palpable absurdity.'

In the back row Stettenhover slumped suddenly in his seat, his heels held out before him, making a loud, dry, disgusted sound. His body sank until his neck rested on the back of his chair. He folded his hands across his belly and looked significantly out of the window, exasperated not only with Tertan, but with Howe, with the class, with the whole system designed to encourage this kind of thing. There was a certain insolence in the movement and Howe flushed. As Tertan continued to speak, Howe stalked casually toward the window and placed himself in the line of Stettenhover's vision. He stared at the great fellow, who pretended not to see him. There was so much power in the big body, so much contempt in the Greek-athlete face under the crisp Greek-athlete curls, that Howe felt almost physical fear. But at last Stettenhover admitted him to focus and under his disapproving gaze sat up with slow indifference. His eyebrows raised high in resignation, he began to examine his hands. Howe relaxed and turned his attention back to Tertan.

'Flux of existence,' Tertan was saying, 'produces all things, so that judgment wavers. Beyond the phenomena, what? But phenomena are adumbrated and to them we are limited.'

Howe saw it for a moment as perhaps it existed in the boy's mind—the world of shadows which are cast by a great light upon a hidden reality as in the old myth of the Cave. But the little brush with Stettenhover had tired him, and he said irritably, 'But come to the point, Mr. Tertan.'

He said it so sharply that some of his class looked at him curiously. For three months he had gently carried Tertan through his verbosities, to the vaguely respectful surprise of the other students, who seemed to conceive that there existed between this strange classmate and their teacher some special understanding from which they were content to be excluded. Tertan looked at him mildly, and at once came brilliantly to the point. 'This is the summation of the play,' he said and took up his book and read, ' "Your poor father never found any outlet for the overmastering joy of life that was in him. And I brought no holiday into his home, either. Everything seemed to turn upon duty and I am afraid I made your poor father's home unbearable to him, Oswald." Spoken by Mrs. Alving.'

Yes that was surely the 'summation' of the play and Tertan had hit it, as he hit, deviously and eventually, the literary point of almost everything. But now, as always, he was wrapping it away from sight. 'For most mortals,' he said, 'there are only joys of biological urgings, gross and crass, such as the sensuous Captain Alving. For certain few there are the transmutations beyond these to a contemplation of the utter whole.'

Oh, the boy was mad. And suddenly the word, used in hyperbole, intended almost for the expression of exasperated admiration, became literal. Now that the word was used, it became simply apparent to Howe that Tertan was mad.

It was a monstrous word and stood like a bestial thing in the room. Yet it so completely comprehended everything that had puzzled Howe, it so arranged and explained what for three months had been perplexing him that almost at once its horror became domesticated. With this word Howe was able to understand why he had never been able to communicate to Tertan the value of a single criticism or correction of his wild, verbose themes. Their conferences had been frequent and long but had done nothing to reduce to order the splendid confusion of the boy's ideas. Yet, impossible though its expression was, Tertan's incandescent mind could always strike for a moment into some dark corner of thought.

And now it was suddenly apparent that it was not a faulty rhetoric that Howe had to contend with. With his new knowledge he looked at Tertan's face and wondered how he could have so long deceived himself. Tertan was still talking, and the class had lapsed into a kind of patient unconsciousness, a coma of respect for words which, for all that most of them knew, might be profound. Almost with a suffusion of shame, Howe believed that in some dim way the class had long ago had some intimation of Tertan's madness. He reached out as decisively as he could to seize the thread of Tertan's discourse before it should be entangled further.

'Mr. Tertan says that the blame must be put upon whoever kills the joy of living in another. We have been assuming that Captain Alving was a wholly bad man, but what if we assume that he became bad only because Mrs. Alving, when they were first married, acted toward him in the prudish way she says she did?'

It was a ticklish idea to advance to freshmen and perhaps not profitable. Not all of them were following.

'That would put the blame on Mrs. Alving herself, whom most of you admire. And she herself seems to think so.' He glanced at his watch. The hour was nearly over. 'What do you think, Mr. De Witt?'

De Witt rose to the idea; he wanted to know if society couldn't be blamed for educating Mrs. Alving's temperament in the wrong way. Casebeer was puzzled, Stettenhover continued to look at his hands until the bell rang.

Tertan, his brows louring in thought, was making as always for a private word. Howe gathered his books and papers to leave quickly. At this moment of his discovery and with the knowledge still raw, he could not engage himself with Tertan. Tertan sucked in his breath to prepare for speech and Howe made ready for the pain and confusion. But at that moment Casebeer detached himself from the group with which he had been conferring and which he seemed to represent. His constituency remained at a tactful distance. The mission involved the time of an assigned essay. Casebeer's presentation of the plea—it was based on the freshmen's heavy duties at the fraternities during Carnival Week—cut across Tertan's preparations for speech. 'And so some of us fellows thought,' Casebeer concluded with heavy solemnity, 'that we could do a better job, give our minds to it more, if we had more time.'

Tertan regarded Casebeer with mingled curiosity and revulsion. Howe not only said that he would postpone the assignment but went on to talk about the Carnival, and even drew the waiting constituency into the conversation. He was conscious of Tertan's stern and astonished stare, then of his sudden departure.

Now that the fact was clear, Howe knew that he must act on it. His course was simple enough. He must lay the case before the Dean. Yet he hesitated. His feeling for Tertan must now, certainly, be in some way invalidated. Yet could he, because of a word, hurry to assign to official and reasonable solicitude what had been, until this moment, so various and warm? He could at least delay and, by moving slowly, lend a poor grace to the necessary, ugly act of making his report.

It was with some notion of keeping the matter in his own hands that he went to the Dean's office to look up Tertan's records. In the outer office the Dean's secretary greeted him brightly, and at his request brought him the manila folder with the small identifying photograph pasted in the corner. She laughed. 'He was looking for the birdie in the wrong place,' she said.

Howe leaned over her shoulder to look at the picture. It was as bad as all the Dean's-office photographs were, but it differed from all that Howe had ever seen. Tertan, instead of looking into the camera, as no doubt he had been bidden, had, at the moment of exposure, turned his eyes upward. His mouth, as though conscious of the trick played on the photographer, had the sly superior look that Howe knew.

The secretary was fascinated by the picture. 'What a funny boy,' she said. 'He looks like Tartuffe!'

And so he did, with the absurd piety of the eyes and the conscious slyness of the mouth and the whole face bloated by the bad lens.

'Is he *like* that?' the secretary said.

'Like Tartuffe? No.'

From the photograph there was little enough comfort to be had. The records themselves gave no clue to madness, though they suggested sadness enough. Howe read of a father, Stanislaus Tertan, born in Budapest and trained in engineering in Berlin, once employed by the Hercules Chemical Corporation—this was one of the factories that dominated the sound end of the town—but now without employment. He read of a mother Erminie (Youngfellow) Tertan, born in Manchester, educated at a Normal School at Leeds, now housewife by profession. The family lived on Greenbriar Street which Howe knew as a row of once elegant homes near what was now the factory district. The old mansion had long ago been divided into small and primitive apartments. Of Ferdinand himself there was little to learn. He lived with his parents, had attended a Detroit high school and had transferred to the local school in his last year. His rating for intelligence, as expressed in numbers, was high, his scholastic record was remarkable, he held a college scholarship for his tuition.

Howe laid the folder on the secretary's desk. 'Did you find what you wanted to know?' she asked.

The phrases from Tertan's momentous first theme came back to him. 'Tertan I am, but what is Tertan? Of this time, of that place, of some parentage, what does it matter?'

'No, I didn't find it,' he said.

Now that he had consulted the sad, half-meaningless record he knew all the more firmly that he must not give the matter out of his own hands. He must not release Tertan to authority. Not that he anticipated from the Dean anything but the greatest kindness for Tertan. The Dean would have the experience and skill which he himself could not have. One way or another the Dean could answer the question, 'What is Tertan?' Yet this was precisely what he feared. He alone could keep alive—not forever but for a somehow important time—the question, 'What is Tertan?' He alone could keep it still a question. Some sure instinct told him that he must not surrender the question to a clean official desk in a clear official light to be dealt with, settled and closed.

He heard himself saying, 'Is the Dean busy at the moment? I'd like to see him.'

His request came thus unbidden, even forbidden, and it was one of the surprising and startling incidents of his life. Later when he reviewed the events, so disconnected in themselves, or so merely odd, of the story that unfolded for him that year, it was over this moment, on its face the least notable, that he paused longest. It was frequently to be with fear and never without a certainty of its meaning in his own knowledge of himself that he would recall this simple, routine request, and the feeling of shame and freedom it gave him as he sent everything down the official chute. In the end, of course, no matter what he did to 'protect' Tertan, he would have had to make the same request and lay the matter on the Dean's clean desk. But it would always be a landmark of his life that, at the very moment when he was rejecting the official way, he had been, without will or intention, so gladly drawn to it.

After the storm's last delicate flurry, the sun had come out. Reflected by the new snow, it filled the office with a golden light which was almost musical in the way it made all the commonplace objects of efficiency shine with a sudden sad and noble significance. And the light, now that he noticed it, made the utterance of his perverse and unwanted request even more momentous.

The secretary consulted the engagement pad. 'He'll be free any minute. Don't you want to wait in the parlor?'

She threw open the door of the large and pleasant room in which the Dean held his Committee meetings, and in which his visitors waited. It was designed with a homely elegance on the masculine side of the eighteenth-century manner. There was a small coal fire in the grate and the handsome mahogany table was strewn with books and magazines. The large windows gave on the snowy lawn, and there was such a fine width of window that the white casements and walls seemed at this moment but a continuation of the snow, the snow but an extension of casement and walls. The outdoors seemed taken in and made safe, the indoors seemed luxuriously freshened and expanded.

Howe sat down by the fire and lighted a cigarette. The room had its intended effect upon him. He felt comfortable and relaxed, yet nicely organized, some young diplomatic agent of the eighteenth century, the newly fledged Swift carrying out Sir William Temple's business. The rawness of Tertan's case quite vanished. He crossed his legs and reached for a magazine.

It was that famous issue of *Life and Letters* that his idle hand had found and his blood raced as he sifted through it, and the shape of his own name, Joseph Howe, sprang out at him, still cabalistic in its power. He tossed the magazine back on the table as the door of the Dean's office opened and the Dean ushered out Theodore Blackburn.

'Ah, Joseph!' the Dean said.

Blackburn said, 'Good morning, Doctor.' Howe winced at the title and caught the flicker of amusement over the Dean's face. The Dean stood with his hand high on the door-jamb and Blackburn, still in the doorway, remained standing almost under the long arm.

Howe nodded briefly to Blackburn, snubbing his eager deference. 'Can you give me a few minutes?' he said to the Dean.

'All the time you want. Come in.' Before the two men could enter the office, Blackburn claimed their attention with a long full 'er.' As they turned to him, Blackburn said, 'Can *you* give *me* a few minutes, Doctor Howe?' His eyes sparkled at the little audacity he had committed, the slightly impudent play with hierarchy. Of the three of them Blackburn kept himself the lowest, but he reminded Howe of his subaltern relation to the Dean.

'I mean, of course,' Blackburn went on easily, 'when you've finished with the Dean.'

'I'll be in my office shortly,' Howe said, turned his back on the ready 'Thank you, sir,' and followed the Dean into the inner room.

'Energetic boy,' said the Dean. 'A bit beyond himself but very energetic. Sit down.'

The Dean lighted a cigarette, leaned back in his chair, sat easy and silent for a moment, giving Howe no signal to go ahead with business. He was a young Dean, not much beyond forty, a tall handsome man with sad, ambitious eyes. He had been a Rhodes scholar. His friends looked for great things from him, and it was generally said that he had notions of education which he was not yet ready to try to put into practice.

His relaxed silence was meant as a compliment to Howe. He smiled and said, 'What's the business, Joseph?'

'Do you know Tertan—Ferdinand Tertan, a freshman?'

The Dean's cigarette was in his mouth and his hands were clasped behind his head. He did not seem to search his memory for the name. He said, 'What about him?'

Clearly the Dean knew something, and he was waiting for Howe to tell him more. Howe moved only tentatively. Now that he was doing what he had resolved not to do, he felt more guilty at having been so long deceived by Tertan and more need to be loyal to his error.

'He's a strange fellow,' he ventured. He said stubbornly, 'In a strange way he's very brilliant.' He concluded, 'But very strange.'

The springs of the Dean's swivel chair creaked as he came out of his sprawl and leaned forward to Howe. 'Do you mean he's so strange that it's something you could give a name to?'

Howe looked at him stupidly. 'What do you mean?' he said.

'What's his trouble?' the Dean said more neutrally.

'He's very brilliant, in a way. I looked him up and he has a top intelligence rating. But somehow, and it's hard to explain just how, what he says is always on the edge of sense and doesn't quite make it.'

The Dean looked at him and Howe flushed up. The Dean had surely read Woolley on the subject of 'the Howes' and the *tour d'ivresse*. Was that quick glance ironical?

The Dean picked up some papers from his desk, and Howe could see that they were in Tertan's impatient scrawl. Perhaps the little gleam in the Dean's glance had come only from putting facts together.

'He sent me this yesterday,' the Dean said. 'After an interview I had with him. I haven't been able to do more than glance at it. When you said what you did, I realized there was something wrong.'

Twisting his mouth, the Dean looked over the letter. 'You seem to be involved,' he said without looking up. 'By the way, what did you give him at mid-term?'

Flushing, setting his shoulders, Howe said firmly, 'I gave him A-minus.'

The Dean chuckled. 'Might be a good idea if some of our nicer boys went crazy—just a little.' He said, 'Well,' to conclude the matter and handed the papers to Howe. 'See if this is the same thing you've been finding. Then we can go into the matter again.'

Before the fire in the parlor, in the chair that Howe had been occupying, sat Blackburn. He sprang to his feet as Howe entered.

'I said my office, Mr. Blackburn.' Howe's voice was sharp. Then he was almost sorry for the rebuke, so clearly and naively did Blackburn seem to relish his stay in the parlor, close to authority.

'I'm in a bit of a hurry, sir,' he said, 'and I did want to be sure to speak to you, sir.'

He was really absurd, yet fifteen years from now he would have grown up to himself, to the assurance and mature beefiness. In banks, in consular offices, in brokerage firms, on the bench, more seriously affable, a little sterner, he would make use of his ability to be administered by his job. It was almost reassuring. Now he was exercising his too-great skill on Howe. 'I owe you an apology, sir,' he said.

Howe knew that he did, but he showed surprise.

'I mean, Doctor, after your having been so kind about letting me attend your class, I stopped coming.' He smiled in deprecation. 'Extracurricular activities take up so much of my time. I'm afraid I undertook more than I could perform.'

Howe had noticed the absence and had been a little irritated by it after Blackburn's elaborate plea. It was an absence that might be interpreted as a comment on the teacher. But there was only one way for him to answer. 'You've no need to apologize,' he said. 'It's wholly your affair.'

Blackburn beamed. 'I'm so glad you feel that way about it, sir. I was worried you might think I had stayed away because I was influenced by—' he stopped and lowered his eyes.

Astonished, Howe said, 'Influenced by what?'

'Well, by—' Blackburn hesitated and for answer pointed to the table on which lay the copy of *Life and Letters*. Without looking at it, he knew where to direct his hand. 'By the unfavorable publicity, sir.' He hurried on. 'And that brings me to another point, sir. I am vice president of Quill and Scroll, sir, the student literary society, and I wonder if you would address us. You could read your own poetry, sir, and defend your own point of view. It would be very interesting.'

It was truly amazing. Howe looked long and cruelly into Blackburn's face, trying to catch the secret of the mind that could have conceived this way of manipulating him, this way so daring and inept—but not entirely inept—with its malice so without malignity. The face did not yield its secret. Howe smiled broadly and said, 'Of course I don't think you were influenced by the unfavorable publicity.'

'I'm still going to take—regularly, for credit—your romantic poets course next term,' Blackburn said.

'Don't worry, my dear fellow, don't worry about it.'

Howe started to leave and Blackburn stopped him with, 'But about Quill, sir?'

'Suppose we wait until next term? I'll be less busy then.'

And Blackburn said, 'Very good, sir, and thank you.'

In his office the little encounter seemed less funny to Howe, was even in some indeterminate way disturbing. He made an effort to put it from his mind by turning to what was sure to disturb him more, the Tertan letter read in the new interpretation. He found what he had always found, the same florid leaps beyond fact and meaning, the same headlong certainty. But as his eye passed over the familiar scrawl it caught his own name, and for the second time that hour he felt the race of his blood.

'The Paraclete,' Tertan had written to the Dean, 'from a Greek word meaning to stand in place of, but going beyond the primitive idea to mean traditionally the helper, the one who comforts and assists, cannot without fundamental loss be jettisoned. Even if taken no longer in the supernatural sense, the concept remains deeply in the human consciousness inevitably. Humanitarianism is no reply, for not every man stands in the place of every other man for this other comrade's comfort. But certain are chosen out of the human race to be the consoler of some other. Of these, for example, is Joseph Barker Howe, Ph.D. Of intellects not the first yet of true intellect and lambent instructions, given to that which is intuitive and irrational, not to what is logical in the strict word, what is judged by him is of the heart and not the head. Here is one chosen, in that he chooses himself to stand in the place of another for comfort and consolation. To him more than another I give my gratitude, with all respect to our Dean who reads this, a noble man, but merely dedicated, not consecrated. But not in the aspect of the Paraclete only is Dr. Joseph Barker Howe established, for he must be the Paraclete to another aspect of himself, that which is driven and persecuted by the lack of understanding in the world at large, so that he in himself embodies the full history of man's tribulations and, overflowing upon others, notably the present writer, is the ultimate end.'

This was love. There was no escape from it. Try as Howe might to remember that Tertan was mad and all his emotions invalidated, he could not destroy the effect upon him of his student's stern, affectionate regard. He had betrayed not only a power of mind but a power of love. And, however firmly he held before his attention the fact of Tertan's madness, he could do nothing to banish the physical sensation of gratitude he felt. He had never thought of himself as 'driven and persecuted' and he did not now. But still he could not make meaningless his sensation of gratitude. The pitiable Tertan sternly pitied him, and comfort came from Tertan's never-to-be-comforted mind.

III

In an academic community, even an efficient one, official matters move slowly. The term drew to a close with no action in the case of Tertan, and Joseph Howe had to confront a curious problem. How should he grade his strange student, Tertan?

Tertan's final examination had been no different from all his other writing, and what did one 'give' such a student? De Witt must have his A, that was clear. Johnson would get a B. With Casebeer it was a question of a B-minus or a C-plus, and Stettenhover, who had been crammed by the team tutor to fill half a blue-book with his thin feminine scrawl, would have his C-minus which he would accept with mingled indifference and resentment. But with Tertan it was not so easy.

The boy was still in the college process and his name could not be omitted from the grade sheet. Yet what should a mind under suspicion of madness be graded? Until the medical verdict was given, it was for Howe to continue as Tertan's teacher and to keep his judgment pedagogical. Impossible to give him an F: he had not failed. B was for Johnson's stolid mediocrity. He could not be put on the edge of passing with Stettenhover, for he exactly did not pass. In energy and richness of intellect he was perhaps even De Witt's superior, and Howe toyed grimly with the notion of giving him an A, but that would lower the value of the A De Witt had won with his beautiful and clear, if still arrogant, mind. There was a notation which the Registrar recognized—Inc., for Incomplete, and in the horrible comedy of the situation, Howe considered that. But really only a mark of M for Mad would serve.

In his perplexity, Howe sought the Dean, but the Dean was out of town. In the end, he decided to maintain the A-minus he had given Tertan at mid-term. After all, there had been no falling away from that quality. He entered it on the grade sheet with something like bravado.

Academic time moves quickly. A college year is not really a year, lacking as it does three months. And it is endlessly divided into units which, at their beginning, appear larger than they are —terms, half-terms, months, weeks. And the ultimate unit, the hour, is not really an hour, lacking as it does ten minutes. And so the new term advanced rapidly, and one day the fields about the town were all brown, cleared of even the few thin patches of snow which had lingered so long.

Howe, as he lectured on the romantic poets, became conscious of Blackburn emanating wrath. Blackburn did it well, did it with enormous dignity. He did not stir in his seat, he kept his eyes fixed on Howe in perfect attention, but he abstained from using his notebook, there was no mistaking what he proposed to himself as an attitude. His elbow on the writing-wing of the chair, his chin on the curled fingers of his hand, he was the embodiment of intellectual indignation. He was thinking his own thoughts, would give no public offense, yet would claim his due, was not to be intimidated. Howe knew that he would present himself at the end of the hour.

Blackburn entered the office without invitation. He did not smile; there was no cajolery about him. Without invitation he sat down beside Howe's desk. He did not speak until he had taken the blue-book from his pocket. He said, 'What does this mean, sir?'

It was a sound and conservative student tactic. Said in the usual way it meant, 'How could you have so misunderstood me?' or 'What does this mean for my future in the course?' But there were none of the humbler tones in Blackburn's way of saying it.

Howe made the established reply, 'I think that's for you to tell me.'

Blackburn continued icy. 'I'm sure I can't, sir.'

There was a silence between them. Both dropped their eyes to the blue-book on the desk. On its cover Howe had penciled: 'F. This is very poor work.'

Howe picked up the blue-book. There was always the possibility of injustice. The teacher may be bored by the mass of papers and not wholly attentive. A phrase, even the student's handwriting, may irritate him unreasonably. 'Well,' said Howe, 'Let's go through it.'

He opened the first page. 'Now here: you write, "In *The Ancient Mariner,* Coleridge lives in and transports us to a honey-sweet world where all is rich and strange, a world of charm to which we can escape from the humdrum existence of our daily lives, the world of romance. Here, in this warm and honey-sweet land of charming dreams we can relax and enjoy ourselves."'

Howe lowered the paper and waited with a neutral look for Blackburn to speak. Blackburn returned the look boldly, did not speak, sat stolid and lofty. At last Howe said, speaking gently, 'Did you mean that, or were you just at a loss for something to say?'

'You imply that I was just "bluffing"?' The quotation marks hung palpable in the air about the word.

'I'd like to know. I'd prefer believing that you were bluffing to believing that you really thought this.'

Blackburn's eyebrows went up. From the height of a great and firm-based idea he looked at his teacher. He clasped the crags for a moment and then pounced, craftily, suavely. 'Do you mean, Doctor Howe, that there aren't two opinions possible?'

It was superbly done in its air of putting all of Howe's intellectual life into the balance. Howe remained patient and simple. 'Yes, many opinions are possible, but not this one. Whatever anyone believes of *The Ancient Mariner,* no one can in reason believe that it represents a—a honey-sweet world in which we can relax.'

'But that is what I *feel,* sir.'

This was well-done, too. Howe said, 'Look, Mr. Blackburn. Do you really relax with hunger and thirst, the heat and the sea-serpents, the dead men with staring eyes, Life in Death and the skeletons? Come now, Mr. Blackburn.'

Blackburn made no answer, and Howe pressed forward. 'Now, you say of Wordsworth, "Of peasant stock himself, he turned from the effete life of the salons and found in the peasant the hope of a flaming revolution which would sweep away all the old ideas. This is the subject of his best poems."'

Beaming at his teacher with youthful eagerness, Blackburn said, 'Yes, sir, a rebel, a bringer of light to suffering mankind. I see him as a kind of Prothemeus.'

'A kind of what?'

'Prothemeus, sir.'

'Think, Mr. Blackburn. We were talking about him only today and I mentioned his name a dozen times. You don't mean Prothemeus. You mean—' Howe waited, but there was no response.

'You mean Prometheus.'

Blackburn gave no assent, and Howe took the reins. 'You've done a bad job here, Mr. Blackburn, about as bad as could be done.' He saw Blackburn stiffen and his genial face harden again. 'It shows either a lack of preparation or a complete lack of understanding.' He saw Blackburn's face begin to go to pieces and he stopped.

'Oh, sir,' Blackburn burst out, 'I've never had a mark like this before, never anything below a B, never. A thing like this has never happened to me before.'

It must be true, it was a statement too easily verified. Could it be that other instructors accepted such flaunting nonsense? Howe wanted to end the interview. 'I'll set it down to lack of preparation,' he said. 'I know you're busy. That's not an excuse, but it's an explanation. Now, suppose you really prepare, and then take another quiz in two weeks. We'll forget this one and count the other.'

Blackburn squirmed with pleasure and gratitude. 'Thank you, sir. You're really very kind, very kind.'

Howe rose to conclude the visit. 'All right, then—in two weeks.'

It was that day that the Dean imparted to Howe the conclusion of the case of Tertan. It was simple and a little anti-climactic. A physician had been called in, and had said the word, given the name.

'A classic case, he called it,' the Dean said. 'Not a doubt in the world,' he said. His eyes were full of miserable pity, and he clutched at a word. 'A classic case, a classic case.' To his aid and to Howe's there came the Parthenon and the form of the Greek drama, the Aristotelian logic, Racine and the Well-Tempered Clavichord, the blueness of the Aegean and its clear sky. Classic —that is to say, without a doubt, perfect in its way, a veritable model, and, as the Dean had been told, sure to take a perfectly predictable and inevitable course to a foreknown conclusion.

It was not only pity that stood in the Dean's eyes. For a moment there was fear too. 'Terrible,' he said, 'it is simply terrible.'

Then he went on briskly. 'Naturally, we've told the boy nothing. And, naturally, we won't. His tuition's paid by his scholarship, and we'll continue him on the rolls until the end of the year. That will be kindest. After that the matter will be out of our control. We'll see, of course, that he gets into the proper hands. I'm told there will be no change, he'll go on like this, be as good as this, for four to six months. And so we'll just go along as usual.'

So Tertan continued to sit in Section 5 of English 1A, to his classmates still a figure of curiously dignified fun, symbol to most of them of the respectable but absurd intellectual life. But to his teacher he was now very different. He had not changed—he was still the greyhound casting for the scent of ideas, and Howe could see that he was still the same Tertan, but he could not feel it. What he felt as he looked at the boy sitting in his accustomed place was the hard blank of a fact. The fact itself was formidable and depressing. But what Howe was chiefly aware of was that he had permitted the metamorphosis of Tertan from person to fact.

As much as possible he avoided seeing Tertan's upraised hand and eager eye. But the fact did not know of its mere factuality, it continued its existence as if it were Tertan, hand up and eye questioning, and one day it appeared in Howe's office with a document.

'Even the spirit who lives egregiously, above the herd, must have its relations with the fellowman,' Tertan declared. He laid the document on Howe's desk. It was headed 'Quill and Scroll Society of Dwight College. Application for Membership.'

'In most ways these are crass minds,' Tertan said, touching the paper. 'Yet as a whole, bound together in their common love of letters, they transcend their intellectual lacks since it is not a paradox that the whole is greater than the sum of its parts.'

'When are the elections?' Howe asked.

'They take place tomorrow.'

'I certainly hope you will be successful.'

'Thank you. Would you wish to implement that hope?' A rather dirty finger pointed to the bottom of the sheet. 'A faculty recommender is necessary,' Tertan said stiffly, and waited.

'And you wish me to recommend you?'

'It would be an honor.'

'You may use my name.'

Tertan's finger pointed again. 'It must be a written sponsorship, signed by the sponsor.' There was a large blank space on the form under the heading, 'Opinion of Faculty Sponsor.'

This was almost another thing and Howe hesitated. Yet there was nothing else to do and he took out his fountain pen. He wrote, 'Mr. Ferdinand Tertan is marked by his intense devotion to letters and by his exceptional love of all things of the mind.' To this he signed his name, which looked bold and assertive on the white page. It disturbed him, the strange affirming power of a name. With a business-like air, Tertan whipped up the paper, folding it with decision, and put it into his pocket. He bowed and took his departure, leaving Howe with the sense of having done something oddly momentous.

And so much now seemed odd and momentous to Howe that should not have seemed so. It was odd and momentous, he felt, when he sat with Blackburn's second quiz before him, and wrote in an excessively firm hand the grade of C-minus. The paper was a clear, an indisputable failure. He was carefully and consciously committing a cowardice. Blackburn had told the truth when he had pleaded his past record. Howe had consulted it in the Dean's office. It showed no grade lower than a B-minus. A canvass of some of Blackburn's previous instructors had brought vague attestations to the adequate powers of a student imperfectly remembered, and sometimes surprise that his abilities could be questioned at all.

As he wrote the grade, Howe told himself that his cowardice sprang from an unwillingness to have more dealings with a student he disliked. He knew it was simpler than that. He knew he feared Blackburn: that was the absurd truth. And cowardice did not solve the matter after all. Blackburn, flushed with a first success, attacked at once. The minimal passing grade had not assuaged his feelings and he sat at Howe's desk and again the blue-book lay between them. Blackburn said nothing. With an enormous impudence, he was waiting for Howe to speak and explain himself.

At last Howe said sharply and rudely, 'Well?' His throat was tense and the blood was hammering in his head. His mouth was tight with anger at himself for his disturbance.

Blackburn's glance was almost baleful. 'This is impossible, sir.'

'But there it is,' Howe answered.

'Sir?' Blackburn had not caught the meaning but his tone was still haughty.

Impatiently Howe said, 'There it is, plain as day. Are you here to complain again?'

'Indeed I am, sir.' There was surprise in Blackburn's voice that Howe should ask the question.

'I shouldn't complain if I were you. You did a thoroughly bad job on your first quiz. This one is a little, only a very little, better.' This was not true. If anything, it was worse.

'That might be a matter of opinion, sir.'

'It is a matter of opinion. Of my opinion.'

'Another opinion might be different, sir.'

'You really believe that?' Howe said.

'Yes.' The omission of the 'sir' was monumental.

'Whose, for example?'

'The Dean's, for example.' Then the fleshy jaw came forward a little. 'Or a certain literary critic's, for example.'

It was colossal and almost too much for Blackburn himself to handle. The solidity of his face almost crumpled under it. But he withstood his own audacity and went on. 'And the Dean's opinion might be guided by the knowledge that the person who gave me this mark is the man whom a famous critic, the most eminent judge of literature in this country, called a drunken man. The Dean might think twice about whether such a man is fit to teach Dwight students.'

Howe said in quiet admonition, 'Blackburn, you're mad,' meaning no more than to check the boy's extravagance.

But Blackburn paid no heed. He had another shot in the locker. 'And the Dean might be guided by the information, of which I have evidence, documentary evidence,'—he slapped his breast pocket twice—'that this same person personally recommended to the college literary society, the oldest in the country, that he personally recommended a student who is crazy, who threw the meeting into an uproar—a psychiatric case. The Dean might take that into account.'

Howe was never to learn the details of that 'uproar.' He had always to content himself with the dim but passionate picture which at that moment sprang into his mind, of Tertan standing on some abstract height and madly denouncing the multitude of Quill and Scroll who howled him down.

He sat quiet a moment and looked at Blackburn. The ferocity had entirely gone from the student's face. He sat regarding his teacher almost benevolently. He had played a good card and now, scarcely at all unfriendly, he was waiting to see the effect. Howe took up the blue-book and negligently sifted through it. He read a page, closed the book, struck out the C-minus and wrote an F.

'Now you may take the paper to the Dean,' he said. 'You may tell him that after reconsidering it, I lowered the grade.'

The gasp was audible. 'Oh, sir!' Blackburn cried. 'Please!' His face was agonized. 'It means my graduation, my livelihood, my future. Don't do this to me.'

'It's done already.'

Blackburn stood up, 'I spoke rashly, sir, hastily. I had no in-

tention, no real intention, of seeing the Dean. It rests with you
—entirely, entirely. I *hope* you will restore the first mark.'

'Take the matter to the Dean or not, just as you choose. The
grade is what you deserve and it stands.'

Blackburn's head dropped. 'And will I be failed at mid-term,
sir?'

'Of course.'

From deep out of Blackburn's great chest rose a cry of anguish.
'Oh, sir, if you want me to go down on my knees to you, I will,
I will.'

Howe looked at him in amazement.

'I will, I will. On my knees, sir. This mustn't, mustn't happen.'

He spoke so literally, meaning so very truly that his knees and
exactly his knees were involved and seeming to think that he was
offering something of tangible value to his teacher, that Howe,
whose head had become icy clear in the nonsensical drama,
thought, 'The boy is mad,' and began to speculate fantastically
whether something in himself attracted or developed aberration.
He could see himself standing absurdly before the Dean and
saying, 'I've found another. This time it's the Vice-president of
the Council, the manager of the debating team and secretary of
Quill and Scroll.'

One more such discovery, he thought, and he himself would be
discovered! And there, suddenly, Blackburn was on his knees with
a thump, his huge thighs straining his trousers, his hand outstretched in a great gesture of supplication.

With a cry, Howe shoved back his swivel chair and it rolled
away on its casters half across the little room. Blackburn knelt for
a moment to nothing at all, then got to his feet.

Howe rose abruptly. He said, 'Blackburn, you will stop acting
like an idiot. Dust your knees off, take your paper and get out.
You've behaved like a fool and a malicious person. You have
half a term to do a decent job. Keep your silly mouth shut and
try to do it. Now get out.'

Blackburn's head was low. He raised it and there was a pious
light in his eyes.'Will you shake hands, sir?" he said. He thrust
out his hand.

'I will not,' Howe said.

Head and hand sank together. Blackburn picked up his blue-
book and walked to the door. He turned and said, 'Thank you,
sir.' His back, as he departed, was heavy with tragedy and state-
liness.

IV

After years of bad luck with the weather, the College had a perfect day for Commencement. It was wonderfully bright, the air so transparent, the wind so brisk that no one could resist talking about it.

As Howe set out for the campus he heard Hilda calling from the back yard. She called, 'Professor, professor,' and came running to him.

Howe said, 'What's this "professor" business?'

'Mother told me,' Hilda said. 'You've been promoted. And I want to take your picture.'

'Next year,' said Howe. 'I won't be a professor until next year. And you know better than to call anybody "professor." '

'It was just in fun,' Hilda said. She seemed disappointed.

'But you can take my picture if you want. I won't look much different next year.' Still, it was frightening. It might mean that he was to stay in this town all his life.

Hilda brightened. 'Can I take it in this?' she said, and touched the gown he carried over his arm.

Howe laughed. 'Yes, you can take it in this.'

'I'll get my things and meet you in front of Otis,' Hilda said. 'I have the background all picked out.'

On the campus the Commencement crowd was already large. It stood about in eager, nervous little family groups. As he crossed, Howe was greeted by a student, capped and gowned, glad of the chance to make an event for his parents by introducing one of his teachers. It was while Howe stood there chatting that he saw Tertan.

He had never seen anyone quite so alone, as though a circle had been woven about him to separate him from the gay crowd on the campus. Not that Tertan was not gay, he was the gayest of all. Three weeks had passed since Howe had last seen him, the weeks of examination, the lazy week before Commencement, and this was now a different Tertan. On his head he wore a panama hat, broad-brimmed and fine, of the shape associated with South American planters. He wore a suit of raw silk, luxurious, but yellowed with age and much too tight, and he sported a whangee cane. He walked sedately, the hat tilted at a devastating angle, the stick coming up and down in time to his measured tread. He had, Howe guessed, outfitted himself to greet the day in the clothes of that ruined father whose existence was on record in the Dean's office. Gravely and arrogantly he surveyed the scene —in it, his whole bearing seemed to say, but not of it. With his haughty step, with his flashing eye, Tertan was coming nearer. Howe did not wish to be seen. He shifted his position slightly. When he looked again, Tertan was not in sight.

The chapel clock struck the quarter hour. Howe detached himself from his chat and hurried to Otis Hall at the far end of the campus. Hilda had not yet come. He went up into the high portico and, using the glass of the door for a mirror, put on his gown, adjusted the hood on his shoulders and set the mortarboard on his head. When he came down the steps, Hilda had arrived.

Nothing could have told him more forcibly that a year had passed than the development of Hilda's photographic possessions from the box camera of the previous fall. By a strap about her neck was hung a leather case, so thick and strong, so carefully stitched and so molded to its contents that it could only hold a costly camera. The appearance was deceptive, Howe knew, for he had been present at the Aikens' pre-Christmas conference about its purchase. It was only a fairly good domestic camera. Still, it looked very impressive. Hilda carried another leather case from which she drew a collapsible tripod. Decisively she extended each of its gleaming legs and set it up on the path. She removed the camera from its case and fixed it to the tripod. In its compact efficiency the camera almost had a life of its own, but Hilda treated it with easy familiarity, looked into its eye, glanced casually at its gauges. Then from a pocket she took still another leather case and drew from it a small instrument through which she looked first at Howe, who began to feel inanimate and lost, and then at the sky. She made some adjustment on the instrument, then some adjustment on the camera. She swept the scene with her eye, found a spot and pointed the camera in its direction. She walked to the spot, stood on it and beckoned to Howe. With each new leather case, with each new instrument, and with each new adjustment she had grown in ease and now she said, 'Joe, will you stand here?'

Obediently Howe stood where he was bidden. She had yet another instrument. She took out a tape-measure on a mechanical spool. Kneeling down before Howe, she put the little metal ring of the tape under the tip of his shoe. At her request, Howe pressed it with his toe. When she had measured her distance, she nodded to Howe who released the tape. At a touch, it sprang back into the spool. 'You have to be careful if you're going to get what you want,' Hilda said. 'I don't believe in all this snap-snap-snapping,' she remarked loftily. Howe nodded in agreement, although he was beginning to think Hilda's care excessive.

Now at last the moment had come. Hilda squinted into the camera, moved the tripod slightly. She stood to the side, holding the plunger of the shutter-cable. 'Ready,' she said. 'Will you relax, Joseph, please?' Howe realized that he was standing frozen. Hilda stood poised and precise as a setter, one hand holding the little cable, the other extended with curled dainty fingers like a dancer's, as if expressing to her subject the precarious delicacy of the moment. She pressed the plunger and there was the click. At once she stirred to action, got behind the camera, turned a new exposure. 'Thank you,' she said. 'Would you stand under that tree and let me do a character study with light and shade?'

The childish absurdity of the remark restored Howe's ease. He went to the little tree. The pattern the leaves made on his gown was what Hilda was after. He had just taken a satisfactory position when he heard in the unmistakable voice, 'Ah, Doctor! Having your picture taken?'

Howe gave up the pose and turned to Blackburn who stood on the walk, his hands behind his back, a little too large for his bachelor's gown. Annoyed that Blackburn should see him posing for a character study in light and shade, Howe said irritably, 'Yes, having my picture taken.'

Blackburn beamed at Hilda. 'And the little photographer?' he said. Hilda fixed her eyes on the ground and stood closer to her brilliant and aggressive camera. Blackburn, teetering on his heels, his hands behind his back, wholly prelatical and benignly patient, was not abashed at the silence. At last Howe said, 'If you'll excuse us, Mr. Blackburn, we'll go on with the picture.'

'Go right ahead, sir. I'm running along.' But he only came closer. 'Doctor Howe,' he said fervently, 'I want to tell you how glad I am that I was able to satisfy your standards at last.'

Howe was surprised at the hard, insulting brightness of his own voice, and even Hilda looked up curiously as he said, 'Nothing you have ever done has satisfied me, and nothing you could ever do would satisfy me, Blackburn.'

With a glance at Hilda, Blackburn made a gesture as if to hush Howe—as though all his former bold malice had taken for granted a kind of understanding between himself and his teacher, a secret which must not be betrayed to a third person. 'I only meant, sir,' he said, 'that I was able to pass your course after all.'

Howe said, 'You didn't pass my course. I passed you out of my course. I passed you without even reading your paper. I wanted to be sure the college would be rid of you. And when all the grades were in and I did read your paper, I saw I was right not to have read it first.'

Blackburn presented a stricken face. 'It was very bad, sir?'

But Howe had turned away. The paper had been fantastic. The paper had been, if he wished to see it so, mad. It was at this moment that the Dean came up behind Howe and caught his arm. 'Hello, Joseph,' he said. 'We'd better be getting along, it's almost late.'

He was not a familiar man, but when he saw Blackburn, who approached to greet him, he took Blackburn's arm, too. 'Hello, Theodore,' he said. Leaning forward on Howe's arm and on Blackburn's, he said, 'Hello, Hilda dear.' Hilda replied quietly, 'Hello, Uncle George.'

Still clinging to their arms, still linking Howe and Blackburn, the Dean said, 'Another year gone, Joe, and we've turned out another crop. After you've been here a few years, you'll find it reasonably upsetting—you wonder how there can be so many graduating classes while you stay the same. But of course you don't stay the same.' Then he said, 'Well,' sharply, to dismiss the thought. He pulled Blackburn's arm and swung him around to Howe. 'Have you heard about Teddy Blackburn?' he asked. 'He has a job already, before graduation—the first man of his class to be placed.' Expectant of congratulations, Blackburn beamed at Howe. Howe remained silent.

'Isn't that good?' the Dean said. Still Howe did not answer and the Dean, puzzled and put out, turned to Hilda. 'That's a very fine-looking camera, Hilda.' She touched it with affectionate pride.

'Instruments of precision,' said a voice. 'Instruments of precision.' Of the three with joined arms, Howe was the nearest to Tertan, whose gaze took in all the scene except the smile and the nod which Howe gave him. The boy leaned on his cane. The broad-brimmed hat, canting jauntily over his eye, confused the image of his face that Howe had established, suppressed the rigid lines of the ascetic and brought out the baroque curves. It made an effect of perverse majesty.

'Instruments of precision,' said Tertan for the last time, addressing no one, making a casual comment to the universe. And it occurred to Howe that Tertan might not be referring to Hilda's equipment. The sense of the thrice-woven circle of the boy's loneliness smote him fiercely. Tertan stood in majestic jauntiness, superior to all the scene, but his isolation made Howe ache with a pity of which Tertan was more the cause than the object, so general and indiscriminate was it.

Whether in his sorrow he made some unintended movement toward Tertan which the Dean checked, or whether the suddenly tightened grip on his arm was the Dean's own sorrow and fear, he did not know. Tertan watched them in the incurious way people watch a photograph being taken, and suddenly the thought that, to the boy, it must seem that the three were posing for a picture together made Howe detach himself almost rudely from the Dean's grasp.

'I promised Hilda another picture,' he announced—needlessly, for Tertan was no longer there, he had vanished in the last sudden flux of visitors who, now that the band had struck up, were rushing nervously to find seats.

'You'd better hurry,' the Dean said. 'I'll go along, it's getting late for me.' He departed and Blackburn walked stately by his side.

Howe again took his position under the little tree which cast its shadow over his face and gown. 'Just hurry, Hilda, won't you?' he said. Hilda held the cable at arm's length, her other arm crooked and her fingers crisped. She rose on her toes and said 'Ready,' and pressed the release. 'Thank you,' she said gravely and began to dismantle her camera as he hurried off to join the procession.

EDITORS' ANALYSIS

In "Of This Time, of That Place," we are taken inside the subtle and sensitive mind of the instructor, Howe, and are asked to commune with him in his preoccupation with Tertan's apparent madness, apparent genius. The story has, as background to this pathos, elements of serious comedy: satire on academic politics and apple-polishing students who try to "sell" themselves to their instructors. It is also richly concerned with Howe's own private anxieties as teacher and poet, his concern over the problems of conformity and originality, genius and madness. The final scene with the camera, all action stopped, Howe confirmed in his promotion, a fixed figure from an academic procession, is a disturbingly realized, sad denouement to the action, and an acute manifestation of Trilling's own symbolic imagination.

QUESTIONS

1. Discuss the apparently casual, but actually very tight, organization of the events of the story. Does the organization seem too contrived? Wholly successful?

2. Discuss the ways in which the author objectifies Tertan's enthusiasm and energy, and Howe's lassitude and willingness to compromise. Are Tertan and Howe complementary pictures of each other, in some ways, and oddly alike in character?

3. Are Casebeer and Blackburn realistic or stylized portraits of collegiate types? Compare the degree of stylization in their sketches with the heightening of feeling about Tertan. Is Tertan, also, a familiar figure on every campus?

4. How does the author use suspense about whether Tertan is a genius or a psychotic in order to build his story? Should he have decided earlier? Why was he unwilling to pigeonhole Tertan with greater dispatch?

5. What is the emotional and symbolic significance of the final scene involving an academic procession, a camera, and Howe posing for his picture? Is Tertan's comment "Instruments of precision," made almost at the end of the story, an indictment of Howe, in this final scene?

The Unvexed Isles

by ROBERT PENN WARREN

Robert Penn Warren (1905-   ), novelist, poet, essayist, college teacher, achieved his first prominence as co-editor, with Cleanth Brooks, of *The Southern Review* (1935-1942), one of the most distinguished of American literary quarterlies. He is usually identified as a regional writer, since most of his fiction has dealt with the South. His best-known novel is *All the King's Men* (1946), a portrait of the rise and fall of a political dictator, not unlike the actual Huey Long of Louisiana. His most recent novel is *The Cave* (1959). Collections of his poetry are: *Selected Poems, 1923-1943*, and *Promises: Poems 1954-1956*. He has published a volume of his critical writings, *Selected Essays* (1958). He has taught at the University of Minnesota (1942-1950) and at Yale (1950-1956). Central to all of his writing, poetry and prose, is a sense of the tremendous diversity in definitions of the meaning of existence from one person to another.

Warren's "The Unvexed Isles" presents the moment when a college professor comes to full realization of the ultimate nature of his own life. It is a much less complex presentation of characters and their problems than was "Of This Time, of That Place." It makes its somber comment about its Professor Dalrymple by great economy in the use of detail and by very careful understatement.

The whisky—the best whisky in Russell Hill—sloshed with unthrifty golden opulence into the third and last of the glasses that stood on the lacquered tray. Professor Dalrymple, something of the crystal-gazer's pious abstraction in his regard, watched the spill and whirl of the liquor in the orbit of bright glass. Professor Dalrymple did not relish whisky, even the best whisky in Russell Hill, which, indeed, he dispensed. But he never entered the warm pantry on a Sunday evening, hearing the competent rustle of the electric refrigerator and the murmur of voices from a farther room, without feeling, as he lifted the decanter, a sense of decorous liberation. It was the same sense of liberation he sometimes felt when, looking at his own fine white hands, he recalled that one visit home and the sight of his brother's hands lying inert on the tablecloth in the lamplight: burned by sun, chapped by wind like rotten leather, grained irrevocably with black dirt from the prairie.

Sacramentally, the whiskey sloshed into the glass. Bubbles of air streamed upward, and at the surface minutely exploded.

Professor Dalrymple set the silver-mounted siphon on the tray beside the silver bucket of ice, picked up the tray, squared his shoulders as he did these days when he detected that unconscious droop, and proceeded through the door, across the dining room, where articles of silver discreetly glimmered in the dimness, across the hall, and into the room where they sat, waiting.

"Not the true, the blushing Hippocrene," he uttered, and approached the bright fire where they sat, "but 'twill serve."

"It'll serve all right, Doctor," Phil Alburt said. "It's as much of a beaker full of the warm South as I ask, even on as lousy cold a night as tonight." His voice filled the room with authority, a kind of aimless vitality that seemed to make the fire burn up brighter and the bulbs behind their parchment shades glow with more assurance. "It was snowing again when I came in."

"So that's what you got out of my English 40, sir?" the Professor demanded.

"Not exactly." His laughter was like his voice.

"Well, Phil, if you didn't get more than that, nobody did. I'll wager on that."

"Don't loiter, George," Mrs. Dalrymple commanded, a tinge of asperity licking along the edge of the pleasantry. "Mr. Alburt can wait for his compliment, but I don't want to wait for my toddy."

"Pardon me, Alice," he said, and with some formality presented the tray.

Looking at the ready tray, she commanded, "Squirt it for me."

Her husband set the tray on the little table, placed his long white thumb with its chalky nail on the siphon lever, and pressed. The liquor swirled, paled in the soft light, rose toward the brim.

"Ice," she said.

"On a night like this," Phil Alburt deplored.

"We always take ice back home in Baltimore," she said.

Professor Dalrymple handed his wife the glass.

"No ice for me," Phil Alburt said, "and not much water."

"I remember," the Professor said. "No ice. Result of your English visits, I suppose."

"Perhaps," Phil Alburt said, and laughed the vital, vacant laugh.

"Not the only result, I'm sure," the Professor said, and carried the tray across to him. The young man laid his cigarette on the receptacle beside him, looked up at his host with a smile of affable toleration, and reached for the siphon. "Thank you, sir," he said.

The Professor regarded the head with its dark hair which lay in neat gleaming curly folds as though carved. As the water hissed peremptorily into the glass, the smoke lifted from the idle cigarette on the tray under the Professor's eyes and swayed in its delicate substance. The Professor's glance rested on the cigarette. *It is most singular,* he thought, *that the tip of that cigarette should be stained with lipstick.* The words came through his head with such emphatic clarity and distinctness that, rattling the glasses, he started as though the sentence had been spoken by an unseen observer.

"That's fine. Thank you," the young man was saying.

Professor Dalrymple, with effort, disengaged his eyes from the cigarette to meet the large features turned up at him in the contortion of amiability. The features were large and suddenly naked: the strong lips, the even white teeth unbared, the thrust of the nose, the wide brown eyes in which swam flecks of gold, the heavy eyebrows where hairs arched sleekly out from some vigor at the root.

"You're welcome," Professor Dalrymple rejoined mechanically, then, aware of his words, flushed. As he turned about and traversed the excessive distance across the blue carpet, he felt that all these objects accumulated around him—table, chair, chair, blue carpet, rug, lamp—were unfamiliar to him, and now for the first time might, if he so chose, be construed in their unique and rich unities. After he had adjusted the tray, with special care, on the stand, he gave to its obscure design a lingering and analytic regard. Lingering, as if he were a schoolboy unwilling at the last moment to lay aside the book before entering the examination room, or as if his attention to the intricacies of the design might postpone the need to inspect those people whose voices, somewhat remotely, impinged upon him.

The liquid was cold and sweetish in his mouth. He set the glass back, and as he did so discovered with some surprise that the muscles of his cheek were warped upward in an attentive smile. He might have caught sight of himself in a random mirror, so surely did he see, not feel, the thin, long, over-sensitive lips lift and recede beneath the accurate line of black bristle in the ambassadorial mustache. *I am making a great fool of myself,* he reflected, *grinning like that.*

Alice Dalrymple had just said, "I guess old Prexy would turn over in his truckle bed if he knew we were plying one of his charges with toddy."

Professor Dalrymple, yet smiling, cleared his throat slightly. "You know, Phil, we are not able to follow the dictates of hospitality as a general thing. Offering refreshment to our undergraduates is, as a general thing, shall I say, tabu. But I feel, we feel, that we are at liberty to do so in certain cases where the undergraduate's background is more liberal—when the undergraduate is more mature, more, shall I say, a man of the world." The words slipped precisely over his lips, and he was aware, at their conclusion, of the lips still warped upward in the smile. He was aware of having uttered the words at some time in the past, of some quality and inflection that implied rehearsal. But as he said "A man of the world," he did not experience that feeling of inner security and relish which customarily was his on like occasions.

Phil Alburt lolled in dark well-tailored mass behind a glass, a look of bland inattention on his features. When he spoke, it was, likewise, with an accent of rehearsal. "I must say I'm mature enough to appreciate the quality of this hospitality," he said, and significantly fingered the glass.

Professor Dalrymple thought, *A man of the world.* He slipped the phrase about in his mind as a child sucks candy, but the words were hard and savorless like marbles. Quite suddenly it occurred to him that the young man opposite, who nodded his head in amused approbation at some remark from the pretty woman, fancied himself as a man of the world. *Because he is rich,* it occurred to him, *because he lives in New York and wears tailor-made clothes and goes to Europe and drinks whisky, and, in fact, has kissed Alice Bogan Dalrymple in my house, he fancies himself a man of the world. I was born in Nebraska in a house that stood on the bare ground with no trees.* Then with a feeling of distant fatality, his sense of warmth for Phil Alburt, somewhat modified but real enough, came back within him. In all perversity, it came back.

Alice Dalrymple gave her gaze to the fire, where flames scrolled ornamentally upward to the black chimney throat. The brass dogs gleamed, the hearth was swept to a sharp border, the flames sprouted upward like flowers from an accurate parterre. *She turns her head so,* Professor Dalrymple observed, *because she knows she looks best in profile. She is thinner these days, she looks tired.* Alice Dalrymple held her head at right angles to the young man's chair: her profile was clean and delicate, with a careful dyspeptic beauty. The young man himself was looking into the fire.

"So you are leaving Tuesday?" she said.

"Tuesday," Phil Alburt said with the air of one gently engrossed in the collaboration of fireside and toddy. "Tuesday, and I get home the next night just in time to hang up my stocking."

"And up early next morning," Professor Dalrymple said, "to see your new velocipede."

"Not to see my new velocipede, to take some Mother Sill's. You see, I've got to hang my stocking up over the wash basin on a boat to Bermuda. Mother is dragging me off down there."

Mrs. Dalrymple laughed, a quick accurate modulation. "And Old Santy comes down the hot water pipe and fills it with little guest cakes of Palmolive and Dr. West toothbrushes." She laughed. "Instead of ashes and switches."

"I won't care if it's full of horsewhips, I'll be feeling so bad that first morning. I'm a rotten sailor."

"Not horsewhips for a good little boy," Professor Dalrymple echoed, and, quite unexpectedly, laughed too.

"I've been planning to go East," Mrs. Dalrymple said in a tone of mild frustration. "To Baltimore."

"Home?" Phil Alburt said.

Home, Professor Dalrymple thought, *Mrs. George Dalrymple lives in Russell Hill in Illinois.* He tabulated the items of her address in his mind. *Mrs. George Dalrymple, 429 Poplar Street, Russell Hill, Illinois, U. S. A.*

"But George here can't go," she said, "and I'm going to be sweet and dutiful and stay right here."

"You ought to go, Alice," Professor Dalrymple said. And he said to himself, *She can't go because she can't buy a ticket on a train to Baltimore. Because she married a poor man.*

"George, you see, wants to finish up some research this vacation. He gets so little time during the year."

"What is it, Doctor?"

"Just a little Chaucer note I've been working on," the Professor answered, and thought for a minute that he might, after all, write a paper. Satisfaction and meaning filled him and velleities slipped away as he lifted his glass to his lips.

"So I'll stay here with him, a martyr to the noble cause of scholarship."

"A mild martyrdom, I would call it, to sit with my heels on the fender," the young man said.

"We used to have some pretty good Christmases in Baltimore, didn't we?" Mrs. Dalrymple gave her husband a full intimate glance, and he noted how the flesh dropped thinly away from the base of her nostrils. "I believe Father made the best eggnog I ever tasted. Everybody used to come in for eggnog on Christmas. Everybody. You ought to let your old research go hang this Christmas, George—"

"Yes, indeed," her husband said. He was conscious of the rhythm of forgotten voices, forgotten excitements, like the sea sound in empty whorls of a shell. Old Mr. Bogan's voice saying, "Gentlemen, gentlemen." Old Mrs. Bogan's voice with the shrillness all drained away in time. Form of voices with no sound.

"—but instead we'll just sit this Christmas."

Eggs. Dozens of eggs. Baskets of eggs. Whisky, sweetish and gold. Hams. Arrogant turkeys. Wine. A steaming mess heaped and poured on the altar of Lucile Bogan's and Alice Bogan's need for a man to share the bed and pay the bills. A steaming, sweating altar, while smoke ascended from twenty-five cent cigars. *Ah*, he thought, and old Mr. Bogan's ritualistic white shirt front obtruded, a-glitter with starch and studs, in the midst of his fancy. *Ah, they spent a lot of money and the best they got was me. But that was when Alice wrote her little verses for the Junior League magazine and showed an English professor to her friends.* Then he concluded with a flat feeling in his head like a run-down clock: *She would know better now.*

"Well," Phil Alburt said, "just sitting has its points. I'm going to do a good deal of sitting myself this vacation. Taking my little school satchel along."

"To Bermuda," Professor Dalrymple said, dryly he hoped, and realized on the instant that he hated Phil Alburt, not because lipstick stained a dead cigarette butt in the ash tray across the hearth, but because Phil Alburt had said those precise words in that précise accent of comfort.

"To Bermuda," Phil Alburt agreed, and laughed without embarrassment.

Mrs. Dalrymple laughed, again the quick accurate modulation. Her husband stonily inspected her mirth: *She has no more self-respect than to laugh after what he just said to her. When she laughs now she holds her head up so the skin won't sag in her neck. Craning her neck like that, she looks like a cigarette adver-tisement.* He looked guiltily across at the tray by Phil Alburt, as if it were necessary to assure himself that the dead butt reposed there in its matrix of ash.

"However, I can't just sit any more right now," the young man said. "I've got to go now and do a little work before bedtime. I just came to say good-bye." He stood in front of his chair, not really tall but erect, broad shoulders appearing broader by the cut of his coat, his hair with a dark waxen gleam in the light, the double-breasted coat buttoned sleek and flat over his hips and belly.

Professor Dalrymple rose.

"Must you go," Mrs. Dalrymple asked, and likewise stood.

"Must," he said.

"Off to the happy isles," Professor Dalrymple said cheerfully. Then: "I'm thinking about a trip myself. I think I'll go home this Christmas." With a certain pleasure he noted his wife's faint movement of surprise—or was it annoyance?

"Fine," Phil Alburt said.

"You see," he continued, "I haven't been home in a long time. Not for nine years. I was born and reared out in Nebraska."

"On a ranch, I bet," the young man said hopefully.

"No. On a dirt farm, that's what they call them. Near a place named Sinking Fork Station. Just a wheat elevator and a siding. Did you ever hear of the place?"

Phil Alburt looked quickly at Mrs. Dalrymple, a glance of appeal for support or enlightenment. Then he managed a smile. "I can't say that I have," he said.

"I didn't really imagine that you had. My brother out there is still running the farm, I believe, unless they have foreclosed his various mortgages."

"Recent times have been difficult for the agriculturist," Phil Alburt said, somehow with a touch of piety.

"Indeed," Professor Dalrymple said, an ambiguous inflection to the word which he himself, for the flicker of an instant, tried in his mind to decipher. But he could scarcely decide what he had intended. He stood passively while his guest, a perturbed

peevish light in his brown eyes, hesitated before taking comfort
in the circumstance of farewell. Phil Alburt and Mrs. Dalrymple
said good-bye. Good-bye and Merry Christmas.

In the hall, while he held Phil Alburt's coat, he felt like a fool.
At the door, he shook, cordially as one trying to make amends,
the hand offered him, refrained from looking at the face of the
parting guest for fear he might find a smile on it, and said,
several times, "Good-bye."

After Phil Alburt had gone down the steps, he yet stood in the
open doorway, while the cold wind blew down the street and a
few small flakes whipped past, and watched the figure proceed
the length of the walk and climb into an automobile. He called
once, "Merry Christmas," but his voice, he knew immediately,
was lost in the easy, vicious whir of gears.

The wind which blew down the street tossed the decorative
conifers by the walk so that they looked like two old women in
tattered black shawls begging at his doorstep. He straightened
his shoulders and experienced again, though but faintly, the
accustomed sense of Sunday night complacency. Then his wife
called, "Shut the door!"

He knew exactly how she would be when he entered the room.
She would be standing before the fireplace, very still, as though
spent by agitations of the evening; the black chiffon, in contrast
to pale skin and pale hair, would hang to her slender figure with
that extravagant flimsiness which once had made him suspect
that a dress was borrowed for the occasion; and her breasts,
defined but flattish, would lift, then decline, in a movement of
disturbing, finicky respiration.

He closed the heavy door, took three paces down the hall,
and entered the room.

There she stood.

"I think, Alice," he announced with a premonitory clearing of
the throat, "I think that I shall do that paper. The subject has
never been approached from precisely—"

She fixed her eyes on him; said, "What paper? . . . Oh, of
course"; and relapsed into her stillness. The cigarette which hung,
almost artificially, from her thin nervous fingers surrendered its
trail of smoke to the air.

As he approached her across the carpet, warily as though he
trod a treacherous surface on which he might slip and lose
dignity, desire, an irritable but profound desire, took him. "Alice,"
he said, unsure of what words were to follow.

She again looked at him. "You were very rude to Phil," she said.

"Rude?" he echoed.

"What ever made you so rude to him?" Her voice was the voice of dutiful catechism.

He almost said: "Under the circumstances I had a right to be rude to him"; but did not. Then he thought: *She is angry because I said what I did to that fool. She doesn't believe I am really going home. I am going home.*

"What made you so rude?" she patiently demanded.

He was conscious of a small kernel of blind, blank rage deep in him. Its tentacles dumbly, blindly, groped within him.

"I never saw you act like that before."

"If I was rude to Mr. Alburt, I am sorry." He framed his words with care. "I assure you that my intentions were of the kindest."

The desire came back, profound and dangerous, but he preserved from it a strange detachment. He felt like a man about to pick a scab: that perverse curiosity, that impulse to view the object, to test his own pain. "Alice," he said, hearing the syllables distantly, and put his arm round her shoulder. His kiss did not reach her mouth; he felt the bristles of his mustache press into the yielding flesh of her cheek.

He did not know whether she had disengaged herself, or whether, in fact, his arm had simply fallen from her shoulders. There she stood, and she lifted one hand, palm against the temple, in that fatalistic gesture which now, as ever, filled him with a sense of insufficiency.

"I am very tired," she said.

"Yes," he agreed, "you look tired." And he felt with gratification that by not having said a moment before, "I love you," he had maintained his self-respect.

"Good night," she said.

She withdrew from him, past the chair where she had sat that evening, past the table where his own drained glass stood, and toward the door. With her movement the black chiffon fluttered and waggled.

He looked at the door through which she had just passed. Words took form in his mind with such special satisfaction that he was tempted to speak them aloud. *I would be doing my friend, Mr. Alburt, a favor if I should tell him that Alice Dalrymple is cold as a snake.* Then, as he surveyed the room, whose articles, now that she had gone, seemed out of focus, he could not help but wonder what she would have said, how she would have taken it, if, after all, he had said, "I love you."

He drifted toward the hall door, and out into the hall. Somewhere on the upper floor a light burned, splaying shadow and angular patches of illumination into the lower section like a gigantic, ghostly pack of cards. Without looking up, he passed down the hall to his study door, opened it, and threw the electric switch. The big bronze lamp on the desk in the center of the room released its steady flooding light over the appointed objects: over the tray of pens which lay in meticulous intimacy side by side, the bronze inkstand, the leather spectacle case. In shadow, just beyond the rim of light, the books, tier on tier, mounted like masonry of some blank, eyeless structure.

He seated himself before the desk; removed the spectacles from the case; dutifully wiped them with a white handkerchief; hooked them over his ears. He opened the book in front of him. He was scarcely aware that he had performed that set of actions, so habitual to him; it was, indeed, with a subdued surprise that to him came recognition of the words on the printed page. It was as if, on relaxing his attention at the end of each sentence, he should say, "Well, well, here I am."

He tried to follow the words that marched cleanly from margin to margin, line by line; but the faces persistently came. He perceived Phil Alburt's naked face set in the rich flaring fur of an overcoat collar, and beyond it another face, undefined, unknown, anonymous, the face of a girl whose body, reclining, was lapped in silk and fur: faces fixed above the dash lamp and the little white unwinking dials that said all was well, all was well, while the bold-flung beams of headlights ripped the snowy road and the dark that whirled toward the faces.

Between the words on the page, between the sentences, he saw the faces appear and reappear as between the spokes of a slowly revolving wheel. *Necking*, he thought, *out necking*. He suddenly discovered as though he had been searching for it, that word he had heard the students use. *And he is going to Bermuda*, he thought, and into his mind crowded the pictures he had seen in travel advertisements, the man and woman on horseback, in bright coats, riding along the white beach by blue water. *To Bermuda*, he thought, *but I am going home. Even if Alice doesn't believe me, I am going home.* That satisfied him and he felt, somehow surprised at his emotion, a deep homesickness.

He tried to comprehend the words on the page, but his mind, like nervous fingers, dropped them. While the wind sweeping down the great valley of the Mississippi beat the town, beat the house, and hurled the sparse lost flakes through the upper reaches of darkness, he sat in the ring of steady light from the bronze lamp on his desk. At length before he possessed the calm, sufficient meaning of the words under his eye, he knew that he would stay here forever in Russell Hill, Illinois, at this sad, pretentious little college on the plain, in this house with the rustling electric refrigerator and the tiers of books; that this Christmas, or any other, he would not go home; that the woman now sleeping upstairs where the single light burned was perfectly his own; and that Phil Alburt, who had, really, nothing to do with them, with George Dalrymple and Alice Bogan Dalrymple, would ride away, forever, on horseback, his naked face smiling as he rode down the white beaches beside the blue water of the unvexed isles.

EDITORS' ANALYSIS

"The Unvexed Isles" is more a light sketch, perhaps, than a fully worked out short story. Its details are organized largely as a series of ironies. Professor Dalrymple feels a glow of security for a brief minute or two, as he plays host to a student. But this security vanishes utterly as he realizes that the student can drink his whisky, kiss his wife behind his back, and have the money to go off to Bermuda for the holidays. At the end of the sketch, he has reached a moment of clear insight, when his having escaped life on a dirt farm in Nebraska for college teaching no longer seems very important. We see him, at the story's end, accepting the grim fact that he has achieved nothing at all but a mildly comfortable existence "in Russell Hill, Illinois, at this sad, pretentious little college on the plain."

QUESTIONS

1. Professor Dalrymple feels "a sense of decorous liberation" at the beginning of the story. How would you describe his feelings at the end?

2. What gives Phil Alburt his "aimless vitality," his voice of authority, in the presence of Dalrymple? His mere youth? His greater wealth? Something less tangible?

3. Is Alice Dalrymple as disenchanted with her husband as he is with her? Comment on the details given in the story which suggest their attitudes toward each other.

4. Trilling's "Of This Time, of That Place" covers a full college year while Warren's sketch covers only a few minutes in one evening. How does this affect the kind of detail which is used in each story? Give examples.

5. Warren's title is an irony in itself. In Shakespeare's *The Tempest* the Bermudas were referred to as "still-vex'd" (i.e., always stormy). Why does Warren, then, call them "unvexed"? To whom are they always calm? Dalrymple? Phil Alburt?

3.

LOVE

Babylon Revisited

by F. SCOTT FITZGERALD

F. Scott Fitzgerald (1896-1940) was the outstanding chronicler
of the moral chaos in lives of members of the so-called "jazz age"
between the two world wars. His first novel, *This Side of Paradise*
(1920), was an immediate success, and set the pattern for his fictional
studies in disillusionment. His best-known novel, *The Great Gatsby*
(1925), summed up the attitudes of a rootless post World War I
generation. His later novel, *Tender is the Night* (1934), attempted a
subtle, psychological penetration of character not found in his earlier
works. Fitzgerald wrote many short stories, uneven in merit, most of
which were aimed at a commercial market. His reputation as a major
writer of the generation of Faulkner and Hemingway went into eclipse
before his death. Interest in Fitzgerald was partly revived with the
publication of *The Crack-Up* (1945), his notebooks and autobiographical papers, edited by Edmund Wilson. Arthur Mizener's critical biography, *The Far Side of Paradise* (1951), helped to bring Fitzgerald
forward as one of the important writers of the first half of the century.

Fitzgerald's "Babylon Revisited" was written after the stock market
crash of 1929 had dried up the incomes of the expatriates and had
brought an end to an epoch. Its story of a defeat in love is also a poignant epilogue to the decade of the "jazz age".

"And where's Mr. Campbell?" Charlie asked.

"Gone to Switzerland. Mr. Campbell's a pretty sick man, Mr.
Wales."

"I'm sorry to hear that. And George Hardt?" Charlie inquired.

"Back in America, gone to work."

"And where is the snow bird?"

"He was in here last week. Anyway, his friend, Mr. Schaeffer, is in Paris."

Two familiar names from the long list of a year and a half ago. Charlie scribbled an address in his notebook and tore out the page.

"If you see Mr. Schaeffer, give him this," he said. "It's my brother-in-law's address. I haven't settled on a hotel yet."

He was not really disappointed to find Paris was so empty. But the stillness in the bar was strange, almost portentous.

It was not an American bar any more—he felt polite in it, and not as if he owned it. It had gone back into France. He had felt the stillness from the moment he got out of the taxi and saw the doorman, usually in a frenzy of activity at this hour, gossiping with a *chasseur* by the servants' entrance.

Passing through the corridor, he heard only a single, bored voice in the once-clamorous women's room. When he turned into the bar he traveled the twenty feet of green carpet with his eyes fixed straight ahead by old habit; and then, with his foot firmly on the rail, he turned and surveyed the room, encountering only a single pair of eyes that fluttered up from a newspaper in the corner. Charlie asked for the head barman, Paul, who in the latter days of the bull market had come to work in his own custom-built car—disembarking, however, with due nicety at the nearest corner. But Paul was at his country house to-day and Alix was giving him his information.

"No, no more. I'm going slow these days."

Alix congratulated him: "Hope you stick to it, Mr. Wales. You were going pretty strong a couple of years ago."

"I'll stick to it all right," Charlie assured him. "I've stuck to it for over a year and a half now."

"How do you find conditions in America?"

"I haven't been to America for months. I'm in business in Prague, representing a couple of concerns there. They don't know about me down there." He smiled faintly. "Remember the night of George Hardt's bachelor dinner here? . . . By the way, what's become of Claude Fessenden?"

Alix lowered his voice confidentially: "He's in Paris, but he doesn't come here any more. Paul doesn't allow it. He ran up a bill of thirty thousand francs, charging all his drinks and his lunches, and usually his dinner, for more than a year. And when Paul finally told him he had to pay, he gave him a bad check."

Alix pressed his lips together and shook his head.

"I don't understand it, such a dandy fellow. Now he's all bloated up—" He made a plump apple of his hands.

A thin world, resting on a common weakness, shredded away now like tissue paper. Turning, Charlie saw a group of effeminate young men installing themselves in a corner.

"Nothing affects them," he thought. "Stocks rise and fall, people loaf or work, but they go on forever." The place oppressed him. He called for the dice and shook with Alix for the drink.

"Here for long, Mr. Wales?"

"I'm here for four or five days to see my little girl."

"Oh-h! You have a little girl?"

Outside, the fire-red, gas-blue, ghost-green signs shone smokily through the tranquil rain. It was late afternoon and the streets were in movement; the *bistros* gleamed. At the corner of the Boulevard des Capucines he took a taxi. The Place de la Concorde moved by in pink majesty; they crossed the logical Seine, and Charlie felt the sudden provincial quality of the left bank.

"I spoiled this city for myself," he thought. "I didn't realize it, but the days came along one after another, and then two years were gone, and everything was gone, and I was gone."

He was thirty-five, a handsome man, with the Irish mobility of his face sobered by a deep wrinkle between his eyes. As he rang his brother-in-law's bell in the Rue Palatine, the wrinkle deepened till it pulled down his brows; he felt a cramping sensation in his belly. From behind the maid who opened the door darted a lovely little girl of nine who shrieked "Daddy!" and flew up, struggling like a fish, into his arms. She pulled his head around by one ear and set her cheek against his.

"My old pie," he said.

"Oh, daddy, daddy, daddy, daddy, dads, dads, dads!"

She drew him into the salon, where the family waited, a boy and girl his daughter's age, his sister-in-law and her husband. He greeted Marion with his voice pitched carefully to avoid either feigned enthusiasm or dislike, but her response was more frankly tepid, and she minimized her expression of unshakable distrust by directing her regard toward his child. The two men clasped hands in a friendly way and Lincoln Peters rested his for a moment on Charlie's shoulder.

The room was warm and comfortably American. The three children moved intimately about, playing through the yellow oblongs that led to other rooms; the cheer of six o'clock spoke in the eager smacks of the fire and the sounds of French activity in the kitchen. But Charlie did not relax; his heart sat up rigidly in his body and he drew confidence from his daughter, who from time to time came close to him, holding in her arms the doll he had brought.

"Really extremely well," he declared in answer to Lincoln's question. "There's a lot of business there that isn't moving at all, but we're doing even better than ever. In fact, damn well. I'm bringing my sister over from America next month to keep house for me. In fact, my income is bigger than it was when I had money. You see, the Czechs—"

His boasting was for a specific purpose; but after a moment, seeing a faint restiveness in Lincoln's eye, he changed the subject:

"Those are fine children of yours, well brought up, good manners."

"We think Honoria's a great little girl too."

Marion Peters came back into the little salon. She was a tall woman with worried eyes, who had once possessed a fresh American loveliness. Charlie had never been sensitive to it and was always surprised when people spoke of how pretty she had been. From the first there had been an instinctive antipathy between them.

"Well, how do you find Honoria?" she asked.

"Wonderful. I was astonished how much she's grown in ten months. All the children are looking well."

"We haven't had a doctor for a year. How do you like being back in Paris?"

"It seems very funny to see so few Americans around."

"I'm delighted," Marion said vehemently. "Now at least you can go into a store without their assuming you're a millionaire. We've suffered like everybody, but on the whole it's a good deal pleasanter."

"But it was nice while it lasted," Charlie said. "We were a sort of royalty, almost infallible, with a sort of magic around us. In the bar this afternoon"—he stumbled, seeing his mistake—"there wasn't a man I knew."

She looked at him keenly. "I should think you'd have had enough of bars."

"I only stayed a minute. I take one drink every afternoon, and no more."

"Don't you want a cocktail before dinner?" Lincoln asked.

"I take only one drink every afternoon, and I've had that."

"I hope you keep to it," said Marion.

Her dislike was evident in the coldness with which she spoke, but Charlie only smiled; he had larger plans. Her very aggressiveness gave him an advantage, and he knew enough to wait. He wanted them to initiate the discussion of what they knew had brought him to Paris.

Honoria was to spend the following afternoon with him. At dinner he couldn't decide whether she was most like him or her mother. Fortunate if she didn't combine the traits of both that had brought them to disaster. A great wave of protectiveness went over him. He thought he knew what to do for her. He believed in character; he wanted to jump back a whole generation and trust in character again as the eternally valuable element. Everything wore out now. Parents expected genius, or at least brilliance, and both the forcing of children and the fear of forcing them, the fear of warping natural abilities, were poor substitutes for that long, careful watchfulness, that checking and balancing and reckoning of accounts, the end of which was that there should be no slipping below a certain level of duty and integrity.

That was what the elders had been unable to teach plausibly since the break between the generations ten or twelve years ago.

He left soon after dinner, but not to go home. He was curious to see Paris by night with clearer and more judicious eyes. He bought a *strapontin* for the Casino and watched Josephine Baker go through her chocolate arabesques.

After an hour he left and strolled toward Montmartre, up the Rue Pigalle into the Place Blanche. The rain had stopped and there were a few people in evening clothes disembarking from taxis in front of cabarets, and *cocottes* prowling singly or in pairs, and many Negroes. He passed a lighted door from which issued music, and stopped with the sense of familiarity; it was Bricktop's, where he had parted with so many hours and so much money. A few doors farther on he found another ancient rendezvous and incautiously put his head inside. Immediately an eager orchestra burst into sound, a pair of professional dancers leaped to their feet and a maître d'hôtel swooped toward him, crying, "Crowd just arriving, sir!" But he withdrew quickly.

"You have to be damn drunk," he thought.

Zelli's was closed, the bleak and sinister cheap hotels surrounding it were dark; up in the Rue Blanche there was more light and a local, colloquial French crowd. The Poet's Cave had disappeared, but the two great mouths of the Café of Heaven and the Café of Hell still yawned—even devoured, as he watched, the meager contents of a tourist bus—a German, a Japanese, and an American couple who glanced at him with frightened eyes.

So much for the effort and ingenuity of Montmartre. All the catering to vice and waste was on an utterly childish scale, and he suddenly realized the meaning of the word "dissipate"—to dissipate into thin air; to make nothing out of something. In the little hours of the night every move from place to place was an enormous human jump, an increase of paying for the privilege of slower and slower motion.

He remembered thousand-franc notes given to an orchestra for playing a single number, hundred-franc notes tossed to a doorman for calling a cab.

But it hadn't been given for nothing.

It had been given, even the most wildly squandered sum, as an offering to destiny that he might not remember the things most worth remembering, the things that now he would always remember—his child taken from his control, his wife escaped to a grave in Vermont.

In the glare of a *brasserie* a woman spoke to him. He bought her some eggs and coffee, and then, eluding her encouraging stare, gave her a twenty-franc note and took a taxi to his hotel.

II

He woke upon a fine fall day—football weather. The depression of yesterday was gone and he liked the people on the streets. At noon he sat opposite Honoria at the Grand Vatel, the only restaurant he could think of not reminiscent of champagne dinners and long luncheons that began at two and ended in a blurred and vague twilight.

"Now, how about vegetables? Oughtn't you to have some vegetables?"

"Well, yes."

"Here's *épinards* and *chou-fleur* and carrots and *haricots*."

"I'd like *choux-fleurs*."

"Wouldn't you like to have two vegetables?"

"I usually only have one at lunch."

The waiter was pretending to be inordinately fond of children. "*Qu'elle est mignonne la petite? Elle parle exactment comme une française.*"

"How about dessert? Shall we wait and see?"

The waiter disappeared. Honoria looked at him expectantly. "What are we going to do?"

"First we're going to that toy store in the Rue St. Honoré and buy you anything you like. And then we're going to the vaudeville at the Empire."

She hesitated. "I like it about the vaudeville, but not the toy store."

"Why not?"

"Well, you brought me this doll." She had it with her. "And I've got lots of things. And we're not rich any more, are we?"

"We never were. But to-day you are to have anything you want."

"All right," she agreed resignedly.

He had always been fond of her, but when there had been her mother and a French nurse he had been inclined to be strict; now he extended himself, reached out for a new tolerance; he must be both parents to her and not shut any of her out of communication.

"I want to get to know you," he said gravely. "First let me introduce myself. My name is Charles J. Wales, of Prague."

"Oh, daddy!" her voice cracked with laughter.

"And who are you, please?" he persisted, and she accepted a rôle immediately: "Honoria Wales, Rue Palatine, Paris."

"Married or single?"

"No, not married. Single."

He indicated the doll. "But I see you have a child, madame."

Unwilling to disinherit it, she took it to her heart and thought quickly: "Yes, I've been married, but I'm not married now. My husband is dead."

He went on quickly, "And the child's name?"

"Simone. That's after my best friend at school."

"I'm very pleased that you're doing so well at school."

"I'm third this month," she boasted. "Elsie"—that was her cousin—"is only about eighteenth, and Richard is about at the bottom."

"You like Richard and Elsie, don't you?"

"Oh, yes. I like Richard quite well and I like her all right."

Cautiously and casually he asked: "And Aunt Marion and Uncle Lincoln—which do you like best?"

"Oh, Uncle Lincoln, I guess."

He was increasingly aware of her presence. As they came in, a murmur of "What an adorable child" followed them, and now the people at the next table bent all their silences upon her, staring as if she were something no more conscious than a flower.

"Why don't I live with you?" she asked suddenly. "Because mamma's dead?"

"You must stay here and learn more French. It would have been hard for daddy to take care of you so well."

"I don't really need much taking care of any more. I do everything for myself."

Going out of the restaurant, a man and a woman unexpectedly hailed him!

"Well, the old Wales!"

"Hello there, Lorraine . . . . Dunc."

Sudden ghosts out of the past: Duncan Schaeffer, a friend from college. Lorraine Quarrles, a lovely, pale blond of thirty; one of a crowd who had helped them make months into days in the lavish times of two years ago.

"My husband couldn't come this year," she said, in answer to his question. "We're poor as hell. So he gave me two hundred a month and told me I could do my worst on that . . . . This your little girl?"

"What about sitting down?" Duncan asked.

"Can't do it." He was glad for an excuse. As always, he felt Lorraine's passionate, provocative attraction, but his own rhythm was different now.

"Well, how about dinner?" she asked.

"I'm not free. Give me your address and let me call you."

"Charlie, I believe you're sober," she said judicially. "I honestly believe he's sober, Dunc. Pinch him and see if he's sober."

Charlie indicated Honoria with his head. They both laughed.

"What's your address?" said Duncan skeptically.

He hesitated, unwilling to give the name of his hotel.

"I'm not settled yet. I'd better call you. We're going to see the vaudeville at the Empire."

"There! That's what I want to do," Lorraine said. "I want to see some clowns and acrobats and jugglers. That's just what we'll do, Dunc."

"We've got to do an errand first," said Charlie. "Perhaps we'll see you there."

"All right, you snob. . . . Good-by, beautiful little girl."

"Good-by." Honoria bobbed politely.

Somehow, an unpleasant encounter, Charlie thought. They liked him because he was functioning, because he was serious; they wanted to see him, because he was stronger than they were now, because they wanted to draw a certain sustenance from his strength.

At the Empire, Honoria proudly refused to sit upon her father's folded coat. She was already an individual with a code of her own, and Charlie was more and more absorbed by the desire of putting a little of himself into her before she crystallized utterly. It was hopeless to try to know her in so short a time.

Between the acts they came upon Duncan and Lorraine in the lobby where the band was playing.

"Have a drink?"

"All right, but not up at the bar. We'll take a table."

"The perfect father."

Listening abstractedly to Lorraine, Charlie watched Honoria's eyes leave them all, and he followed them wistfully about the room, wondering what they saw. He met them and she smiled.

"I liked that lemonade," she said.

What had she said? What had he expected? Going home in a taxi afterward, he pulled her over until her head rested against his chest.

"Darling, do you ever think about your mother?"

"Yes, sometimes," she answered vaguely.

"I don't want you to forget her. Have you got a picture of her?"

"Yes, I think so. Anyhow, Aunt Marion has. Why don't you want me to forget her?"

"She loved you very much."

"I loved her too."

They were silent for a moment.

"Daddy, I want to come and live with you," she said suddenly.

His heart leaped; he had wanted it to come like this.

"Aren't you perfectly happy?"

"Yes, but I love you better than anybody. And you love me better than anybody, don't you, now that mummy's dead?"

"Of course I do. But you won't always like me best, honey. You'll grow up and meet somebody your own age and go marry him and forget you ever had a daddy."

"Yes, that's true," she agreed tranquilly.

He didn't go in. He was coming back at nine o'clock and he wanted to keep himself fresh and new for the thing he must say then.

"When you're safe inside, just show yourself in that window."

"All right. Good-by, dads, dads, dads, dads."

He waited in the dark street until she appeared, all warm and glowing, in the window above and kissed her fingers out into the night.

III

They were waiting. Marion sat behind empty coffee cups in a dignified black dinner dress that just faintly suggested mourning. Lincoln was walking up and down with the animation of one who had already been talking. They were as anxious as he was to get into the question. He opened it almost immediately:

"I suppose you know what I want to see you about—why I really came to Paris."

Marion fiddled with the glass grapes on her necklace and frowned.

"I'm awfully anxious to have a home," he continued. "And I'm awfully anxious to have Honoria in it. I appreciate your taking in Honoria for her mother's sake, but things have changed now"—he hesitated and then continued strongly—"changed radically with me, and I want to ask you to reconsider the matter. It would be silly for me to deny that about two years ago I was acting badly—"

Marion looked up at him with hard eyes.

"—but all that's over. As I told you, I haven't had more than a drink a day for over a year, and I take that drink deliberately, so that the idea of alcohol won't get too big in my imagination. You see the idea?"

"No," said Marion succinctly.

"It's a sort of stunt I set myself. It keeps the matter in proportion."

"I get you," said Lincoln. "You don't want to admit it's got any attraction for you."

"Something like that. Sometimes I forget and don't take it. But I try to take it. Anyhow, I couldn't afford to drink in my position. The people I represent are more than satisfied with what I've done, and I'm bringing my sister over from Burlington to keep house for me, and I want awfully to have Honoria too. You know that even when her mother and I weren't getting along well I never let anything that happened touch Honoria. I know she's fond of me and I know I'm able to take care of her and—well, there you are. How do you feel about it?"

He knew that now he would have to take a beating. It would last an hour or two hours, and it would be difficult, but if he modulated his inevitable resentment to the chastened attitude of the reformed sinner, he might win his point in the end. "Keep your temper," he told himself. "You don't want to be justified. You want Honoria."

Lincoln spoke first: "We've been talking it over ever since we got your letter last month. We're happy to have Honoria here. She's a dear little thing, and we're glad to be able to help her, but of course that isn't the question—"

Marion interrupted suddenly. "How long are you going to stay sober, Charlie?" she asked.

"Permanently, I hope."

"How can anybody count on that?"

"You know I never did drink heavily until I gave up business and came over here with nothing to do. Then Helen and I began to run around with—"

"Please leave Helen out of it. I can't bear to hear you talk about her like that."

He stared at her grimly; he had never been certain how fond of each other the sisters were in life.

"My drinking only lasted about a year and a half—from the time we came over until I—collapsed."

"It was time enough."

"It was time enough," he agreed.

"My duty is entirely to Helen," she said. "I try to think what she would have wanted me to do. Frankly, from the night you did that terrible thing you haven't really existed for me. I can't help that. She was my sister."

"Yes."

"When she was dying she asked me to look out for Honoria. If you hadn't been in a sanitarium then, it might have helped matters."

He had no answer.

"I'll never in my life be able to forget the morning when Helen knocked at my door, soaked to the skin and shivering, and said you'd locked her out."

Charlie gripped the sides of the chair. This was more difficult than he expected; he wanted to launch out into a long expostulation and explanation, but he only said: "The night I locked her out—" and she interrupted, "I don't feel up to going over that again."

After a moment's silence Lincoln said: "We're getting off the subject. You want Marion to set aside her legal guardianship and give you Honoria. I think the main point for her is whether she has confidence in you or not."

"I don't blame Marion," Charlie said slowly, "but I think she can have entire confidence in me. I had a good record up to three years ago. Of course, it's within human possibilities I might go wrong any time. But if we wait much longer I'll lose Honoria's childhood and my chance for a home. I'll simply lose her, don't you see?"

"Yes, I see," said Lincoln.

"Why didn't you think of all this before?" Marion asked.

"I suppose I did, from time to time, but Helen and I were getting along badly. When I consented to the guardianship, I was flat on my back in a sanitarium and the market had cleaned me out of every sou. I knew I'd acted badly, and I thought if it would bring any peace to Helen, I'd agree to anything. But now it's different. I'm well, I'm functioning, I'm behaving damn well, so far as—"

"Please don't swear at me," Marion said.

He looked at her, startled. With each remark the force of her dislike became more and more apparent. She had built up all her fear of life into one wall and faced it toward him. This trivial reproof was possibly the result of some trouble with the cook several hours before. Charlie became increasingly alarmed at leaving Honoria in this atmosphere of hostility against himself; sooner or later it would come out, in a word here, a shake of the head there, and some of that distrust would be irrevocably implanted in Honoria. But he pulled his temper down out of his face and shut it up inside him; he had won a point, for Lincoln realized the absurdity of Marion's remark and asked her lightly since when she had objected to the word "damn."

"Another thing," Charlie said: "I'm able to give her certain advantages now. I'm going to take a French governess to Prague with me. I've got a lease on a new apartment—"

He stopped, realizing that he was blundering. They couldn't be expected to accept with equanimity the fact that his income was again twice as large as their own.

"I suppose you can give her more luxuries than we can," said Marion. "When you were throwing away money we were living along watching every ten francs. . . . I suppose you'll start doing it again."

"Oh, no," he said. "I've learned. I worked hard for ten years, you know—until I got lucky in the market, like so many people. Terribly lucky. It didn't seem any use working any more, so I quit. It won't happen again."

There was a long silence. All of them felt their nerves straining, and for the first time in a year Charlie wanted a drink. He was sure now that Lincoln Peters wanted him to have his child.

Marion shuddered suddenly; part of her saw that Charlie's feet were planted on the earth now, and her own maternal feeling recognized the naturalness of his desire; but she had lived for a long time with a prejudice—a prejudice founded on a curious disbelief in her sister's happiness, and which, in the shock of one terrible night, had turned to hatred for him. It had all happened at a point in her life where the discouragement of ill-health and adverse circumstances made it necessary for her to believe in tangible villainy and a tangible villain.

"I can't help what I think!" she cried out suddenly. "How much you were responsible for Helen's death, I don't know. It's something you'll have to square with your own conscience."

An electric current of agony surged through him; for a moment he was almost on his feet, an unuttered sound echoing in his throat. He hung on to himself for a moment, another moment.

"Hold on there," said Lincoln uncomfortably. "I never thought you were responsible for that."

"Helen died of heart trouble," Charlie said dully.

"Yes, heart trouble." Marion spoke as if the phrase had another meaning for her.

Then, in the flatness that followed her outburst, she saw him plainly and she knew he had somehow arrived at control over the situation. Glancing at her husband, she found no help from him, and as abruptly as if it were a matter of no importance, she threw up the sponge.

"Do what you like!" she cried, springing up from her chair. "She's your child. I'm not the person to stand in your way. I think if it were my child I'd rather see her—" She managed to check herself. "You two decide it. I can't stand this. I'm sick. I'm going to bed."

She hurried from the room; after a moment Lincoln said:

"This has been a hard day for her. You know how strongly she feels—" His voice was almost apologetic: "When a woman gets an idea in her head."

"Of course."

"It's going to be all right. I think she sees now that you—can provide for the child, and so we can't very well stand in your way or Honoria's way."

"Thank you, Lincoln."

"I'd better go along and see how she is."

"I'm going."

He was still trembling when he reached the street, but a walk down the Rue Bonaparte to the quais set him up, and as he crossed the Seine, dotted with many cold moons, he felt exultant.

But back in his room he couldn't sleep. The image of Helen haunted him. Helen whom he had loved so until they had sense- lessly begun to abuse each other's love and tear it into shreds. On that terrible February night that Marion remembered so vividly, a slow quarrel that had gone on for hours. There was a scene at the Florida, and then he attempted to take her home, and then Helen kissed Ted Wilder at a table, and what she had hysterically said. Charlie's departure and, on his arrival home, his turning the key in the lock in wild anger. How could he know she would arrive an hour later alone, that there would be a snowstorm in which she wandered about in slippers for an hour, too confused to find a taxi? Then the aftermath, her escaping pneumonia by a miracle, and all the attendant horror. They were "reconciled," but that was the beginning of the end, and Marion, who had seen with her own eyes and who imagined it to be one of many scenes from her sister's martyrdom, never forgot.

Going over it again brought Helen nearer, and in the white, soft light that steals upon half sleep near morning he found him- self talking to her again. She said that he was perfectly right about Honoria and that she wanted Honoria to be with him. She said she was glad he was being good and doing better. She said a lot of other things—very friendly things—but she was in a swing in a white dress, and swinging faster and faster all the time, so that at the end he could not hear clearly all that she said.

IV

He woke up feeling happy. The door of the world was open again. He made plans, vistas, futures for Honoria and himself, but suddenly he grew sad, remembering all the plans he and Helen had made. She had not planned to die. The present was the thing—work to do and some one to love. But not to love too much, for Charlie had read in D. H. Lawrence about the injury that a father can do to a daughter or a mother to a son by attach- ing them too closely. Afterward, out in the world, the child would seek in the marriage partner the same blind, unselfish ten- derness and, failing in all human probability to find it, develop a grudge against love and life.

It was another bright, crisp day. He called Lincoln Peters at the bank where he worked and asked if he could count on taking Honoria when he left for Prague. Lincoln agreed that there was no reason for delay. One thing—the legal guardianship. Marion wanted to retain that a while longer. She was upset by the whole matter, and it would oil things if she felt that the situation was still in her control for another year. Charlie agreed, wanting only the tangible, visible child.

Then the question of a governess. Charlie sat in a gloomy agency and talked to a buxom Breton peasant whom he knew he couldn't endure. There were others whom he could see to-morrow.

He lunched with Lincoln Peters at the Griffon, trying to keep down his exultation.

"There's nothing quite like your own child," Lincoln said. "But you understand how Marion feels too."

"She's forgotten how hard I worked for seven years there," Charlie said. "She just remembers one night."

"There's another thing." Lincoln hesitated. "While you and Helen were tearing around Europe throwing money away, we were just getting along. I didn't touch any of the prosperity because I never got ahead enough to carry anything but my insurance. I think Marion felt there was some kind of injustice in it—you not even working and getting richer and richer."

"It went just as quick as it came," said Charlie.

"A lot did. And a lot of it stayed in the hands of *chasseurs* and saxophone players and maîtres d'hôtel—well, the big party's over now. I just said that to explain Marion's feeling about those crazy years. If you drop in about six o'clock to-night before Marion's too tired, we'll settle the details on the spot."

Back at his hotel, Charlie took from his pocket a *pneumatique* that Lincoln had given him at luncheon. It had been redirected by Paul from the hotel bar.

> DEAR CHARLIE: You were so strange when we saw you the other day that I wondered if I did something to offend you. If so, I'm not conscious of it. In fact, I have thought about you too much for the last year, and it's always been in the back of my mind that I might see you if I came over here. We did have such good times that crazy spring, like the night you and I stole the butcher's tricycle, and the time we tried to call on the president and you had the old derby and the wire cane. Everybody seems so old lately, but I don't feel old a bit. Couldn't we get together sometime to-day for old time's sake? I've got a vile hang-over for the moment, but will be feeling better this afternoon and will look for you about five at the bar.
>
> Always devotedly,
> LORRAINE.

His first feeling was one of awe that he had actually, in his mature years, stolen a tricycle and pedaled Lorraine all over the Étoile between the small hours and dawn. In retrospect it was a nightmare. Locking out Helen didn't fit in with any other act of his life, but the tricycle incident did—it was one of many. How many weeks or months of dissipation to arrive at that condition of utter irresponsibility?

He tried to picture how Lorraine had appeared to him then— very attractive; so much so that Helen had been jealous. Yesterday, in the restaurant, she had seemed trite, blurred, worn away. He emphatically did not want to see her, and he was glad no one knew at what hotel he was staying. It was a relief to think of Honoria, to think of Sundays spent with her and of saying good morning to her and of knowing she was there in his house at night, breathing quietly in the darkness.

At five he took a taxi and bought presents for all the Peterses— a piquant cloth doll, a box of Roman soldiers, flowers for Marion, big linen handkerchiefs for Lincoln.

He saw, when he arrived in the apartment, that Marion had accepted the inevitable. She greeted him now as though he were a recalcitrant member of the family, rather than a menacing outsider. Honoria had been told she was going, and Charlie was glad to see that her tact was sufficient to conceal her excessive happiness. Only on his lap did she whisper her delight and the question "When?" before she slipped away.

He and Marion were alone for a minute in the room, and on an impulse he spoke out boldly:

"Family quarrels are bitter things. They don't go according to my rules. They're not like aches or wounds; they're more like splits in the skin that won't heal because there's not enough material. I wish you and I could be on better terms."

"Some things are hard to forget," she answered. "It's a question of confidence. If you behave yourself in the future I won't have any criticism." There was no answer to this, and presently she asked, "When do you propose to take her?"

"As soon as I can get a governess. I hoped the day after tomorrow."

"That's impossible. I've got to get her things in shape. Not before Saturday."

He yielded. Coming back into the room, Lincoln offered him a drink.

"I'll take my daily whisky," he said.

It was warm here, it was a home, people together by a fire. The children felt very safe and important; the mother and father were serious, watchful. They had things to do for the children more important than his visit here. A spoonful of medicine was, after all, more important than the strained relations between Marion and himself. They were not dull people, but they were very much in the grip of life and circumstances, and their gestures as they turned in a cramped space lacked largeness and grace. He wondered if he couldn't do something to get Lincoln out of that rut at the bank.

There was a long peal at the doorbell; the maid crossed the room and went down the corridor. The door opened upon another long ring, and then voices, and the three in the salon looked up expectantly; Richard moved to bring the corridor within his range of vision, and Marion rose. Then the maid came along the corridor, closely followed by the voices, which developed under the light into Duncan Schaeffer and Lorraine Quarrles.

They were gay, they were hilarious, they were roaring with laughter. For a moment Charlie was astounded; then he realized they had got the address he had left at the bar.

"Ah-h-h!" Duncan wagged his finger roguishly at Charlie. "Ah-h-h!"

They both slid down into another cascade of laughter. Anxious and at a loss, Charlie shook hands with them quickly and presented them to Lincoln and Marion. Marion nodded, scarcely speaking. She had drawn back a step toward the fire; her little girl stood beside her, and Marion put an arm about her shoulder.

With growing annoyance at the intrusion, Charlie waited for them to explain themselves. After some concentration Duncan said:

"We came to take you to dinner. Lorraine and I insist that all this shi-shi, cagy business got to stop."

Charlie came closer to them, as if to force them backward down the corridor.

"Sorry, but I can't. Tell me where you'll be and we'll call you in half an hour."

This made no impression. Lorraine sat down suddenly on the side of a chair, and focusing her eyes on Richard, cried, "Oh, what a nice little boy! Come here, little boy." Richard glanced at his mother, but did not move. With a perceptible shrug of her shoulders, Lorraine turned back to Charlie:

"Come on out to dinner. Be yourself, Charlie. Come on."

"How about a little drink?" said Duncan to the room at large.

Lincoln Peters had been somewhat uneasily occupying himself by swinging Honoria from side to side with her feet off the ground.

"I'm sorry, but there isn't a thing in the house," he said. "We just this minute emptied the only bottle."

"All the more reason for coming to dinner," Lorraine assured Charlie.

"I can't," said Charlie almost sharply. "You two go have dinner and I'll phone you."

"Oh, you will, will you?" Her voice became suddenly unpleasant. "All right, we'll go along. But I remember, when you used to hammer on my door, I used to be enough of a good sport to give you a drink. Come on, Dunc."

Still in slow motion, with blurred, angry faces, with uncertain feet, they retired along the corridor.

"Good night," Charlie said.

"Good night!" responded Lorraine emphatically.

When he went back into the salon Marion had not moved, only now her son was standing in the circle of her other arm. Lincoln was still swinging Honoria back and forth like a pendulum from side to side.

"What an outrage!" Charlie broke out. "What an absolute outrage!"

Neither of them answered. Charlie dropped down into an armchair, picked up his drink, set it down again and said:

"People I haven't seen for two years having the colossal nerve—"

He broke off. Marion had made the sound "Oh!" in one swift, furious breath, turned her body from him with a jerk and left the room.

Lincoln set down Honoria carefully.

"You children go in and start your soup," he said, and when they obeyed, he said to Charlie:

"Marion's not well and she can't stand shocks. That kind of people make her really physically sick."

"I didn't tell them to come here. They wormed this address out of Paul at the bar. They deliberately—"

"Well, it's too bad. It doesn't help matters. Excuse me a minute."

Left alone, Charlie sat tense in his chair. In the next room he could hear the children eating, talking in monosyllables, already oblivious of the scene among their elders. He heard a murmur of conversation from a farther room and then the ticking bell of a phone picked up, and in a panic he moved to the other side of the room and out of earshot.

In a minute Lincoln came back. "Look here, Charlie. I think we'd better call off dinner for to-night. Marion's in bad shape."

"Is she angry with me?"

"Sort of," he said, almost roughly. "She's not strong and—"

"You mean she's changed her mind about Honoria?"

"She's pretty bitter right now. I don't know. You phone me at the bank to-morrow."

"I wish you'd explain to her I never dreamed these people would come here. I'm just as sore as you are."

"I couldn't explain anything to her now."

Charlie got up. He took his coat and hat and started down the corridor. Then he opened the door of the dining room and said in a strange voice, "Good night, children."

Honoria rose and ran around the table to hug him.

"Good night, sweetheart," he said vaguely, and then trying to make his voice more tender, trying to conciliate something, "Good night, dear children."

V

Charlie went directly to the bar with the furious idea of finding Lorraine and Duncan, but they were not there, and he realized that in any case there was nothing he could do. He had not touched his drink at the Peterses,' and now he ordered a whisky-and-soda. Paul came over to say hello.

"It's a great change," he said sadly. "We do about half the business we did. So many fellows I hear about back in the States lost everything, maybe not in the first crash, but then in the second, and now when everything keeps going down. Your friend George Hardt lost every cent, I hear. Are you back in the States?"

"No, I'm in business in Prague."

"I heard that you lost a lot in the crash."

"I did," and he added grimly, "but I lost everything I wanted in the boom."

"Selling short."

"Something like that."

Again the memory of those days swept over him like a nightmare—the people they had met traveling; then people who couldn't add a row of figures or speak a coherent sentence. The little man Helen had consented to dance with at the ship's party, who had insulted her ten feet from the table; the human mosaic of pearls who sat behind them at the Russian ballet and, when the curtain rose on a scene, remarked to her companion: "Luffly; just luffly. Zomebody ought to baint a bicture of it." Men who locked their wives out in the snow, because the snow of twenty-nine wasn't real snow. If you didn't want it to be snow, you just paid some money.

He went to the phone and called the Peters apartment; Lincoln himself answered.

"I called up because, as you can imagine, this thing is on my mind. Has Marion said anything definite?"

"Marion's sick," Lincoln answered shortly. "I know this thing isn't altogether your fault, but I can't have her go to pieces about this. I'm afraid we'll have to let it slide for six months; I can't take the chance of working her up to this state again."

"I see."

"I'm sorry, Charlie."

He went back to his table. His whisky glass was empty, but he shook his head when Alix looked at it questioningly. There wasn't much he could do now except send Honoria some things; he would send her a lot of things to-morrow. He thought rather angrily that that was just money—he had given so many people money.

"No, no more," he said to another waiter. "What do I owe you?"

He would come back some day; they couldn't make him pay forever. But he wanted his child, and nothing was much good now, beside that fact. He wasn't young any more, with a lot of nice thoughts and dreams to have by himself. He was absolutely sure Helen wouldn't have wanted him to be so alone.

EDITORS' ANALYSIS

In Fitzgerald's "Babylon Revisited" the personal loss in love is very nearly total, the inevitable result of a man's relegation of himself and his wife to what had seemed an exciting way of living, but which was actually a way of self-destruction. The story does not moralize, though its title surely carries an evaluative sting to it. The international setting suggests that the debacle of Charlie Wales was not merely that of one man. It leads us to an awareness that his plight was a typical product of the American expatriate's effort to break away from conventional moral tradition.

QUESTIONS

1. How is the title related to the events of the story? What suggestions, satiric or otherwise, does it convey?

2. The story is rich in suggestive detail. Could any of it be omitted and have the story survive? Would the omission of any of it make the ending seem less bleak?

3. What is the nature of the "instinctive antipathy" between Charlie Wales and his sister-in-law? In the story, your sympathy is with Wales, but you may feel that his sister-in-law is also justified in her views. Does this add to the tension of the story?

4. Is "Babylon Revisited" wholly concerned with the lives of members of the "lost generation," or does it have a larger meaning? Does the meaning transcend the circumstances of the story?

5. At the story's end, when Charlie Wales is thinking of what his dead wife might have wished for him, is our sense of his tragic plight enhanced by his own self-evident sense of guilt? If so, how?

The Brooch

by WILLIAM FAULKNER

William Faulkner (1897-   ) is considered by many critics to be the most important American writer of the first half of this century, and his having been awarded the Nobel Prize for Literature in 1950 is partial confirmation of his stature. He has invented a distinct fictional world, a mythological county in a real Mississippi, into which his great fabric of stories and novels has been threaded. One of the dominant themes of his fiction, touched upon very lightly in "The Brooch," is the conflict between the decadent families whose way of life still reflects the "Old South," and the pushing, half-literate new-comers who have supplanted them. His trilogy *The Hamlet* (1940) *The Town* (1957) and *The Mansion* (1959) is almost wholly based upon this theme. Faulkner's greatness as a writer, at least in part, lies in his ability to evoke in the reader an awareness of the deeply rooted nature of the loves, hatreds, and fears which haunt his characters, and the human race. His comparatively short novel *Light in August* (1932) exemplifies this ability at its best. Useful critical studies of Faulkner include: *William Faulkner: Two Decades of Criticism,* ed. Frederick J. Hoffman and Olga W. Vickery (1951); *William Faulkner, A Critical Study,* by Irving Howe (1952); and *The Tangled Fire of William Faulkner,* by William Van O'Connor (1954).

Faulkner's "The Brooch," without his art, could be described as a fictional treatment of a commonplace of everyday experience: a young man's loss of his wife to her lover. But the story takes on added depth from the conflict between the old tradition of the South represented by the mother, and the new as represented by the wife. Its real power over us, however, is less easily explained. It has to do with the young husband's own discovery of the completeness of his need for love.

The telephone waked him. He waked already hurrying, fumbling in the dark for robe and slippers, because he knew

---

before waking that the bed beside his own was still empty, and the instrument was downstairs just opposite the door beyond which his mother had lain propped upright in bed for five years, and he knew on waking that he would be too late because she would already have heard it, just as she heard everything that happened at any hour in the house.

She was a widow, he the only child. When he went away to college she went with him; she kept a house in Charlottesville, Virginia, for four years while he graduated. She was the daughter of a well-to-do merchant. Her husband had been a travelling man who came one summer to the town with letters of introduction: one to a minister, the other to her father. Three months later the travelling man and the daughter were married. His name was Boyd. He resigned his position within the year and moved into his wife's house and spent his days sitting in front of the hotel with the lawyers and the cotton-planters—a dark man with a gallant swaggering way of removing his hat to ladies. In the second year, the son was born. Six months later, Boyd departed. He just went away, leaving a note to his wife in which he told her that he could no longer bear to lie in bed at night and watch her rolling onto empty spools the string saved from parcels from the stores. His wife never heard of him again, though she refused to let her father have the marriage annulled and change the son's name.

Then the merchant died, leaving all his property to the daughter and the grandson who, though he had been out of Fauntleroy suits since he was seven or eight, at twelve wore even on weekdays clothes which made him look not like a child but like a midget; he probably could not have long associated with other children even if his mother had let him. In due time the mother found a boy's school where the boy could wear a round jacket and a man's hard hat with impunity, though by the time the two of them removed to Charlottesville for these next four years, the son did not look like a midget. He looked now like a character out of Dante—a man a little slighter than his father but with something of his father's dark handsomeness, who hurried with averted head, even when his mother was not with him, past the young girls on the streets not only of Charlottesville but of the little lost Mississippi hamlet to which they presently returned, with an expression of face like the young monks or angels in fifteenth-century allegories. Then his mother had her stroke, and presently the mother's friends brought to her bed reports of almost exactly the sort of girl which perhaps even the mother might have expected the son to become not only involved with but to marry.

Her name was Amy, daughter of a railroad conductor who had been killed in a wreck. She lived now with an aunt who kept a boarding-house—a vivid, daring girl whose later reputation was due more to folly and the caste handicap of the little Southern town than to badness and which at the last was doubtless more smoke than fire; whose name, though she always had invitations to the more public dances, was a light word, especially among the older women, daughters of decaying old houses like this in which her future husband had been born.

So presently the son had acquired some skill in entering the house and passing the door beyond which his mother lay propped in bed, and mounting the stairs in the dark to his own room. But one night he failed to do so. When he entered the house the transom above his mother's door was dark, as usual, and even if it had not been he could not have known that this was the afternoon on which the mother's friends had called and told her about Amy, and that his mother had lain for five hours, propped bolt upright, in the darkness, watching the invisible door. He entered quietly as usual, his shoes in his hand, yet he had not even closed the front door when she called his name. Her voice was not raised. She called his name once:

"Howard."

He opened the door. As he did so the lamp beside her bed came on. It sat on a table beside the bed; beside it sat a clock with a dead face; to stop it had been the first act of his mother when she could move her hands two years ago. He approached the bed from which she watched him—a thick woman with a face the color of tallow and dark eyes apparently both pupil-less and iris-less beneath perfectly white hair. "What?" he said. "Are you sick?"

"Come closer." she said. He came nearer. They looked at one another. Then he seemed to know; perhaps he had been expecting it.

"I know who's been talking to you," he said. "Those damned old buzzards."

"I'm glad to hear it's carrion," she said. "Now I can rest easy that you won't bring it into our house."

"Go on. Say, your house."

"Not necessary. Any house where a lady lives." They looked at one another in the steady lamp which possessed that stale glow of sickroom lights. "You are a man. I don't reproach you. I am not even surprised. I just want to warn you before you make yourself ridiculous. Don't confuse the house with the stable."

"With the—Hah!" he said. He stepped back and jerked the door open with something of his father's swaggering theatricalism. "With your permission," he said. He did not close the door. She lay bolt upright on the pillows and looked into the dark hall and listened to him go to the telephone, call the girl, and ask her to marry him tomorrow. Then he reappeared at the door. "With your permission," he said again, with that swaggering reminiscence of his father, closing the door. After a while the mother turned the light off. It was daylight in the room then.

They were not married the next day, however. "I'm scared to," Amy said. "I'm scared of your mother. What does she say about me?"

"I don't know. I never talk to her about you."

"You don't even tell her you love me?"

"What does it matter? Let's get married."

"And live there with her?" They looked at one another. "Will you go to work, get us a house of our own?"

"What for? I have enough money. And it's a big house."

"Her house. Her money."

"It'll be mine—ours some day. Please."

"Come on. Let's try to dance again." This was in the parlor of the boarding-house, where she was trying to teach him to dance, but without success. The music meant nothing to him; the noise of it or perhaps the touch of her body destroyed what little co-ordination he could have had. But he took her to the Country Club dances; they were known to be engaged. Yet she still staid out dances with other men, in the parked cars about the dark lawn. He tried to argue with her about it, and about drinking.

"Sit out and drink with me, then," he said.

"We're engaged. It's no fun with you."

"Yes," he said, with the docility with which he accepted each refusal; then he stopped suddenly and faced her. "What's no fun with me?" She fell back a little as he gripped her shoulder. "What's no fun with me?"

"Oh," she said. "You're hurting me!"

"I know it. What's no fun with me?"

Then another couple came up and he let her go. Then an hour later, during an intermission, he dragged her, screaming and struggling, out of a dark car and across the dance floor, empty now and lined with chaperones like a theater audience, and drew out a chair and took her across his lap and spanked her. By daylight they had driven twenty miles to another town and were married.

That morning Amy called Mrs. Boyd "Mother" for the first and (except one, and that perhaps shocked out of her by surprise or perhaps by exultation) last time, though the same day Mrs. Boyd formally presented Amy with the brooch: an ancient, clumsy thing, yet valuable. Amy carried it back to their room, and he watched her stand looking at it perfectly cold, perfectly inscrutable. Then she put it into a drawer. She held it over the open drawer with two fingers and released it and then drew the two fingers across her thigh.

"You will have to wear it sometimes," Howard said.

"Oh, I will. I'll show my gratitude. Don't worry." Presently it seemed to him that she took pleasure in wearing it. That is, she began to wear it quite often. Then he realized that it was not pleasure but vindictive incongruity; she wore it for an entire week once on the bosom of a gingham house dress, an apron. But she always wore it where Mrs. Boyd would see it, always when she and Howard had dressed to go out and would stop in the mother's room to say good night.

They lived upstairs, where, a year later, their child was born. They took the child down for Mrs. Boyd to see it. She turned her head on the pillows and looked at the child once. "Ah," she said. "I never saw Amy's father, that I know of. But then, I never travelled on a train a great deal."

"The old—the old—" Amy cried, shuddering and clinging to Howard. "Why does she hate me so? What have I ever done to her? Let's move. You can work."

"No. She won't live always."

"Yes, she will. She'll live forever, just to hate me."

"No," Howard said. In the next year the child died. Again Amy tried to get him to move.

"Anywhere. I won't care how we have to live."

"No. I can't leave her helpless on her back. You will have to start going out again. Dance. Then it won't be so bad."

"Yes," she said, quieter. "I'll have to. I can't stand this."

One said "you," the other, "I." Neither of them said "we." So, on Saturday nights Amy would dress and Howard would put on scarf and overcoat, sometimes over his shirt-sleeves, and they would descend the stairs and stop at Mrs. Boyd's door and then

Howard would put Amy into the car and watch her drive away. Then he would re-enter the house and with his shoes in his hand return up the stairs, as he had used to do before they married, slipping past the lighted transom. Just before midnight, in the overcoat and scarf again, he would slip back down the stairs and past the still lighted transom and be waiting on the porch when Amy drove up. Then they would enter the house and look into Mrs. Boyd's room and say good night.

One night it was one o'clock before she returned. He had been waiting for an hour in slippers and pajamas on the porch; it was November. The transom above Mrs. Boyd's door was dark and they did not stop.

"Some jelly beans set the clock back," she said. She did not look at him, dragging her clothes off, flinging the brooch along with her other jewelry onto the dressing table. "I had hoped you wouldn't be fool enough to stand out there and wait for me."

"Maybe next time they set the clock back I won't."

She stopped, suddenly and perfectly still, looking at him over her shoulder. "Do you mean that?" she said. He was not looking at her; he heard, felt, her approach and stand beside him. Then she touched his shoulder. "Howard?" she said. He didn't move. Then she was clinging to him, flung onto his lap, crying wildly: "What's happening to us?" striking herself against him with a wild abandon: "What is it? What is it?" He held her quiet, though after they were each in their beds (they already had two of them) he heard and then felt her cross the intervening gap and fling herself against him again with that wild terrified abandon not of a woman but of a child in the dark, enveloping him, whispering: "You don't *have* to trust me, Howard! You can! You can! You don't *have* to!"

"Yes," he said. "I know. It's all right. It's all right." So after that, just before twelve, he would put on the overcoat and scarf, creep down the stairs and past the lighted transom, open and close the front door noisily, and then open his mother's door where the mother would be propped high on the pillows, the book open and face down on her knees.

"Back already?" Mrs. Boyd would say.

"Yes. Amy's gone on up. Do you want anything?"

"No. Good night."

"Good night."

Then he would go up and go to bed, and after a time (sometimes) to sleep. But before this sometimes, taking it sometimes into sleep with him, he would think, tell himself with that quiet and fatalistic pessimism of the impotent intelligent: *But this cannot go on forever. Some night something is going to happen; she is going to catch Amy. And I know what she is going to do. But what am I going to do?* He believed that he did know. That is, the top of his mind assured him that it knew, but he discounted this; the intelligence again: not to bury it, flee from it: just discounting, the intelligence speaking out of the impotence: *Because no man ever knows what he will do in any given situation, set of circumstances: the wise, others perhaps, drawing conclusions, but never himself.* The next morning Amy would be in the other bed, and then, in the light of day, it would be gone. But now and then, even by daylight, it returned and he from the detachment of his cerebration contemplating his life, that faulty whole whose third the two of them had produced yet whose lack the two of them could not fill, telling himself, *Yes. I know what she will do and I know what Amy will ask me to do and I know that I will not do that. But what will I do?* but not for long, telling himself now that it had not happened so far, and that anyway it was six long days until Saturday: the impotence now, not even the intellect.

II

So it was that when he waked to the bell's shrilling he already knew that the bed beside his own was still empty, just as he knew that, no matter how quickly he reached the telephone, it would already be too late. He did not even wait for his slippers; he ran down the now icy stairs, seeing the transom above his mother's door come alight as he passed it and went to the phone and took the receiver down: "Oh, Howard, I'm so sorry—this is Martha Ross—so sorry to disturb you, but I knew that Amy would be anxious about it. I found it in the car, tell her, when we got back home."

"Yes," he said. "In the car."

"In our car. After she lost her switch key and we brought her home, to the corner. We tried to get her to come on home with us and have some ham and eggs, but she—" Then the voice died away. He held the cold receiver to his ear and heard the other end of the wire, the silence, fill with a sort of consternation like an indrawn breath: something instinctive and feminine and self-protective. But the pause itself was hardly a pause; almost immediately the voice went on, though completely changed now, blank, smooth, reserved: "Amy's in bed, I suppose."

"Yes. She's in bed."

"Oh. So sorry I bothered you, got you up. But I knew she would be anxious about it, since it was your mother's, the family piece. But of course, if she hasn't missed it yet, you won't need to bother her." The wire hummed, tense. "That I called or anything." The wire hummed. "Hello. Howard?"

"No," he said. "I won't bother her tonight. You can call her in the morning."

"Yes, I will. So sorry I bothered you. I hope I didn't wake your mother."

He put the receiver back. He was cold. He could feel his bare toes curling back from the icelike floor as he stood looking at the blank door beyond which his mother would be sitting, high-propped on the pillows, with her tallow face and dark inscrutable eyes and the hair which Amy said resembled weathered cotton, beside the clock whose hands she had stopped herself at ten minutes to four on the afternoon five years ago when she first moved again. When he opened the door his picture had been exact, almost to the position of the hands even.

"She is not in this house," Mrs. Boyd said.

"Yes. She's in bed. You know when we came in. She just left one of her rings with Martha Ross tonight and Martha telephoned."

But apparently she had not even listened to him. "So you swear she is in this house this minute."

"Yes. Of course she is. She's asleep, I tell you."

"Then send her down here to say good night to me."

"Nonsense. Of course I won't."

They looked at one another across the bed's footboard.

"You refuse?"

"Yes."

They looked at one another a moment longer. Then he began to turn away; he could feel her watching him. "Then tell me something else. It was the brooch she lost."

He did not answer this either. He just looked at her again as he closed the door: the two of them curiously similar, mortal and implacable foes in the fierce close antipathy of blood. He went out.

He returned to the bedroom and turned on the light and found his slippers and went to the fire and put some coal on the embers and punched and prodded it into flame. The clock on the mantel said twenty minutes to one. Presently he had a fair blaze; he had quit shivering. He went back to bed and turned off the light, leaving only the firelight pulsing and gleaming on the furniture and among the phials and mirrors of the dressing table, and in the smaller mirror above his own chest of drawers, upon which sat the three silver photograph frames, the two larger ones containing himself and Amy, the smaller one between them empty. He just lay. He was not thinking at all. He had just thought once, quietly, *So that's that. So now I suppose I will know, find out what I am going to do* and then no more, not even thinking that again.

The house seemed still to be filled with the shrill sound of the telephone like a stubborn echo. Then he began to hear the clock on the mantel, reiterant, cold, not loud. He turned on the light and took up the book face down and open from the table beside his pillow, but he found that he could not keep his mind on the words for the sound which the clock made, so he rose and went to the mantel. The hands were now at half past two. He stopped the clock and turned its face to the wall and brought his book to the fire and found that he could now keep his mind on the words, the sense, reading on now untroubled by time. So he could not have said just when it was that he found he had ceased to read, had jerked his head up. He had heard no sound, yet he knew that Amy was in the house. He did not know how he knew: he just sat holding his breath, immobile, the peaceful book raised and motionless, waiting. Then he heard Amy say, "It's me, Mother."

She said "Mother," he thought, not moving yet. *She called her "Mother" again.* He moved now, putting the book carefully down, his place marked, but as he crossed the room he walked naturally, not trying to deaden his footsteps, to the door and opened it and saw Amy just emerging from Mrs. Boyd's room. She began to mount the stairs, walking naturally too, her hard heels sharp and unnaturally loud in the nightbound house. *She must have stooped when Mother called her and put her slippers on again,* he thought. She had not seen him yet, mounting steadily, her face in the dim hall light vague and petal-like against the collar of her fur coat, projecting already ahead of her to where he waited a sort of rosy and crystal fragrance of the frozen night out of which she had just emerged. Then she saw him at the head of the stairs. For just a second, an instant, she stopped dead still, though she was moving again before it could have been called pause, already speaking as she passed him where he stood aside, and entered the bedroom: "Is it very late? I was with the Rosses.

They just let me out at the corner; I lost my car key out at the club. Maybe it was the car that waked her."

"No. She was already awake. It was the telephone."

She went on to the fire and spread her hands to it, still in her coat; she did not seem to have heard him, her face rosy in the firelight, her presence emanating that smell of cold, that frosty fragrance which had preceded her up the stairs: "I suppose so. Her light was already on. I knew as soon as I opened the front door that we were sunk. I hadn't even got in the house good when she said 'Amy' and I said 'It's me, Mother' and she said, 'Come in here, please,' and there she was with those eyes that haven't got any edges to them and that hair that looks like somebody pulled it out of the middle of a last year's cotton bale, and she said, 'Of course you understand that you will have to leave this house at once. Good night.'"

"Yes," he said. "She has been awake since about half past twelve. But there wasn't anything to do but insist that you were already in bed asleep and trust to luck."

"You mean, she hasn't been asleep at all?"

"No. It was the telephone, like I told you. About half past twelve."

With her hands still spread to the fire she glanced at him over her furred shoulder, her face rosy, her eyes at once bright and heavy, like a woman's eyes after pleasure, with a kind of inattentive conspiratorial commiseration. "Telephone? Here? At half past twelve? What absolutely putrid—But no matter." She turned now, facing him, as if she had only been waiting until she became warm, the rich coat open upon the fragile glitter of her dress; there was a quality actually beautiful about her now—not of the face whose impeccable replica looks out from the covers of a thousand magazines each month, nor of the figure, the shape of deliberately epicene provocation into which the miles of celluloid film have constricted the female body of an entire race; but a quality completely female in the old eternal fashion, primitive assured and ruthless as she approached him, already raising her arms. "Yes! I say luck too!" she said, putting her arms around him, her upper body leaned back to look into his face, her own face triumphant, the smell now warm woman-odor where the frosty fragrance had thawed. "She said at once, now. So we can go. You see? Do you understand? We can leave now. Give her the money, let her have it all. We won't care. You can find work; I won't care how and where we will have to live. You don't have to stay here now, with her now. She has—what do you call it? absolved you herself. Only I have lost the car key. But no matter: we can walk. Yes, walk; with nothing, taking nothing of hers, like we came here."

"Now?" he said. "Tonight?"

"Yes! She said at once. So it will have to be tonight."

"No," he said. That was all, no indication of which question he had answered, which denied. But then, he did not need to because she still held him; it was only the expression of her face that changed. It did not die yet nor even become terrified yet: it just became unbelieving, like a child's incredulity. "You mean, you still won't go? You still won't leave her? That you would just take me to the hotel for tonight and that you will come back here tomorrow? Or do you mean you won't even stay at the hotel with me tonight? That you will take me there and leave me and then you—" She held him, staring at him; she began to say, "Wait, wait. There must be some reason, something—Wait," she cried; "wait! You said, telephone. At half past twelve." She still stared at him, her hands hard, her pupils like pinpoints, her face ferocious. "That's it. That's the reason. Who was it that telephoned here about me? Tell me! I defy you to! I will explain it. Tell me!"

"It was Martha Ross. She said she had just let you out at the corner."

"She lied!" she cried at once, immediately, scarce waiting to hear the name. "She lied! They did bring me home then but it was still early and so I decided to go on with them to their house and have some ham and eggs. So I called to Frank before he got turned around and I went with them. Frank will prove it! She lied! They just this minute put me out at the corner!"

She looked at him. They stared at one another for a full immobile moment. Then he said, "Then where is the brooch?"

"The brooch?" she said. "What brooch?" But already he had seen her hand move upward beneath the coat; besides, he could see her face and watch it gape like that of a child which has lost its breath before she began to cry with a wild yet immobile abandon, so that she spoke through the weeping in the choked gasping of a child, with complete and despairing surrender: "Oh, Howard! I wouldn't have done that to you! I wouldn't have! I wouldn't have!"

"All right," he said. "Hush, now. Hush, Amy. She will hear you."

"All right. I'm trying to." But she still faced him with that wrung and curiously rigid face beneath its incredible flow of moisture, as though not the eyes but all the pores had sprung at once; now she too spoke directly out of thinking, without mention of subject or circumstance, nothing more of defiance or denial: "Would you have gone with me if you hadn't found out?"

"No. Not even then. I won't leave her. I will not, until she is dead. Or this house. I won't. I can't. I—" They looked at one another, she staring at him as if she saw reflected in his pupils not herself but the parchment-colored face below stairs—the piled dirty white hair, the fierce implacable eyes—her own image blanked out by something beyond mere blindness: by a quality determined, invincible, and crucified.

"Yes," she said. From somewhere she produced a scrap of chiffon and began to dab at her eyes, delicately, even now by instinct careful of the streaked mascara. "She beat us. She lay there in that bed and beat us." She turned and went to the closet and drew out an overnight bag and put the crystal objects from the dressing-table into it and opened a drawer. "I can't take everything tonight. I will have to——"

He moved also; from the chest of drawers where the small empty photograph frame sat he took his wallet and removed the bills from it and returned and put the money into her hand. "I don't think there is very much here. But you won't need money until tomorrow."

"Yes," she said. "You can send the rest of my things then, too."

"Yes," he said. She folded and smoothed the notes in her fingers; she was not looking at him. He did not know what she was looking at except it was not at the money. "Haven't you got a purse or something to carry it in?"

"Yes," she said. But she did not stop folding and smoothing the bills, still not looking at them, apparently not aware of them, as if they had no value and she had merely picked them idly up without being aware of it. "Yes," she said. "She beat us. She lay there in that bed she will never move from until they come in and carry her out some day, and took that brooch and beat us both." Then she began to cry. It was as quiet now as the way she had spoken. "My little baby," she said. "My dear little baby."

He didn't even say Hush now. He just waited until she dried her eyes again, almost briskly, rousing, looking at him with an expression almost like smiling, her face, the make-up, the careful evening face haggard and streaked and filled with the weary and peaceful aftermath of tears. "Well," she said. "It's late." She stooped, but he anticipated her and took the bag; they descended the stairs together; they could see the lighted transom above Mrs. Boyd's door.

"It's too bad you haven't got the car," he said.

"Yes. I lost the key at the club. But I telephoned the garage. They will bring it in in the morning."

They stopped in the hall while he telephoned for a cab. Then they waited, talking quietly now and then. "You had better go straight to bed."

"Yes. I'm tired. I danced a good deal."

"What was the music? Was it good?"

"Yes. I don't know. I suppose so. When you are dancing yourself, you don't usually notice whether the music is or isn't."

"Yes, I guess that's so." Then the car came. They went out to it, he in pajamas and robe; the earth was frozen and iron-hard, the sky bitter and brilliant. He helped her in.

"Now you run back into the house," she said. "You didn't even put on your overcoat."

"Yes. I'll get your things to the hotel early."

"Not too early. Run, now." She had already sat back, the coat close about her. He had already remarked how sometime, at some moment back in the bedroom, the warm woman-odor had congealed again and that she now emanated once more that faint frosty fragrance, fragile, impermanent and forlorn; the car moved away, he did not look back. As he was closing the front door his mother called his name. But he did not pause or even glance toward the door. He just mounted the stairs, out of the dead, level, unsleeping, peremptory voice. The fire had burned down: a strong rosy glow, peaceful and quiet and warmly reflected from mirror and polished wood. The book still lay, face down and open, in the chair. He took it up and went to the table between the two beds and sought and found the cellophane envelope which had once contained pipe cleaners, which he used for a bookmark, and marked his place and put the book down. It was the coat-pocket size, Modern Library *Green Mansions*. He had discovered the book during adolescence; he had read it ever since. During that period he read only the part about the journey of the three people in search of the Riolama which did not exist, seeking this part out and reading it in secret as the normal boy would have normal and conventional erotica or obscenity, mounting the barren mountain with Rima toward the cave, not knowing then that it was the cave-symbol which he sought, escaping it at last through the same desire and need to flee and escape which Rima had, following her on past the cave to where she poised, not even waiting for him, impermanent as a match flame and as weak, in the cold and ungrieving moon. In his innocence then he believed, with a sort of urgent and despairing joy, that the mystery about her was not mystery since it was physical: that she was corporeally impenetrable, incomplete; with peaceful despair justifying, vindicating, what he was through (so he believed) no fault of his own, with what he read in books, as the young do. But after his marriage he did not read the book again until the child died and the Saturday nights began. And then he avoided the journey to Riolama as he had used to seek it out. Now he read only where Abel (the one man on earth who knew that he was alone) wandered in the impervious and interdict forest filled with the sound of birds. Then he went to the chest and opened again the drawer where he kept the wallet and stood for a moment, his hand still lying on the edge of the drawer. "Yes," he said quietly, aloud: "it seems to have been right all the time about what I will do."

The bathroom was at the end of the hall, built onto the house later, warm too where he had left the electric heater on for Amy and they had forgot it. It was here that he kept his whiskey also. He had begun to drink after his mother's stroke, in the beginning of what he had believed to be his freedom, and since the death of the child he had begun to keep a two-gallon keg of corn whiskey in the bathroom. Although it was detached from the house proper and the whole depth of it from his mother's room, he nevertheless stuffed towels carefully about and beneath the door, and then removed them and returned to the bedroom and took the down coverlet from Amy's bed and returned and stuffed the door again and then hung the coverlet before it. But even then he was not satisfied. He stood there, thoughtful, musing, a little pudgy (he had never taken any exercise since he gave up trying to learn to dance, and now what with the steady drinking, there was little of the young Italian novice about his figure any more), the pistol hanging from his hand. He began to look about. His glance fell upon the bath mat folded over the edge of the tub. He wrapped his hand, pistol and all, in the mat and pointed it toward the rear wall and fired it, the report muffled and jarring though not loud. Yet even now he stood and listened as if he expected to hear from this distance. But he heard nothing; even when, the door freed again, he moved quietly down the hall and then down the steps to where he could see clearly the dark transom above his mother's door. But again he did not pause. He returned up the stairs, quietly, hearing the cold and impotent ratiocination without listening to it: *Like your father, you cannot seem to live with either of them, but unlike your father you cannot seem to live without them;* telling himself quietly, "Yes, it seems that it was right. It seems to have known us better than I did," and he shut the bathroom door again and stuffed the towels carefully about and beneath it. But he did not hang the coverlet this time. He drew it over himself, squatting, huddling into it, the muzzle of the pistol between his teeth like a pipe, wadding the thick soft coverlet about his head, hurrying, moving swiftly now because he was already beginning to suffocate.

EDITORS' ANALYSIS

In "The Brooch," the loss in love is absolute for the young man, Howard. It ends on a moment when he faces the fact that he cannot break loose from the undertow of his childhood and adolescent commitment to his mother, and must inevitably drown. Faulkner creates the story with great skill around the moment in time present when the young man's suicidal feelings well up in him. And we are made to understand by the carefully related circumstances preceding this moment why the young man has to kill himself. Part of the power of the story is that though the man seems to have been trapped by fate or circumstance, his suicide is, paradoxically, an act of free will, of choice, because it is a result of his own terrible and final awareness of himself.

QUESTIONS

1. Why is Amy, the wife in the story, described as "exactly the sort of girl" whom Howard would be expected to marry? What does this reveal about Howard? About his mother?

2. Why cannot Howard break away from his mother? Is the brooch of the title suggestive of his problem? Does Faulkner prepare you wholly for his final decision through a description of his childhood? Are the roots of Howard's character fully revealed? Does some mystery remain?

3. Do all of these characters seem to you without will, caught up in some way of life from which they cannot escape? Do you agree with the editors' analysis that Howard is at least in part responsible for his final act?

4. Discuss the individualizing qualities of Faulkner's style in this story. Comment on the way in which Faulkner is able to give you, by suggestion, the whole of Howard's character, in little, in the first paragraph.

5. What is especially revealing about Howard in the elaborate preparations which he makes for his own death?

The Whole World Knows

by EUDORA WELTY

Eudora Welty (1909-   ) is one of the outstanding Southern writers of fiction. Her novel *Delta Wedding* (1946) established her reputation as a regional writer and made clear the peculiar qualities of her art. Her interest in fiction is less in action and plot than in a sense of atmosphere, an awareness of place, and a burning concern for the nature of the emotions experienced by her created characters. Her novel *The Ponder Heart* (1954) won the Howells Medal in 1955, given by the American Academy of Arts to the "most distinguished work of American fiction" of the preceding five years. *The Golden Apples* (1949) and *The Bride of the Innisfallen, and Other Stories* (1955) are recent collections of her shorter fiction. Miss Welty's work runs the danger of appearing to be overly subtle to some readers, "difficult" as a result of a self-indulgent preciousness on her part. Her best work transcends these dangers.

"The Whole World Knows" is an example of Miss Welty's art at its most compelling. The title suggests the central event which lies in back of the story, the infidelity of Jinny, the young wife of the bank clerk, Ran MacLain. But the story itself is presented as a montage of the emotions at loose in Ran MacLain as he thinks about his wife, visits her with a friend, makes love to another woman. In her "Introduction" to Eudora Welty's *A Curtain of Green* (1941), Katherine Anne Porter noted that Miss Welty portrayed moments in characters' lives in which "external act and the internal voiceless life of the human imagination almost meet and mingle on the mysterious threshold between dream and waking." This remark also seems to characterize "The Whole World Knows."

Father, I wish I could talk to you, wherever you are right now.

Mother said, *Where have you been, son?*—Nowhere, Mother.—

I wish you wouldn't sound so unhappy, son. You could come back to MacLain and live with me now.—I can't do that, Mother. You know I have to stay in Morgana.

When I slammed the door of the bank I rolled down my sleeves and stood for some time looking out at the cotton field behind Mr. Wiley Bowles' across the street, until it nearly put me to sleep and then woke me up like a light turned on in my face. Woodrow Spights had been gone a few minutes or so. I got in my car and drove up the street, turned around at the foot of Jinny's driveway (yonder went Woody) and drove down again. I turned around in our old driveway, where Miss Francine had the sprinkler running, and made the same trip. The thing everybody does every day, except not by themselves.

There was Maideen Sumrall on the drugstore step waving a little green handkerchief. When I didn't remember to stop I saw the handkerchief pulled down. I turned again, to pick her up, but she'd caught her ride with Red Ferguson.

So I went to my room. Bella, Miss Francine Murphy's little dog, panted all the time—she was sick. I always went out in the backyard and spoke to her. Poor Bella, how do you do, lady? Is it hot, do they leave you alone?

Mother said on the phone, *Have you been out somewhere, son?*—Just to get a little air.—*I can tell you're all peaked. And you keep things from me, I don't understand. You're as bad as Eugene Hudson. Now I have two sons keeping things from me.* —I haven't been anywhere, where would I go?—*If you came back with me, to MacLain Courthouse, everything would be all right. I know you won't eat at Miss Francine's table, not her biscuit.*—It's as good as Jinny's, Mother.

But Eugene's safe in California, that's what we think.

When the bank opened, Miss Perdita Mayo came up to my window and hollered, "Randall, when are you going back to your precious wife? You forgive her, now you hear? That's no way to do, bear grudges. Your mother never bore your father a single grudge in her life, and he made her life right hard. I tell you, how do you suppose he made her life? She don't bear him a grudge. We're all human on earth. Where's little old Woodrow this morning, late to work or you done something to him? I still think of him a boy in knee britches and Buster Brown bob, riding that pony, that extravagant pony, cost a hundred dollars. Wood-

row: a little common but so smart. Felix Spights never over-
charged a customer, and Miss Billy Texas amounted to a good
deal before she got like she is now; and Missie could always play
the piano better than average; Little Sister too young to tell yet.
Ah, I'm a woman that's been clear around the world in my
rocking chair, and I tell you we all get surprises now and then.
But you march on back to your wife, Ran MacLain. You hear?
It's a thing of the flesh not the spirit, it'll pass. Jinny'll get over
this in three four months. You hear me? And you go back *nice*."

"Still hotter today, isn't it?"
I picked up Maideen Sumrall and we rode up and down the
street. She was from the Sissum community. She was eighteen
years old. "Look! Citified," she said, and pushed both hands at
me; she had new white cotton gloves on. Maideen would ride
there by me and talk about things I didn't mind hearing about—
the Seed and Feed where she clerked and kept the books, Old
Man Moody that she worked for, the way working in Morgana
seemed after the country and junior college. Her first job: her
mother still didn't like the idea. And people could be so nice:
getting a ride home with me sometimes like this, instead of with
Red Ferguson in the Coca-Cola truck. So she told me now. "And
I didn't think you were going to see me at first, Ran. I saved my
gloves to wear riding home in a car."
I told her my eyes had gone bad. She said she was sorry. She
was country-prim and liked to have something to put in words
that she could be sorry about. I drove, idling along, up and down
a few times more. Mr. Steptoe was dragging the mail sack into
the postoffice—he and Maideen waved. In the Presbyterian
church Missie Spights was playing "Will There Be Any Stars in
My Crown?", and Maideen listened. And on the street the same
ones stood in doorways or rode in their cars, and waved at my
car. Maideen's little blue handkerchief was busy waving back.
She waved at them as she did at me.
"I wouldn't be surprised if it *wasn't* hard on the eyes, to be
cooped up and just count money all day, Ran"—to say something
to me.
She knew what anybody in Morgana told her; and for four or
five afternoons after the first one I picked her up and took her
up and down the street a few turns, bought her a coke at Johnny
Loomis's, and drove her home out by Old Forks and let her
out, and she never said a word except a kind one, like about

counting money. She was kind; her company was the next thing to being alone.

I drove her home and then drove back to Morgana to the room I had at Miss Francine Murphy's.

Next time, there at the end of the pavement, I turned up the cut to the Starks'. I couldn't stand it any longer.

Maideen didn't say a word till we reached the head of the drive and stopped.

"Ran?" she said. She wasn't asking anything. She meant just to remind me I had company, but that was what I knew. I got out and went around and opened her door.

"You want to take me in yonder?" she said. "Please, I'd just as soon you wouldn't." Her head hung. I saw the extra-white part in her hair.

I said, "Sure. Let's go in and see Jinny. Why not?"

I couldn't stand it any longer, that was why.

"I'm going and taking you."

It wasn't as if Mr. Drewsie Carmichael didn't say to me every afternoon, "Come on home with me, boy"—argue, while he banged that big Panama—like yours, Father—down on his head, "no sense in your not sleeping cool, with one of our fans turned on you. Mamie's mad at you for roasting in that room across the street from us—you could move in five minutes. Well, Ran, look: Mamie has something to say to you: I don't." And he'd wait a minute in the door before he left. He'd stand and hold his cane— the one Woody Spights and I had bought him together when he was elected Mayor—up by his head, to threaten me with comfort, till I answered him, "No thanks, sir."

Maideen was at my side. We walked across the Starks' baked yard to the front porch, passing under the heavy heads of those crape myrtles, the too bright blooms that hang down like fruits that might drop. My wife's mother—Miss Lizzie Morgan, Father —put her face to her bedroom window first thing. She'd know it first if I came back, all right. Parting her curtains with a steel crochet hook, she looked down at Randall MacLain coming to her door, and bringing who-on-earth with him.

"What are you doing here, Ran MacLain?"

When I didn't look up, she rapped on the window sill with her hook.

"I've never been inside the Stark home," Maideen said, and I began to smile. I felt curiously light-hearted. Lilies must have been in bloom somewhere near, and I took a full breath of their ether smell: consciousness could go or not. I pulled open the screen door. From above, inside somewhere, Miss Lizzie was calling, "Jinny Love!" like Jinny had a date.

Jinny—not out playing croquet—stood with her legs apart, cutting off locks of her hair at the hall mirror. The locks fell at her feet. She had on straw sandals, the kind that would have to be ordered, boy's shorts. She looked up at me, short range, and said "Just in time, to tell me when to stop." She'd cut bangs. Her smile reminded me of the way a child will open its mouth all right, but not let out the cry till it sees the right person.

And turning to the mirror she cut again. "Obey that impulse—" She had seen Maideen then, and she went right on cutting her hair with those stork-shaped scissors. "Come in *too*, take off your gloves."

That's right: she would know, with her quickness like fore-knowledge, first that I would come back when the summer got too much for me, and second that I'd just as soon bring a stranger if I could find one, somebody who didn't know any better, to come in the house with me when I came.

Father, I wished I could go back.

I looked at Jinny's head with the ragged points all over it, and there was Miss Lizzie coming down; she had just stopped to change her shoes, of course. For the kind that came down stairs like a march. As we all fell in together, we were leaving where we met too, starting down the hall with nobody pairing, and over each other's names or whatever we said, Jinny's voice hollered at Tellie for cokes. She counted us with her finger. That lightness came right back. Just to step on the matting, that billows a little anyway, and with Jinny's hair scattered like feathers on it, I could have floated, risen and floated.

In rockers—we sat on the back porch—we were all not rocking. The chairs, white wicker, had a new coat of paint—their thou-sandth-and-first, but one new coat since I left Jinny. The outside —a sheet of white light—was in my eyes. The ferns close around us were hushing on their stands, they had just been watered. I could listen to women and hear pieces of the story, of what happened to us, of course—but I listened to the ferns.

No matter, it was being told. Not in Miss Lizzie's voice, which wouldn't think of it, certainly not in Jinny's, but in the clear voice of Maideen where it had never existed—all the worse for the voice not even questioning what it said—just repeating, just rushing, old—the town words.

Telling what she was told she saw, repeating what she listened to—young girls are outlandish little birds that talk. They can be taught, some each day, to sing a song *people* have made. . . . Even Miss Lizzie put her head on one side, to let Maideen be.

He walked out on her and took his clothes down to the other end of the street. Now everybody's waiting to see how soon he'll go back. They say Jinny MacLain invites Woody out there to eat, a year younger than she is, remember when they were born. Invites, under her mama's nose. Sure, it's Woodrow Spights she invites. Who else in Morgana would there be for Jinny Stark after Ran, with even Eugene MacLain gone? She's kin to the Nesbitts. They don't say when it started, can anybody tell? At the Circle, at Miss Francine's, at Sunday School, they say, they say she will marry Woodrow: Woodrow'd jump at it but Ran will kill somebody first. And there's Ran's papa and the way he was and is, remember, remember? And Eugene gone that could sometimes hold him down. Poor Snowdie, it's her burden. He used to be sweet but too much devil in him from Time was, that's Ran. He'll do something bad. He won't divorce Jinny but he'll do something bad. Maybe kill them all. They say Jinny's not scared of that. Maybe she drinks and hides the bottle, you know her father's side. And just as prissy as ever on the street. And oh, don't you know, they run into each other every day of the world, all three. Sure, how could they help it if they wanted to help it, how could you get away from it, right in Morgana? You can't get away in Morgana. Away from anything at all, you know that.

Father! You didn't listen.

And Tellie was mad at all of us. She still held the tray, she held it about an inch and a half too high. When Maideen took her coke in her white glove, she said to Miss Lizzie, "I look too tacky and mussed when I work in the store all day to be coming in anybody's strange house."

"You're by the far the freshest one here, my dear."

Who else had Maideen ever known to talk about but herself?

But she looked like Jinny. She was a child's copy of Jinny. Jinny's first steady look at me, coming just then, made that plain all at once. (Oh, her look always made contamination plain. Or plainer.) That resemblance I knew *post-mortem*, so to speak— and it made me right pleased with myself. I don't mean there was any mockery in Maideen's little face—no—but there was something of Maideen in Jinny's, that went back early—to whatever I knew my Jinny would never be now.

The slow breeze from that ceiling fan—its old white blades frosted like a cake, with the flies riding on it—lifted the girls' hair like one passing hand, Maideen's brown hair shoulder-long and Jinny's brown hair short, ruined—she ruined it herself, as she liked doing. Maideen was even more polite than she'd ever been to me, and making intervals in the quiet, like the ferns dripping, she talked about herself and the Seed and Feed; but she glowed with something she didn't know about, yet, there in the room with Jinny. And Jinny sat not rocking, yet, with her clever, not-listening smile.

I looked from Jinny to Maideen and back to Jinny, and almost listened for some compliment—a compliment from somewhere— Father!—for my good eyes, my vision. It took me, after all, to bring it out. There was nothing but time between them.

There were those annoying sounds keeping on out there— people and croquet. We finished the cokes. Miss Lizzie just sat there—hot. She still held the crochet hook, straight up like a ruler, and nobody was rapped, done to death. Jinny was on her feet, inviting us out to play croquet.

But it had been long enough.

They were slowly moving across the shade of the far backyard—Woody, Johnnie and Etta Loomis, Nina Carmichael and Jinny's cousin Junior Nesbitt, and the fourteen-year-old child that they let play—with Woody Spights knocking his ball through a wicket. He was too young for me—I'd never really looked at him before this year; he was coming up in the world. I looked down through the yard and the usual crowd seemed to have dwindled a little, I could not think who was out. Jinny went down there. It was myself.

Mother said, *Son, you're walking around in a dream.*

Miss Perdita came and said, "I hear you went back yesterday and wouldn't open your mouth, left again. Might as well not go at all. But no raring up now and doing anything we'll all be sorry to hear about. I know you won't. I knew your father, was crazy about your father, glad to see him come every time, sorry to see him go, and love your mother. Sweetest people in the world, most happily mated people in the world, long as he was home. Tell your mother I said so, next time you see her. And you march back to that precious wife. March back and have you some chirren. My Circle declares Jinny's going to divorce you, marry Woodrow. I said, Why? Thing of the flesh, I told my Circle, won't last. Sister said you'd kill him, and I said Sister, who are you talking about? If it's Ran MacLain that *I* knew in his buggy, I said, he's not at all likely to take on to that extent. And little Jinny. Who's going to tell Lizzie to spank her, though? I couldn't help but laugh at Jinny: she says, It's my own business! We was in Hardware, old Holifield just scowling his head off. I says, How did it happen, Jinny, tell old Miss Perdita, you monkey, and she says, Oh, Miss Perdita, do like *me*. Do like *me*, she says, and just go on like nothing's happened. I declare, and she says I have to write my checks on the Morgana bank, and Woody Spights works in it, there's just him and Ran, so I go up to Woody and cash them. And I says, Child—how could you all get away from each other if you tried? You couldn't. It's a pity you had to run to a Spights, though. Oh, if there'd just been some Carmichael *boys*, I often say! No matter who you are, though, it's an endless circle. That's what a thing of the flesh is, endless circle. And you won't get away from that in Morgana. Even our little town.

"All right, I said to Old Man Moody while ago, look. Jinny was unfaithful to Ran—that's the up-and-down of it. There you have what it's all *about*. That's the brunt of it. Face it, I told Dave Moody. Like Lizzie Stark does, she's brave. Though she's seven miles south of here, Snowdie MacLain's another brave one. Poor Billy Texas Spights is beyond knowing. You're just a seed and feed man and the marshal here, you don't form opinions enough to suit me.

"Jinny was never scared of the Devil himself as a growing girl, so she certainly shouldn't be now, she's twenty-five. She's Lizzie's own. And Woodrow Spights won't ever quit at the bank, will he? It's so much cleaner than the store, and he'll get the store too. So it's up to you, Ran, looks like.

"And I'd go back to my lawful spouse!" Miss Perdita puts both hands on the bars of my cage and raises her voice. "You or I or the Man in the Moon got no business sleeping in that little hot upstairs room with a western exposure at Miss Francine Murphy's for all the pride on earth, not in August! And even if it is the house you grew up in, it's a different room. And listen here to me. Don't you ruin a *country* girl in the bargain. Make what you will of that."

She backs away leaving her hands out, pulling-like at the air, like I'm floating on my ear suspended, hypnotized, and she can leave. But she just goes as far as the next window—Woody Spights'.

I went back to the room I had at Miss Francine Murphy's. Father, it used to be the trunk room. It had Mother's pieced quilts and her wedding dress and all the terrible accumulation of a long time you wouldn't have known about.

After work I would cut the grass or something in Miss Francine's backyard so it would be cooler for Bella. It kept the fleas away from her to some extent. It didn't do much good. The heat held on.

I tried going to Jinny's a little later in the afternoon. The men were playing, still playing croquet with a little girl, and the women had taken off to themselves, on the porch. I tried without Maideen.

It was the long Mississippi evening, the waiting till it was cool enough to eat. The voice of Miss Lizzie carried. Like the hum of the gin, it was there, but the evening was still quiet, still very hot and quiet.

Somebody called to me, "You're dead on Woody." It was just a little Williams girl in pigtails.

I may have answered with a joke. I felt light-headed, not serious at all, really doing it for a child when I lifted my mallet— the one with the red band that had always been mine. But I brought Woody Spights down with it. He toppled and shook the ground. I felt the air rush up. Then I beat on him. I went over his whole length, and cracked his head apart with that soft girl's hair and all the ideas, beat on him without stopping till every bone, all the way down to the numerous little bones in the foot, was cracked in two. I didn't have done with Woody Spights till then. And I proved the male human body—it has a too positive, too special shape, you know, not to be hurt—it could be finished up pretty fast. It just takes one good loud blow after another—Jinny should be taught that.

I looked at Woodrow down there. And his blue eyes were just as unharmed. Just as unharmed as bubbles a child blows, the most impervious things—you've seen grass blades go through bubbles and they still reflect the world, give it back unbroken. Woodrow Spights I declare was dead. "Now you watch," he said.

He spoke with no sign of pain. Just that edge of competition

was in his voice. He was ever the most ambitious fool. To me
ambition's always been a mystery, but now it was his try to
deceive us—me and him both. I didn't know how it could open
again, the broken jawbone of Woody Spights, but it could. I
heard him say, "Now you watch."

He was dead on the ruined grass. But he had risen up. Just to
call attention to it, he gave the fat little Williams girl a spank. I
could see the spank, but I couldn't hear it—the most familiar
sound in the world.

And I should have called out *then*—All is disgrace! Human
beings' cries could swell if locusts' could, in the last of evening
like this, and cross the grass in a backyard, if only THEY enough
of them cried. At our feet the shadows faded out light into no
shadows left and the locusts sang in long waves, O-E, O-E, and
the gin ran on. Our grass in August is like the floor of the sea,
and we walk on it slowly playing, and the sky turns green before
dark, Father, as you know. The sweat ran over my back and down
my arms and legs, branching, like an upside-down tree.

Then, "You all come in!" They were calling from the porch—
the well-known lamps suddenly all went on. They called us in
their calling women's voices, of disguise, all but Jinny. "Fools,
you're playing in the dark!" she said. "Supper's ready, if anybody
cares."

The bright porch across the dark was like a boat on the river
to me; an excursion boat I wasn't going on. I was going to Miss
Francine Murphy's, as everybody knew.

Each evening to avoid Miss Francine and the three school
teachers, I ran through the porch and hall both like a man
through a burning building. In the backyard, with fig trees black,
otherwise moonlit, Bella opened her eyes and looked at me. Her
eyes both showed the moon. If she drank water, she vomited it
up—yet she went with effort to her pan and drank again, for
me. I held her. Poor Bella. I thought she suffered from a tumor,
and stayed with her most of the night.

Mother said, *Son, I was glad to see you but I noticed that old
pistol of your father's in your nice coat pocket, what do you want
with that? Your father never cared for it, went off and left it.
Not any robbers coming to the Morgana bank that I know of. Son,
if you'd just saved your money you could take a little trip to the
coast. I'd go with you. They always have a breeze at Gulfport,
nearly always.*

Where the driveway ends at Jinny's, there are Spanish daggers and the bare front yard with the forked tree with the seat around it—like some old playground of a consolidated school, with the school back out of sight. Just the sharp, overgrown Spanish daggers, and the spiderwebs draped over them like clothes-rags. You can go under trees to the house by going all around the yard and opening the old gate by the summerhouse. Somewhere back in the shade there's a statue from Morgan days, of a dancing girl with her finger to her chin, all pockmarked, with some initials on her legs.

Maideen liked the statue but she said, "Are you taking me back in? I thought maybe now you weren't going to."

I saw my hand on the gate and said, "Now you wait. I've lost a button." I held out my sleeve to Maideen. All at once I felt so unlike myself I was ready to shed tears.

"A button? Why, I'll sew you one on, if you come on and take me home," Maideen said. That's what I wanted her to say, but she touched my sleeve. A chameleon ran up a leaf, and held there panting. "Then Mama can meet you. She'd be glad to have you stay to supper."

I unlatched the little old gate. I caught a whiff of the sour pears on the ground, the smell of August. I'd never told Maideen I was coming to supper, at any time, or would see her mama, of course; but also I kept forgetting about the old ways, the eternal politeness of the people you hope not to know.

"Oh, Jinny can sew it on now," I said.

"Oh, I can?" Jinny said. She'd of course been listening all the time from the summerhouse. She came out, alone, with the old broken wicker basket full of speckled pears. She didn't say go back and shut the gate.

I carried the rolling basket for her and we went ahead of Maideen but I knew she was coming behind; she wouldn't know very well how not to. There in the flower beds walked the same robins. The sprinkler dripped now. Once again we went into the house by the back door. Our hands touched. We had stepped on Tellie's patch of mint. The yellow cat was waiting to go in with us, the door handle was as hot as the hand, and on the step, getting under the feet of two people who went in together, the Mason jars with the busy cuttings in water—"Watch out for Mama's—!" A thousand times we'd gone in like that. As a thousand bees had droned and burrowed in the pears that lay on the ground.

Miss Lizzie shrank with a cry and started abruptly up the back stairs—bosom lifted—her shadow trotted up the boarding beside her like a bear with a nose. But she couldn't get to the top; she turned. She came down, carefully, and held up a finger at me. She needed to be careful. That stairs was the one Mr. Comus Stark fell down and broke his neck on one night, going up the back way drunk. Did I call it to attention?—Jinny got away.

"Randall. I can't help but tell you about a hand I held yesterday. My partner was Mamie Carmichael and you know she always plays her own hand with no more regard for her partner than you have. Well, she opened with a spade and Etta Loomis doubled. I held: a singleton spade, five clubs to the king-queen, five hearts to the king, and two little diamonds. I said two clubs. Parnell Moody said two diamonds, Mamie two spades, all passed. And when I laid down my hand Mamie said, Oh, *partner!* Why didn't you bid your hearts! I said, Hardly. At the level of three with the opponents doubling for a takeout. It developed of course she was two-suited—six spades to the ace-jack and four hearts to the ace-jack-ten, also my ace of clubs. Now, Randall. It would have been just as easy for Mamie to bid three hearts on that second go-round. But no! She could see only her own hand and took us down two, and we could have made five hearts. Now do *you* say I should have bid three hearts?"

I said, "You were justified not to, Miss Lizzie."

She began to cry on the stairs. Tears stood on her powdered face. "You men. You got us beat in the end. May be I'm getting old. Oh no, that's not it. Because I can tell you where you got us beat. We'd know you through and through except we never know what ails you. Don't you look at me like that. Of course I see what Jinny's doing, the fool, but you ailed first. You just got her answer to it, Ran." Then she glared again, turned, and went back upstairs.

And what ails me I don't know, Father, unless maybe you know. All through what she had to say I stood holding the cooking-pears. Then I set the basket on the table.

Jinny was in the little back study, "Mama's office," with the landscape wallpaper and Mr. Comus's old desk full-up with U.D.C. correspondence and plat maps that cracked like thunder when the fan blew them. She was yelling at Tellie. Tellie came in with the workbasket and then just waited, eyeing her.

"Put it down, Tellie, I'll use it when I get ready. Now you go on. Pull your mouth in, you hear?"

Tellie put down the basket and Jinny flicked it open and fished in it. The stork scissors fell out. She found a button that belonged to me, and waited on Tellie.

"I hear you's a mess." Tellie went out.

Jinny looked at me and didn't mind. I minded. I fired point-blank at Jinny—more than once. It was close range—there was barely room between us suddenly for the pistol to come up. And she only stood frowning at the needle I had forgotten the reason for. Her hand never deviated, never shook from the noise. The dim clock on the mantel was striking—the pistol hadn't drowned that out. I was watching Jinny and I saw her pouting childish breasts, excuses for breasts, sprung full of bright holes where my bullets had gone. But Jinny didn't feel it. She threaded her needle. She made her little face of success. Her thread always went straight in the eye.

"Will you hold still."

She far from acknowledged pain—anything but sorrow and pain. When I couldn't give her something she wanted she would hum a little tune. In our room, her voice would go low and soft to complete disparagement. Then I loved her a lot. The little cheat. I waited on, while she darted the needle and pulled at my sleeve, the sleeve to my helpless hand. It was like counting my breaths. I let out my fury and breathed the pure disappointment in: that she was not dead on earth. She bit the thread—magnificently. When she took her mouth away I nearly fell. The cheat.

I didn't dare say good-bye to Jinny any more. "All right, now you're ready for croquet," she told me. She went upstairs too.

Old Tellie spat a drop of nothing into the stove and clanged the lid down as I went out through the kitchen. Maideen was out in the swing, sitting. I told her to come on down to the croquet yard, where we all played Jinny's game, without Jinny.

Going to my room, I saw Miss Billy Texas Spights outdoors in her wrapper, whipping the flowers to make them bloom.

Father! Dear God wipe it clean. Wipe it clean, wipe it out. Don't let it be.

At last Miss Francine caught hold of me in the hall. "Do me a favor, Ran. Do me a favor and put Bella out of her misery. None of these school teachers any better at it than I'd be. And my friend coming to supper too tenderhearted. You do it. Just do it and don't tell us about it, hear?"

Where have you been, Son, it's so late.—Nowhere, Mother, nowhere.—*If you were back under my roof,* Mother said, *if*

Eugene hadn't gone away too. He's gone and you won't listen to anybody.—It's too hot to sleep, Mother.—*I stayed awake by the telephone. The Lord never meant us all to separate. To go and be cut off. One from the other, off in some little room.*

"I remember your wedding," old Miss Jefferson Moody said at my window, nodding on the other side of the bars. "Never knew it would turn out like this, the prettiest and longest wedding I ever saw. Look! If all that money belonged to you, you could leave town."

And I was getting tired, oh so tired, of Maideen waiting on me. I felt cornered when she told me, still as kind as ever, about the Seed and Feed. Because ever since I was born, Old Man Moody lined his sidewalk with pie pans full of shelled corn and stuff like bird-shot. The window used to be so clouded up it looked like stained glass. She'd scrubbed it for him, and exposed the barrels and cannisters and the sacks and bins of stuff inside, and Old Man Moody in an eyeshade sitting on a stool, making cat's-cradles; and her poking food at the bird. There were cotton blooms across the window and door, and then it would be sugar-cane, and she told me she was thinking already about the Christmas tree. No telling what she was going to string on Old Man Moody's Christmas tree. And now I was told her mother's maiden name. God help me, the name Sojourner was laid on my head like the top teetering crown of a pile of things to remember. Not to forget, never to forget the name of Sojourner.

And then always having to take the little Williams girl home at night. She was the bridge player. That was a game Maideen had never learned to play. Maideen: I never kissed her.

But the Sunday came when I took her to Vicksburg.

Already on the road I began to miss my bridge. We could get our old game now, Jinny, Woody, myself, and either Nina Carmichael or Junior Nesbitt, or both and sit in. Miss Lizzie of course would walk out on us now, never be our fourth, holding no brief for what a single one of us had done; she couldn't stand the Nesbitts to begin with. I always won—Nina used to win, but anybody could see she was pressed too much about Nesbitt to play her cards, and sometimes she didn't come to play at all, or Nesbitt either, and we had to go get the little Williams girl and take her home.

Maideen never put in a word to our silence now. She sat holding some women's magazine. Every now and then she'd turn over a page, moistening her finger first, like my mother. When she

lifted her eyes to me, I didn't look up. Every night I would take
their money. Then at Miss Francine's I would be sick, going out-
doors so the teachers wouldn't wonder.

"Now you really must get these two home. Their mothers will
be wondering." Jinny's voice.

Maideen would stand up with the little Williams girl to leave,
and I thought whatever I let her in for, I could trust her.

She would get stupefied for sleep. She would lean farther and
farther over in the Starks' chair. She would never have a rum
and coke with us, but would be simply dead for sleep. She slept
sitting up in the car gong home, where her mama, now large-
eyed, maiden name Sojourner, sat up listening. I'd wake Maideen
and tell her where we were. The little Williams girl would be
chatting away in the back seat, there and as far as her house
wide awake as an owl.

Vicksburg: nineteen miles over the gravel and the thirteen
little bridges and the Big Black. And suddenly all sensation
returned.

Morgana I had looked at too long. Till the street was a pencil
mark on the sky. The street was there just the same, red-brick
scallops, two steeples and the water tank and the branchy trees,
but if I saw it, it was not with love, it was a pencil mark on the
sky that jumped with the shaking of the gin. If some indelible
red false-fronts joined one to the other like a little toy train went
by, I didn't think of my childhood any more. I saw Old Man
Holifield turn his back, his suspenders looked cross, very cross.

In Vicksburg, I stopped my car at the foot of the street under
the wall, by the canal. There was that dazzling light, water-
marked light. I woke Maideen and asked her if she was thirsty.
She smoothed her dress and lifted her head at the sounds of a
city, the traffic on cobblestones just behind the wall. I watched
the water taxi come to get us, chopping over the canal strip,
babyish as a rocking horse.

"Duck your head," I told Maideen.

"In here?"

It was sunset. The island was very near across the water—a
waste of willows, yellow and green strands loosely woven
together, like a basket that let the light spill out uncontrollably.
We all stood up and bent our heads under the ceiling in the tiny
cabin, and shaded our eyes. The Negro who ran the put-put
never said a word, "Get in" or "Get out." "Where is this we're

going?" Maideen said. In two minutes we were touching the barge.

Nobody was inside but the barkeep—a silent, relegated place like a barn, old and tired. I let him bring some rum cokes out to the card table on the back where the two cane chairs were. It was open back there. The sun was going down on the island side while we sat, and making Vicksburg all picked out on the other. East and West were in our eyes.

"Don't make me drink it. I don't want to drink it," Maideen said.

"Go on and drink it."

"You drink it if you like it. Don't make me drink it."

"You drink it too."

I looked at her take some of it, and sit shading her eyes. There were wasps dipping from a nest over the old screen door and skimming her hair. There was a smell of fish and of the floating roots fringing the island, and of the oilcloth top of our table, and endless deals. A load of Negroes came over on the water taxi and stepped out sulphur-yellow all over, coated with cottonseed meal. They disappeared in the colored barge at the other end, in single file, carrying their buckets, like they were sentenced to it.

"Sure enough, I don't want to drink it."

"Look, you drink it and then tell me if it tastes bad, and I'll pour 'em both in the river."

"It will be too late."

Through the screen door I could see into the dim saloon. Two men with black cocks under their arms had come in. Without noise they each set a muddy boot on the rail and drank, the cocks absolutely still. They got off the barge on the island side and were lost in a minute in a hot blur of willow trees. They might never be seen again.

The heat shook on the water and on the other side shook along the edges of the old white buildings and the concrete slabs and the wall. From the barge Vicksburg looked like an image of itself in some old mirror—like a portrait at a sad time of life.

A short cowboy and his girl came in, walking alike. They dropped a nickel in the nickelodeon, and came together.

There weren't any waves visible, yet the water did tremble under our chairs. I was aware of it like the sound of a winter fire in the room.

"You don't ever dance, do you," Maideen said.

It was a long time before we left. A good many people had
come out to the barge. There was old Gordon Nesbitt, dancing.
When we left, the white barge and the nigger barge had both
filled up, and it was good-dark.

The lights were far between on shore—sheds and warehouses,
long walls that needed propping. High up on the ramparts of
town some old iron bells were ringing.

"Are you a Catholic?" I asked her suddenly, and she shook
her head.

Nobody was a Catholic but I looked at her—I made it plain
she disappointed some hope of mine, and she had, standing there
with a foreign bell ringing on the air.

"We're all Baptists. Why, are you a Catholic? Is that what
you are?"

Without touching her except by accident with my knee I
walked her ahead of me up the steep uneven way to where my
car was parked listing downhill. Inside, she couldn't shut her
door. I stood outside and waited, the door hung heavily and she
had drunk all I had made her drink. Now she couldn't shut her
door.

"Shut it."

"I'll fall out. I'll fall in your arms. If I fall, catch me."

"No. Shut it. You have to shut it. I can't. All your might."

At last. I leaned against her shut door, and held on for a
moment.

I grated up the steep hills, turned and followed the river road
along the bluff, turned again off into a deep rutted dirt way
under shaggy banks, Father, dark and circling and rushing down.

"Don't lean on me," I said. "Better to sit up and get air."

"Don't want to."

"Pull up your head." I could hardly understand what she said
any more. "You want to lie down?"

"Don't want to lie down."

"You get some air."

"Don't want to do a thing, Ran, do we, from now and on till
evermore."

We circled down. The sounds of the river tossing and teasing
its great load, its load of trash, I could hear through the dark
now. It made the noise of a moving wall, and up it fishes and
reptiles and uprooted trees and man's throw-aways played and
climbed all alike in a splashing like innocence. A great wave of
smell beat at my face. The track had come down here deep as a

tunnel. We were on the floor of the world. The trees met and their branches matted overhead, the cedars came together, and through them the stars of Morgana looked sifted and fine as seed, so high, so far. Away off, there was the sound of a shot.

"Yonder's the river," she said, and sat up. "I see it—the Mississippi River."

"You don't see it. You only hear it."

"I see it, I see it."

"Haven't you ever seen the river before? You baby."

"I thought we were on it on the boat. Where's this?"

"The road's ended. You can see that."

"Yes, I can. Why does it come this far and stop?"

"How should I know?"

"What do they come down here for?"

"There're all kinds of people in the world." Far away, somebody was burning something.

"You mean bad people? Niggers?"

"Oh, fishermen. River men. See, you're waked up."

"I think we're lost," she said.

Mother said, *If I thought you'd ever go back to that Jinny Stark, I couldn't stand it.*—No, Mother, I'm not going back.—*The whole world knows what she did to you. It's different from when it's the man.*

"You dreamed we're lost. That's all right, you can lie down a little."

"You can't get lost in Morgana."

"After you lie down a little you'll be all right again. We'll go somewhere where you can lie down good."

"Don't want to lie down."

"Did you know my car would back up a hill as steep as this?"

"You'll be killed."

"I bet nobody ever saw such a crazy thing. Do you think anybody ever saw such a crazy thing?"

We were almost straight up and down, Father, hanging on the wall of the bluff, and the rear end of the car bumping and rising like something that wanted to fly, lifting and dropping us. At last we backed back over the brink, like a bee pulling out of a flower cup, and skidded a little. Without that last drink, maybe I wouldn't have made it at all.

We drove a long way then. All through the dark part, the same old statues and stances, the stone rifles at point again and again on the hills, lost and the same. The towers they've condemned, the lookout towers, lost and the same.

Maybe I didn't have my bearings, but I looked for the moon, due to be in the last quarter. There she was. The air wasn't darkness but faint light and floating sound. It was the breath of all the people in the world who were breathing out into the late night looking at the moon, knowing her quarter. And all along I knew I rode in the open world and took bearings by the stars.

We rode in wildernesses under the lifting moon. Maideen was awake because I heard her sighing faintly, as if she longed for something for herself. A coon, white as a ghost, pressed low like an enemy, crossed over the road.

We crossed a highway and there a light burned in a white-washed tree. Under hanging moss it showed a half-circle of white-washed cabins, dark, and all along it a fence of pale palings. A little nigger boy leaned on the gate where our lights moved on him; he was wearing a train engineer's cap. Sunset Oaks.

The little nigger hopped on the runningboard, and I paid. I guided Maideen by the shoulders. She had been asleep after all.

"One step up," I told her at the door.

We fell dead asleep in our clothes across the iron bed.

The naked light hung far down into the room and our sleep, a long cord with the strands almost untwisted. Maideen got up after some time and turned the light off, and the night descended like a bucket let down a well, and I woke up. It was never dark enough, the enormous sky flashing with August light rushing into the emptiest rooms, the loneliest windows. The month of falling stars. I hate the time of year this is, Father.

I saw Maideen taking her dress off. She bent over all tender toward it, smoothing its skirt and shaking it and laying it, at last, on the room's chair; and tenderly like it was any chair, not that one. I propped myself up against the rods of the bed with my back pressing them. I was sighing—deep sigh after deep sigh. I heard myself. When she turned back to the bed, I said, "Don't come close to me."

And I showed I had the pistol. I said, "I want the whole bed." I told her she hadn't needed to be here. I got down in the bed and pointed the pistol at her, without much hope, the way I used to lie cherishing a dream in the morning, and she the way Jinny would come pull me out of it.

Maideen came into the space before my eyes, plain in the lighted night. She held her bare arms. She was disarrayed. There was blood on her, blood and disgrace. Or perhaps there wasn't. For a minute I saw her double. But I pointed the gun at her the best I could.

"Don't come close to me," I said.

Then while she spoke to me I could hear all the noises of the place we were in—the frogs and nightbirds of Sunset Oaks, and the little idiot nigger running up and down the fence, up and down, as far as it went and back, sounding the palings with his stick.

"Don't, Ran. Don't do that, Ran. Don't do it, please don't do it." She came closer, but when she spoke I wasn't hearing what she said. I was reading her lips, the conscientious way people do through train windows. Outside, I thought the little nigger at the gate would keep that up for ever, no matter what I did, or what anyone did—running a stick along the fence, up and then down, to the end and back again.

Then that stopped. I thought, he's still running. The fence stopped, and he ran on without knowing it.

I drew back the pistol, and turned it. I put the pistol's mouth to my own. My instinct is always quick and ardent and hungry and doesn't lose any time. There was Maideen still, coming, coming in her petticoat.

"Don't do it, Ran. Please don't do it." Just the same.

I made it—made the awful sound.

And *she* said, "Now you see. It didn't go off. Give me that. Give that old thing to me, I'll take care of it."

She took it from me. Dainty as she always was, she carried it over to the chair; and prissy as she was, like she knew some long-tried way to deal with a gun, she folded it in her dress. She came back to the bed again, and dropped down on it.

In a minute she put her hand out again, differently, and laid it cold on my shoulder. And I had her so quick.

I could have been asleep then. I was lying there.

"You're so stuck up," she said.

I lay there and after a while I heard her again. She lay there by the side of me, weeping for herself. The kind of soft, patient meditative sobs a child will venture long after punishment.

So I slept.

How was I to know she would go and hurt herself? She cheated, she cheated too.

Father, Eugene! What you went and found, was it better than this?

And where's Jinny?

EDITORS' ANALYSIS

Eudora Welty presents the central character of her story, Ran MacLain, so directly to us that all we see or hear is as it is seen or heard by him. There is no outside point of view at all by which to view Ran, except as he remembers, or turns over half-consciously in his mind, what various people in the small town of Morgana have said to him about himself. It is this glaring directness which makes "The Whole World Knows" both a difficult story and one which invites a strong emotional response from the reader. The story begins with Ran's sense of helplessness, in his wish to talk things over with a father who has skipped out long before. It ends with his poignant awareness of loss, not so much of the actual person Jinny who was having an affair with a fellow bank clerk, as of the Jinny he wanted to love. Between these two moments of deep feeling, we get a mixture of events which Ran describes and then responds to, at varying levels of his conscious mind. The grief at the end of the story is reinforced by Maideen Sumrall's weeping beside Ran, lost in her own sense of the vast distance between love and love-making.

QUESTIONS

1. There seem to be few decisions, only a flow of feelings and events in this story. Does this give its central character a peculiar, dream-like quality? Does it make him seem less or more real to you than a more conventional presentation of him might?

2. Comment on the italicized portions of the story, where Ran hears his mother's voice, and her comment. What keeps him from returning to her?

3. Ran imagines beating his rival to death and shooting his estranged wife. The desire is so strong in him that he imagines the wish to be the reality. How does Miss Welty make it evident that Ran only imagines killing these two?

4. Is Ran as careless of Maideen's feelings as Jinny has been of his? Discuss.

5. Compare Faulkner's young husband, in "The Brooch," with Eudora Welty's Ran MacLain. Which study in love moves you to greater compassion? Why?

4·

MARRIAGE

MARRIAGE

"The Country Husband," by John Cheever

"A Domestic Dilemma," by Carson McCullers

"Sandra," by George P. Elliott

The Country Husband

by JOHN CHEEVER

John Cheever (1912-   ) is the author of the novel *The Wapshot Chronicle* (1957) which won the National Book Award as the finest novel of its year. He is better known as a prolific writer of short stories, most of which have been published in *The New Yorker*. Both the *Wapshot Chronicle* and many of his short stories have taken as their subject matter problems in love and marriage among the upper middle-class, men and women living for the most part in the suburbs of New York, eager for the excitements of adulterous love but also pulled by the forces of moral conservatism.

The major concern of "The Country Husband" is with a romantic dreamer who turns momentarily from his wife and the routine complexities of domestic life to fall impossibly in love with the family's babysitter. In the richness of its detail and in the amplitude of its exploration of the husband, it is almost a miniature novel. It shows both Cheever and his kind of story at their best.

To begin at the beginning, the airplane from Minneapolis in which Francis Weed was travelling East ran into heavy weather. The sky had been a hazy blue, with the clouds below the plane lying so close together that nothing could be seen of the earth. Then mist began to form outside the windows, and they flew into a white cloud of such density that it reflected the exhaust fires. The color of the cloud darkened to gray, and the plane began to rock. Francis had been in heavy weather before, but he had never been shaken up so much. The man in the seat beside him pulled a flask out of his pocket and took a drink. Francis smiled at his neighbor, but the man looked away; he wasn't sharing his painkiller with anyone. The plane had begun to drop and flounder wildly. A child was crying. The air in the

---

cabin was overheated and stale, and Francis' left foot went to sleep. He read a little from a paper book that he had bought at the airport, but the violence of the storm divided his attention. The exhaust fires blazed and shed sparks in the dark, and, inside, the shaded lights, the stuffiness, and the window curtains gave the cabin an atmosphere of intense and misplaced domesticity. Then the lights flickered and went out. "You know what I've always wanted to do?" the man beside Francis said suddenly. "I've always wanted to buy a farm in New Hampshire and raise beef cattle." The stewardess announced that they were going to make an emergency landing. All but the child saw in their minds the spreading wings of the Angel of Death. The pilot could be heard singing faintly, "I've got sixpence, jolly, jolly sixpence. I've got sixpence to last me all my life . . ." There was no other sound.

The loud groaning of the hydraulic valves swallowed up the pilot's song, and there was a shrieking high in the air, like automobile brakes, and the plane hit flat on its belly in a corn-field and shook them so violently that an old man up forward howled, "Me kidneys! Me kidneys!" The stewardess flung open the door, and someone opened an emergency door at the back, letting in the sweet noise of their continuing mortality—the idle splash and smell of a heavy rain. Anxious for their lives, they filed out of the doors and scattered over the cornfield in all direc-tions, praying that the thread would hold. It did. Nothing happened. When it was clear that the plane would not burn or explode, the crew and the stewardess gathered the passengers together and led them to the shelter of a barn. They were not far from Philadelphia, and in a little while a string of taxis took them into the city. "It's just like the Marne," someone said, but there was surprisingly little relaxation of that suspiciousness with which many Americans regard their fellow-travellers.

In Philadelphia, Francis Weed got a train to New York. At the end of that journey, he crossed the city and caught, just as it was about to pull out, the commuting train that he took five nights a week to his home in Shady Hill.

He sat with Trace Bearden. "You know, I was in that plane that just crashed outside Philadelphia," he said. "We came down in a field . . ." He had travelled faster than the newspapers or the rain, and the weather in New York was sunny and mild. It was a day in late September, as fragrant and shapely as an apple. Trace listened to the story, but how could he get excited? Francis had no powers that would let him re-create a brush with death—

particularly in the atmosphere of a commuting train, journeying through a sunny countryside where already, in the slum gardens, there were signs of harvest. Trace picked up his newspaper, and Francis was left alone with his thoughts. He said good night to Trace on the platform at Shady Hill and drove in his second-hand Volkswagen up to the Blenhollow neighborhood, where he lived.

The Weeds' Dutch Colonial house was larger than it appeared to be from the driveway. The living room was spacious and divided like Gaul into three parts. Around an ell to the left as one entered from the vestibule was the long table, laid for six, with candles and a bowl of fruit in the center. The sounds and smells that came from the open kitchen door were appetizing, for Julia Weed was a good cook. The largest part of the living room centered around a fireplace. On the right were some bookshelves and a piano. The room was polished and tranquil, and from the windows that opened to the west there was some late-summer sunlight, brilliant and as clear as water. Nothing here was neglected; nothing had not been burnished. It was not the kind of household where, after prying open a stuck cigarette box, you would find an old shirt button and a tarnished nickel. The hearth was swept, the roses on the piano were reflected in the polish of the broad top, and there was an album of Schubert waltzes on the rack. Louisa Weed, a pretty girl of nine, was looking out the western windows. Her younger brother Henry was standing beside her. Her still younger brother, Toby, was studying the figures of some tonsured monks drinking beer on the polished brass of the wood box. Francis, taking off his hat and putting down his paper, was not consciously pleased with the scene; he was not that reflective. It was his element, his creation, and he returned to it with that sense of lightness and strength with which any creature returns to its home. "Hi, everybody," he said. "The plane from Minneapolis . . ."

Nine times out of ten, Francis would be greeted with affection, but tonight the children are absorbed in their own antagonisms. Francis had not finished his sentence about the plane crash before Henry plants a kick in Louisa's behind. Louisa swings around, saying "*Damn* you!" Francis makes the mistake of scolding Louisa for bad language before he punishes Henry. Now Louisa turns on her father and accuses him of favoritism. Henry is always right; she is persecuted and lonely; her lot is hopeless. Francis turns to his son, but the boy has justification for the kick—she hit him first; she hit him on the ear, which is dangerous. Louisa agrees with this passionately. She hit him on the ear, and she *meant* to hit him on the ear, because he messed up her china collection. Henry says that this is a lie. Little Toby turns away from the wood box to throw in some evidence for Louisa. Henry claps his hand over little Toby's mouth. Francis separates the two boys but accidentally pushes Toby into the wood box. Toby begins to cry. Louisa is already crying. Just then, Julia Weed comes into that part of the room where the table is laid. She is a pretty, intelligent woman, and the white in her hair is premature. She does not seem to notice the fracas. "Hello, darling," she says serenely to Francis. "Wash your hands, everyone. Dinner is ready." She strikes a match and lights the six candles in this vale of tears.

This simple announcement, like the war cries of the Scottish chieftains, only refreshes the ferocity of the combatants. Louisa gives Henry a blow on the shoulder. Henry, although he seldom cries, has pitched nine innings and is tired. He bursts into tears. Little Toby discovers a splinter in his hand and begins to howl. Francis says loudly that he has been in a plane crash and that he is tired. Julia appears again, from the kitchen, and, still ignoring the chaos, asks Francis to go upstairs and tell Helen that everything is ready. Francis is happy to go; it is like getting back to headquarters company. He is planning to tell his oldest daughter about the airplane crash, but Helen is lying on her bed reading a *True Romance* magazine, and the first thing Francis does is to take the magazine from her hand and remind Helen that he has forbidden her to buy it. She did not buy it, Helen replies. It was given to her by her best friend, Bessie Black. Everybody reads *True Romance*. Bessie Black's father reads *True Romance*. There isn't a girl in Helen's class who doesn't read *True Romance*. Francis expresses his detestation of the magazine and then tells her that dinner is ready—although from the sounds downstairs it doesn't seem so. Helen follows him down the stairs. Julia has seated herself in the candle-light and spread a napkin over her lap. Neither Louisa nor Henry has come to the table. Little Toby is still howling, lying face down on the floor. Francis speaks to him gently: "Daddy was in a plane crash this afternoon, Toby. Don't you want to hear about it?" Toby goes on crying. "If you don't come to the table now, Toby," Francis says, "I'll have to send you to bed without any supper." The little boy rises, gives him a cunning look, flies up the stairs to his bedroom, and slams the door. "Oh dear," Julia says, and starts to go after him. Francis says that she will spoil him. Julia says that Toby is ten pounds underweight and has to be encouraged to eat. Winter is coming, and he will spend the cold months in bed unless he has his dinner. Julia goes upstairs. Francis sits down at the table with Helen. Helen is suffering from the dismal feeling of having read too intently on a fine day, and she gives her father and the room a jaded look. She doesn't understand about the plane crash, because there wasn't a drop of rain in Shady Hill.

Julia returns with Toby, and they all sit down and are served. "Do I have to look at that big, fat slob?" Henry says, of Louisa. Everybody but Toby enters into this skirmish, and it rages up and down the table for five minutes. Toward the end, Henry puts his napkin over his head and, trying to eat that way, spills spinach all over his shirt. Francis asks Julia if the children couldn't have their dinner earlier. Julia's guns are loaded for this. She can't cook two dinners and lay two tables. She paints with lightning strokes that panorama of drudgery in which her youth, her beauty, and her wit have been lost. Francis says that he must be understood; he was nearly killed in an airplane crash, and he doesn't like to come home every night to a battlefield. Now Julia is deeply committed. Her voice trembles. He doesn't come home every night to a battlefield. The accusation is stupid and mean. Everything was tranquil until he arrived. She stops speaking, puts down her knife and fork, and looks into her plate as if it is a gulf. She begins to cry. "Poor Mummy" Toby says, and when Julia gets up from the table, drying her tears with a napkin, Toby goes to her side. "Poor Mummy," he says. "Poor Mummy!" And they climb the stairs together. The other children drift away from the battlefield and Francis goes into the back garden for a cigarette and some air.

It was a pleasant garden, with walks and flower beds and places to sit. The sunset had nearly burned out, but there was still plenty of light. Put into a thoughtful mood by the crash and the battle, Francis listened to the evening sounds of Shady Hill. "Varmits! Rascals!" old Mr. Nixon shouted to the squirrels in his bird-feeding station. "Avaunt and quit my sight!" A door slammed. Someone was playing tennis on the Babcocks' court; someone was cutting grass. Then Donald Goslin, who lived at the corner, began to play the "Moonlight Sonata." He did this nearly every night. He threw the tempo out the window and played it *rubato* from beginning to end, like an outpouring of tearful petulance, lonesomeness, and self-pity—of everything it was Beethoven's greatness not to know. The music rang up and down the street beneath the trees like an appeal for love, for tenderness, aimed at some lonely housemaid—some fresh-faced, homesick girl from Galway, looking at old snapshots in her third-floor room. "Here, Jupiter, here Jupiter," Francis called to the Mercers' retriever. Jupiter crashed through the tomato vines with the remains of a felt hat in his mouth.

Jupiter was an anomaly. His retrieving instincts and his high spirits were out of place in Shady Hill. He was as black as coal, with a long, alert, intelligent, rakehell face. His eyes gleamed with mischief, and he held his head high. It was the fierce, heavily collared dog's head that appears in heraldry, in tapestry, and that used to appear on umbrella handles and walking sticks. Jupiter went where he pleased, ransacking wastebaskets, clotheslines, garbage pails, and shoe bags. He broke up garden parties and tennis matches, and got mixed up in the processional at Christ's Church on Sunday, barking at the men in red dresses. He crashed through old Mr. Nixon's rose garden two or three times a day, cutting a wide swath through the Condesa de Sastagos, and as soon as Donald Goslin lighted his barbecue fire on Thursday nights, Jupiter would get the scent. Nothing the Goslins did could drive him away. Sticks and stones and rude commands only moved him to the edge of the terrace, where he remained, with his gallant and heraldic muzzle, waiting for Donald Goslin to turn his back and reach for the salt. Then he would spring onto the terrace, lift the steak lightly off the fire, and run away with the Goslins' dinner. Jupiter's days were numbered. The Wrightsons' German gardener or the Farquarsons' cook would soon poison him. Even old Mr. Nixon might put some arsenic in the garbage that Jupiter loved. "Here, Jupiter, Jupiter!" Francis called, but the dog pranced off, shaking the hat in his white teeth. Looking in at the windows of his house, Francis saw that Julia had come down and was blowing out the candles.

Julia and Francis Weed went out a great deal. Julia was well liked and gregarious, and her love of parties sprang from a most natural dread of chaos and loneliness. She went through her morning mail with real anxiety, looking for invitations, and she usually found some, but she was insatiable, and if she had gone out seven nights a week, it would not have cured her of a reflective look —the look of someone who hears distant music—for she would always suppose that there was a more brilliant party somewhere else. Francis limited her to two week-night parties, putting a flexible interpretation on Friday, and rode through the weekend like a dory in a gale. The day after the airplane crash, the Weeds were to have dinner with the Farquarsons.

Francis got home late from town, and Julia got the sitter while he dressed, and then hurried him out of the house. The party was small and pleasant, and Francis settled down to enjoy himself. A new maid passed the drinks. Her hair was dark, and her face was round and pale and seemed familiar to Francis. He had not developed his memory as a sentimental faculty. Wood smoke, lilac, and other such perfumes did not not stir him, and his memory was something like his appendix—a vestigial repository. It was not his limitation at all to be unable to escape the past; it was perhaps his limitation that he had escaped it so successfully. He might have seen the maid at other parties, he might have seen her taking a walk on Sunday afternoons, but in either case he would not be searching his memory now. Her face was, in a wonderful way, a moon face—Norman or Irish—but it was not beautiful enough to account for his feeling that he had seen her before, in circumstances that he ought to be able to remember. He asked Nellie Farquarson who she was. Nellie said that the maid had come through an agency, and that her home was Trénon, in Normandy—a small place with a church and a restaurant that Nellie had once visited. While Nellie talked on about her travels abroad, Francis realized where he had seen the woman before. It had been at the end of the war. He had left a replacement depot with some other men and taken a three-day pass in Trénon. On their second day, they had walked out to a crossroads to see the public chastisement of a young woman who had lived with the German commandant during the Occupation.

It was a cool morning in the fall. The sky was overcast, and poured down onto the dirt crossroads a very discouraging light. They were on high land and could see how like one another the shapes of the clouds and the hills were as they stretched off toward the sea. The prisoner arrived sitting on a three-legged stool in a farm cart. She stood by the cart while the mayor read the accusation and the sentence. Her head was bent and her face was set in that empty half smile behind which the whipped soul is suspended. When the mayor was finished, she undid her hair and let it fall across her back. A little man with a gray mustache cut off her hair with shears and dropped it on the ground. Then, with a bowl of soapy water and a straight razor, he shaved her skull clean. A woman approached and began to undo the fastenings of her clothes, but the prisoner pushed her aside and undressed herself. When she pulled her chemise over her head and threw it on the ground, she was naked. The women jeered; the men were still. There was no change in the falseness or the plaintiveness of the prisoner's smile. The cold wind made her white skin rough and hardened the nipples of her breasts. The jeering ended gradually, put down by the recognition of their common humanity. One woman spat on her, but some inviolable grandeur in her nakedness lasted through the ordeal. When the crowd was quiet, she turned—she had begun to cry—and, with nothing on but a pair of worn black shoes and stockings, walked down the dirt road alone away from the village. The round white face had aged a little, but there was no question but that the maid who passed his cocktails and later served Francis his dinner was the woman who had been punished at the crossroads.

The war seemed now so distant and that world where the cost of partisanship had been death or torture so long ago. Francis had lost track of the men who had been with him in Vésey. He could not count on Julia's discretion. He could not tell anyone. And if he had told the story now, at the dinner table, it would have been a social as well as a human error. The people in the Farquarsons' living room seemed united in their tacit claim that there had been no past, no war—that there was no danger or trouble in the world. In the recorded history of human arrangements, this extraordinary meeting would have fallen into place, but the atmosphere of Shady Hill made the memory unseemingly and impolite. The prisoner withdrew after passing the coffee, but the encounter left Francis feeling languid; it had opened his memory and his senses, and left them dilated. He and Julia drove home when the party ended, and Julia went into the house. Francis stayed in the car to take the sitter home.

Expecting to see Mrs. Henlein, the old lady who usually stayed with the children, he was surprised when a young girl opened the door and came out onto the lighted stoop. She stayed in the light to count her textbooks. She was frowning and beautiful. Now, the world is full of beautiful young girls, but Francis saw here

the difference between beauty and perfection. All those endear-
ing flaws, moles, birthmarks, and healed wounds were missing,
and he experienced in his consciousness that moment when music
breaks glass, and felt a pang of recognition as strange, deep, and
wonderful as anything in his life. It hung from her frown, from
an impalpable darkness in her face—a look that impressed him
as a direct appeal for love. When she had counted her books,
she came down the steps and opened the car door. In the light,
he saw that her cheeks were wet. She got in and shut the door.

"You're new," Francis said.

"Yes, Mrs. Henlein is sick. I'm Anne Murchison."

"Did the children give you any trouble?"

"Oh, no, no." She turned and smiled at him unhappily in the
dim dashboard light. Her light hair caught on the collar of her
jacket, and she shook her head to set it loose.

"You've been crying."

"Yes."

"I hope it was nothing that happened in our house."

"No, no, it was nothing that happened in your house." Her
voice was bleak. "It's no secret. Everybody in the village knows.
Daddy's an alcoholic, and he just called me from some saloon and
gave me a piece of his mind. He thinks I'm immoral. He called
just before Mrs. Weed came back."

"I'm sorry."

"Oh, *Lord!*" She gasped and began to cry. She turned toward
Francis, and he took her in his arms and let her cry on his
shoulder. She shook in his embrace, and this movement accentu-
ated his sense of the fineness of her flesh and bone. The layers
of their clothing felt thin, and when her shuddering began to
diminish, it was so much like a paroxysm of love that Francis
lost his head and pulled her roughly against him. She drew
away. "I live on Belleview Avenue," she said. "You go down Lan-
sing Street to the railroad bridge."

"All right." He started the car.

"You turn left at the traffic light. . . . Now you turn right here
and go straight on toward the tracks."

The road Francis took brought him out of his own neighborhood, across the tracks, and toward the river, to a street where
the near-poor lived, in houses whose peaked gables and trimmings
of wooden lace conveyed the purest feelings of pride and romance, although the houses themselves could not have offered
much privacy or comfort, they were all so small. The street was

dark, and, stirred by the grace and beauty of the troubled girl, he seemed, in turning in to it, to have come into the deepest part of some submerged memory. In the distance, he saw a porch light burning. It was the only one, and she said that the house with the light was where she lived. When he stopped the car, he could see beyond the porch light into a dimly lighted hall-way with an old-fashioned clothes tree. "Well, here we are," he said, conscious that a young man would have said something different.

She did not move her hands from the books, where they were folded, and she turned and faced him. There were tears of lust in his eyes. Determinedly—not sadly—he opened the door on his side and walked around to open hers. He took her free hand, letting his fingers in between hers, climbed at her side the two concrete steps, and went up a narrow walk through a front garden where dahlias, marigolds, and roses—things that had withstood the light frosts—still bloomed, and made a bittersweet smell in the night air. At the steps, she freed her hand and then turned and kissed him swiftly. Then she crossed the porch and shut the door. The porch light went out, then the light in the hall. A second later, a light went on upstairs at the side of the house, shining into a tree that was still covered with leaves. It took her only a few minutes to undress and get into bed, and then the house was dark.

Julia was asleep when Francis got home. He opened a second window and got into bed to shut his eyes on that night, but as soon as they were shut—as soon as he had dropped off to sleep—the girl entered his mind, moving with perfect freedom through its shut doors and filling chamber after chamber with her light, her perfume, and the music of her voice. He was crossing the At-lantic with her on the old Mauretania and, later, living with her in Paris. When he woke from this dream, he got up and smoked a cigarette at the open window. Getting back into bed, he cast around in his mind for something he desired to do that would injure no one, and he thought of skiing. Up through the dimness in his mind rose the image of a mountain deep in snow. It was late in the day. Wherever his eyes looked, he saw broad and heartening things. Over his shoulder, there was a snow-filled valley, rising into wooded hills where the trees dimmed the whiteness like a sparse coat of hair. The cold deadened all sound but the loud, iron clanking of the lift machinery. The light on the trails was blue, and it was harder than it had been a minute or two earlier to pick the turns, harder to judge—now that the snow was all deep blue—the crust, the ice, the bare spots, and the deep piles of dry powder. Down the mountain he swung, matching his speed against the contours of a slope that had been formed in the first ice age, seeking with ardor some simplicity of feeling and circumstance. Night fell then, and he drank a Martini with some old friend in a dirty country bar.

In the morning, Francis' snow-covered mountain was gone, and he was left with his vivid memories of Paris and the Mauretania. He had been bitten gravely. He washed his body, shaved his jaws, drank his coffee, and missed the seven-thirty-one. The train pulled out just as he brought his car to the station, and the longing he felt for the coaches as they drew stubbornly away from him reminded him of the humors of love. He waited for the eight-two, on what was now an empty platform. It was a clear morning; the morning seemed thrown like a gleaming bridge of light over his mixed affairs. His spirits were feverish and high. The image of the girl seemed to put him into a relationship to the world that was mysterious and enthralling. Cars were beginning to fill up the parking lot, and he noticed that those that had driven down from the high land above Shady Hill were white with hoarfrost. This first clear sign of autumn thrilled him. An express train—a night train from Buffalo or Albany—came down the tracks between the platforms, and he saw that the roofs of the foremost cars were covered with a skin of ice. Struck by the miraculous physicalness of everything, he smiled at the passengers in the dining car, who could be seen eating eggs and wiping their mouths with napkins as they travelled. The sleeping-car compartments, with their soiled bed linen, trailed through the fresh morning like a string of rooming-house windows. Then he saw an extraordinary thing; at one of the bedroom windows sat an unclothed woman of exceptional beauty, combing her golden hair. She passed like an apparition through Shady Hill, combing and combing her hair, and Francis followed her with his eyes until she was out of sight. Then old Mrs. Wrightson joined him on the platform and began to talk.

"Well, I guess you must be surprised to see me here the third morning in a row," she said, "but because of my window curtains I'm becoming a regular commuter. The curtains I bought on Monday I returned on Tuesday, and the curtains I bought on Tuesday, I'm returning today. On Monday, I got exactly what I wanted—it's a wool tapestry with roses and birds—but when I got them home, I found they were the wrong length. Well, I exchanged them yesterday, and when I got them home, I found they were still the wrong length. Now I'm praying to high Heaven that the decorator will have them in the right length, because you know my house, you *know* my living-room windows, and you can imagine what a problem they present. I don't know what to do with them."

"I know what to do with them," Francis said.

"What?"

"Paint them black on the inside, and shut up."

There was a gasp from Mrs. Wrightson, and Francis looked down at her to be sure that she knew he meant to be rude. She turned and walked away from him, so damaged in spirit that she limped. A wonderful feeling enveloped him, as if light were being shaken about him, and he thought again of Venus combing and combing her hair as she drifted through the Bronx. The realization of how many years had passed since he had enjoyed being deliberately impolite sobered him. Among his friends and neighbors, there were brilliant and gifted people—he saw that—but many of them, also, were bores and fools, and he had made the mistake of listening to them all with equal attention. He had confused a lack of discrimination with Christian love, and the confusion seemed general and destructive. He was grateful to the girl for this bracing sensation of independence. Birds were singing—cardinals and the last of the robins. The sky shone like enamel. Even the smell of ink from his morning paper honed his appetite for life, and the world that was spread out around him was plainly a paradise.

If Francis had believed in some hierarchy of love—in spirits armed with hunting bows, in the capriciousness of Venus and Eros—or even in magical potions, philtres, and stews, in scapulae and quarters of the moon, it might have explained his susceptibility and his feverish high spirits. The autumnal loves of middle age are well publicized, and he guessed that he was face to face with one of these, but there was not a trace of autumn in what he felt. He wanted to sport in the green woods, scratch where he itched, and drink from the same cup.

His secretary, Miss Rainey, was late that morning—she went to a psychiatrist three mornings a week—and when she came in, Francis wondered what advice a psychiatrist would have for him. But the girl promised to bring back into his life something like the sound of music. The realization that this music might lead him straight to a trial for statutory rape at the county court-house collapsed his happiness. The photograph of his four children laughing into the camera on the beach at Gay Head reproached him. On the letterhead of his firm there was a drawing of the Laocoön, and the figure of the priest and his sons in the coils of the snake appeared to him to have the deepest meaning.

He had lunch with Pinky Trabert, who told him a couple of dirty stories. At a conversational level, the mores of his friends were robust and elastic, but he knew that the moral card house would come down on them all—on Julia and the children as well —if he got caught taking advantage of a baby-sitter. Looking back over the recent history of Shady Hill for some precedent, he found there was none. There was no turpitude; there had not been a divorce since he lived there; there had not even been a breath of scandal. Things seemed arranged with more propriety even than in the Kingdom of Heaven. After leaving Pinky, Francis went to a jeweller's and bought the girl a bracelet. How happy this clandestine purchase made him, how stuffy and comical the jeweller's clerks seemed, how sweet the women who passed at his back smelled! On Fifth Avenue, passing Atlas with his shoulders bent under the weight of the world, Francis thought of the stren-uousness of containing his physicalness within the patterns he had chosen.

He did not know when he would see the girl next. He had the bracelet in his inside pocket when he got home. Opening the door of his house, he found her in the hall. Her back was to him, and she turned when she heard the door close. Her smile was open and loving. Her perfection stunned him like a fine day—a day after a thunderstorm. He seized her and covered her lips with his, and she struggled but she did not have to struggle for long, because just then little Gertrude Flannery appeared from some-where and said, "Oh, Mr. Weed . . ."

Gertrude was a stray. She had been born with a taste for ex-ploration, and she did not have it in her to center her life with her affectionate parents. People who did not know the Flannerys concluded from Gertrude's behavior that she was the child of a bitterly divided family, where drunken quarrels were the rule. This was not true. The fact that little Gertrude's clothing was ragged and thin was her own triumph over her mother's struggle to dress her warmly and neatly. Garrulous, skinny, and unwashed, she drifted from house to house around the Blenhollow neighbor-hood, forming and breaking alliances based on an attachment to babies, animals, children her own age, adolescents, and sometimes adults. Opening your front door in the morning, you would find Gertrude sitting on your stoop. Going into the bathroom to shave, you would find Gertrude using the toilet. Looking into your son's crib, you would find it empty, and, looking further, you would find that Gertrude had pushed him in his baby carriage into the next village. She was helpful, pervasive, honest, hungry, and loyal. She never went home of her own choice. When the time to go arrived, she was indifferent to all its signs. "Go home, Gertrude," people could be heard saying in one house or another, night after night. "Go home, Gertrude." "It's time for you to go home now, Gertrude." "You had better go home and get your supper, Gertrude." "I told you to go home twenty minutes ago, Gertrude." "Your mother will be worrying about you, Gertrude." "Go home, Gertrude, go home.'

There are times when the lines around the human eye seem like shelves of eroded stone and when the staring eye itself strikes us with such a wilderness of animal feeling that we are at a loss. The look Francis gave the little girl was ugly and queer, and it frightened her. He reached into his pocket—his hands were shaking—and took out a quarter. "Go home, Gertrude, go home, and don't tell anyone, Gertrude. Don't—" He choked and ran into the living room as Julia called to him from upstairs to hurry and dress.

The thought that he would drive Anne Murchison home later that night ran like a golden thread through the events of the party that Francis and Julia went to, and he laughed uproariously at dull jokes, dried a tear when Mabel Mercer told him about the death of her kitten, and stretched, yawned, sighed, and grunted like any other man with a rendezvous at the back of his mind. The bracelet was in his pocket. As he sat talking, the smell of grass was in his nose, and he was wondering where he would park the car. Nobody lived in the old Parker mansion, and the driveway was used as a lovers' lane. Townsend Street was a dead end, and he could park there, beyond the last house. The old lane that used to connect Elm Street to the riverbanks was overgrown, but he had walked there with his children, and he could drive his car deep enough into the brushwoods to be concealed.

The Weeds were the last to leave the party, and their host and hostess spoke of their own marriage happiness while they all four stood in the hallway saying good night. "She's my girl," their host said, squeezing his wife. "She's my blue sky. After sixteen years,

I still bite her shoulders. She makes me feel like Hannibal crossing the Alps."

The Weeds drove home in silence. Francis brought the car up the driveway and sat still, with the motor running. "You can put the car in the garage," Julia said as she got out. "I told the Murchison girl she could leave at eleven. Someone drove her home." She shut the door, and Francis sat in the dark. He would be spared nothing then, it seemed, that a fool was not spared: ravening lewdness, jealousy, this hurt to his feelings that put tears in his eyes, even scorn—for he could see clearly the image he now presented, his arms spread over the steering wheel and his head buried in them for love.

Francis had been a dedicated Boy Scout when he was young, and, remembering the precepts of his youth, he left his office early the next afternoon and played some round-robin squash, but, with his body toned up by exercise and a shower, he realized that he might better have stayed at his desk. It was a frosty night when he got home. The air smelled sharply of change. When he stepped into the house, he sensed an unusual stir. The children were in their best clothes, and when Julia came down, she was wearing a lavender dress and her diamond sunburst. She explained the stir: Mr. Hubber was coming at seven to take their photograph for the Christmas card. She had put out Francis' blue suit and a tie with some color in it because the picture was going to be in color this year. Julia was lighthearted at the thought of being photographed for Christmas. It was the kind of ceremony she enjoyed.

Francis went upstairs to change his clothes. He was tired from the day's work and tired with longing, and sitting on the edge of the bed had the effect of deepening his weariness. He thought of Anne Murchison, and the physical need to express himself, instead of being restrained by the pink lamps on Julia's dressing table, engulfed him. He went to Julia's desk, took a piece of writing paper, and began to write on it. "Dear Anne, I love you, I love you, I love you . . ." No one would see the letter, and he used no restraint. He used phrases like "heavenly bliss," and "love nest." He salivated, sighed, and trembled. When Julia called him to come down, the abyss between his fantasy and the practical world opened so wide that he felt it affect the muscles of his heart.

Julia and the children were on the stoop, and the photographer and his assistant had set up a double battery of floodlights to show the family and the architectural beauty of the entrance to their house. People who had come home on a late train slowed their cars to see the Weeds being photographed for their Christmas card. A few waved and called to the family. It took half an hour of smiling and wetting their lips before Mr. Hubber was satisfied. The heat of the lights made an unfresh smell in the frosty air, and when they were turned off, they lingered on the retina of Francis' eyes.

Later that night, while Francis and Julia were drinking their coffee in the living room, the doorbell rang. Julia answered the door and let in Clayton Thomas. He had come to pay her for some theatre tickets that she had given his mother some time ago, and that Helen Thomas had scrupulously insisted on paying for, though Julia had asked her not to. Julia invited him in to have a cup of coffee. "I won't have any coffee," Clayton said, "but I will come in for a minute." He followed her into the living room, said good evening to Francis, and sat awkwardly in a chair.

Clayton's father had been killed in the war, and the young man's fatherlessness surrounded him like an element. This may have been conspicuous in Shady Hill because the Thomases were the only family that lacked a piece; all the other marriages were intact and productive. Clayton was in his second or third year of college, and he and his mother lived alone in a large house, which she hoped to sell. Clayton had once made some trouble. Years ago, he had stolen some money and run away; he had got to California before they caught up with him. He was tall and homely, wore horn-rimmed glasses, and spoke in a deep voice.

"When do you go back to college, Clayton?" Francis asked.

"I'm not going back," Clayton said. "Mother doesn't have the money, and there's no sense in all this pretense. I'm going to get a job, and if we sell the house, we'll take an apartment in New York."

"Won't you miss Shady Hill?" Julia asked.

"No," Clayton said. "I don't like it."

"Why not?" Francis asked.

"Well, there's a lot here I don't approve of," Clayton said gravely. "Things like the club dances. Last Saturday night, I looked in toward the end and saw Mr. Granner trying to put Mrs. Minot into the trophy case. They were both drunk. I disapprove of so much drinking."

"It was Saturday night," Francis said.

"And all the dovecotes are phony," Clayton said. "And the way people clutter up their lives. I've thought about it a lot, and what seems to me to be really wrong with Shady Hill is that it doesn't have any future. So much energy is spent in perpetuating the place—in keeping out undesirables, and so forth—that the only idea of the future anyone has is just more and more commuting trains and more parties. I don't think that's healthy. I think people ought to be able to dream big dreams about the future. I think people ought to be able to dream great dreams."

"Its too bad you couldn't continue with college," Julia said.

"I wanted to go to divinity school," Clayton said.

"What's your church?" Francis asked.

"Unitarian, Theosophist, Transcendentalist, Humanist," Clayton said.

"Wasn't Emerson a transcendentalist?" Julia asked.

"I mean the English transcendentalists," Clayton said. "All the American transcendentalists were goops."

"What kind of a job do you expect to get?" Francis asked.

"Well, I'd like to work for a publisher," Clayton said, "but everyone tells me there's nothing doing. But it's the kind of thing I'm interested in. I'm writing a long verse play about good and evil. Uncle Charlie might get me into a bank, and that would be good for me. I need the discipline. I have a long way to go in forming my character. I have some terrible habits. I talk too much. I think I ought to take vows of silence. I ought to try not to speak for a week, and discipline myself. I've thought of making a retreat at one of the Episcopalian monasteries, but I don't like Trinitarianism."

"Do you have any girl friends?" Francis asked.

"I'm engaged to be married," Clayton said. "Of course, I'm not old enough or rich enough to have my engagement observed or respected or anything, but I bought a simulated emerald for Anne Murchison with the money I made cutting lawns this summer. We're going to be married as soon as she finishes school."

Francis recoiled at the mention of the girl's name. Then a dingy light seemed to emanate from his spirit, showing everything—Julia, the boy, the chairs—in their true colorlessness. It was like a bitter turn of the weather.

"We're going to have a large family," Clayton said. "Her father's a terrible rummy, and I've had my hard times, and we want to have lots of children. Oh, she's wonderful, Mr. and Mrs.

Weed, and we have so much in common. We like all the same things. We sent out the same Christmas card last year without planning it, and we both have an allergy to tomatoes, and our eyebrows grow together in the middle. Well, good night."

Julia went to the door with him. When she returned, Francis said that Clayton was lazy, irresponsible, affected, and smelly. Julia said that Francis seemed to be getting intolerant; the Thomas boy was young and should be given a chance. Julia had noticed other cases where Francis had been short-tempered. "Mrs. Wrightson has asked everyone in Shady Hill to her anniversary party but us," she said.

"I'm sorry, Julia."

"Do you know why they didn't ask us?"

"Why?"

"Because you insulted Mrs. Wrightson."

"Then you know about it?"

"June Masterson told me. She was standing behind you."

Julia walked in front of the sofa with a small step that expressed, Francis knew, a feeling of anger.

"I did insult Mrs. Wrightson, Julia, and I meant to. I've never liked her parties, and I'm glad she's dropped us."

"What about Helen?"

"How does Helen come into this?"

"Mrs. Wrightson's the one who decides who goes to the assemblies."

"You mean she can keep Helen from going to the dances?"

"Yes."

"I hadn't thought of that."

"Oh, I knew you hadn't thought of it," Julia cried, thrusting hilt-deep into this chink of his armor. "And it makes me furious to see this kind of stupid thoughtlessness wreck everyone's happiness."

"I don't think I've wrecked anyone's happiness."

"Mrs. Wrightson runs Shady Hill and has run it for the last forty years. I don't know what makes you think that in a community like this you can indulge every impulse you have to be insulting, vulgar, and offensive."

"I have very good manners," Francis said, trying to give the evening a turn toward the light.

"Damn you, Francis Weed!" Julia cried, and the spit of her words struck him in the face. "I've worked hard for the social position we enjoy in this place, and I won't stand by and see you wreck it. You must have understood when you settled here that you couldn't expect to live like a bear in a cave."

"I've got to express my likes and dislikes."

"You can conceal your dislikes. You don't have to meet everything head-on, like a child. Unless you're anxious to be a social leper. It's no accident that we get asked out a great deal. It's no accident that Helen has so many friends. How would you like to spend your Saturday nights at the movies? How would you like to spend your Sundays raking up leaves? How would you like it if your daughter spent the assembly nights sitting at her window, listening to the music from the club? How would you like it—" He did something then that was, after all, not so unaccountable, since her words seemed to raise up between them a wall so deadening that he gagged: He struck her full in the face. She went up the stairs to their room. She didn't slam the door. When Francis followed, a few minutes later, he found her packing a suitcase.

"Julia, I'm very sorry."

"It doesn't matter," she said. She was crying.

"Where do you think you're going?"

"I don't know. I just looked at a timetable. There's an eleven-sixteen into New York. I'll take that."

"You can't go, Julia."

"I can't stay. I know that."

"I'm sorry about Mrs. Wrightson, Julia, and I'm—"

"It doesn't matter about Mrs. Wrightson. That isn't the trouble."

"What is the trouble?"

"You don't love me."

"I do love you, Julia."

"No, you don't."

"Julia, I do love you, and I would like to be as we were—sweet and bawdy and dark—but now there are so many people."

"You hate me."

"I don't hate you, Julia."

"You have no idea of how much you hate me. I think it's subconscious. You don't realize the cruel things you've done."

"What cruel things, Julia?"

"The cruel acts your subconscious drives you to in order to express your hatred of me."

"What, Julia?"

"I've never complained."

"Tell me."

"You don't know what you're doing."

"Tell me."

"Your clothes."

"What do you mean?"

"I mean the way you leave your dirty clothes around in order to express your subconscious hatred for me."

"I don't understand."

"I mean your dirty socks and your dirty pajamas and your dirty underwear and your dirty shirts!" She rose from kneeling by the suitcase and faced him, her eyes blazing and her voice ringing with emotion. "I'm talking about the fact that you've never learned to hang up anything. You just leave your clothes all over the floor where they drop, in order to humiliate me. You do it on purpose!" She fell on the bed, sobbing.

"Julia, darling!" he said, but when she felt his hand on her shoulder she got up.

"Leave me alone," she said. "I have to go." She brushed past him to the closet and came back with a dress. "I'm not taking any of the things you've given me," she said. "I'm leaving my pearls and the fur jacket."

"Oh, Julia!" Her figure, so helpless in its self-deceptions, bent over the suitcase made him nearly sick with pity. She did not understand how desolate her life would be without him. She didn't understand the hours that working women have to keep. She didn't understand that most of her friendships existed within the framework of their marriage, and that without this she would find herself alone. She didn't understand about travel, about hotels, about money. "Julia, I can't let you go! What you don't understand, Julia, is that you've come to be dependent on me."

She tossed her head back and covered her face with her hands. "Did you say that I was dependent on you?" she asked. "Is that what you said? And who is it that tells you what time to get up in the morning and when to go to bed at night? Who is it that prepares your meals and picks up your dirty closet and invites your friends to dinner? If it weren't for me, your neckties would be greasy and your clothing would be full of moth holes. You were alone when I met you, Francis Weed, and you'll be alone when I leave. When Mother asked you for a list to send out invitations to our wedding, how many names did you have to give her? Fourteen!"

"Cleveland wasn't my home, Julia."

"And how many of your friends came to the church? Two!"

"Cleveland wasn't my home, Julia."

"Since I'm not taking the fur jacket," she said quietly, "you'd better put it back into storage. There's an insurance policy on the pearls that comes due in January. The name of the laundry and the maid's telephone number—all those things are in my desk. I hope you won't drink too much, Francis. I hope that nothing bad will happen to you. If you do get into serious trouble, you can call me."

"Oh my darling, I can't let you go!" Francis said. "I can't let you go, Julia!" He took her in his arms.

"I guess I'd better stay and take care of you for a little while longer," she said.

Riding to work in the morning, Francis saw the girl walk down the aisle of the coach. He was surprised; he hadn't realized that the school she went to was in the city, but she was carrying books, she seemed to be going to school. His surprise delayed his re-action, but then he got up clumsily and stepped into the aisle. Several people had come between them, but he could see her ahead of him, waiting for someone to open the car door, and then, as the train swerved, putting out her hand to support herself as she crossed the platform into the next car. He followed her through that car and halfway through another before calling her name—"Anne! Anne!"—but she didn't turn. He followed her into still another car, and she sat down in an aisle seat. Coming up to her, all his feelings warm and bent in her direction, he put his hand on the back of her seat—even this touch warmed him—and, leaning down to speak to her, he saw it was not Anne. It was an older woman wearing glasses. He went on deliberately into another car, his face red with embarrassment and the much deeper feeling of having his good sense challenged; for if he couldn't tell one person from another, what evidence was there that his life with Julia and the children had as much reality as his dreams of iniquity in Paris or the litter, the grass smell, and the cave-shaped trees in Lovers' Lane.

Late that afternoon, Julia called to remind Francis that they were going out for dinner. A few minutes later, Trace Bearden called. "Look, feller," Trace said. "I'm calling for Mrs. Thomas. You know? Clayton, that boy of hers, doesn't seem able to get a job, and I wondered if you could help. If you'd call Charlie Bell

—I know he's indebted to you—and say a good word for the kid,
I think Charlie would—"

"Trace, I hate to say this," Francis said, "but I don't feel that I
can do anything for that boy. The kid's worthless. I know it's a
harsh thing to say, but it's a fact. Any kindness done for him
would backfire in everybody's face. He's just a worthless kid,
Trace, and there's nothing to be done about it. Even if we got him
a job, he wouldn't be able to keep it for a week. I know that to
be a fact. It's an awful thing, Trace, and I know it is, but instead
of recommending that kid, I'd feel obliged to warn people against
him—people who knew his father and would naturally want to
step in and do something. I'd feel obliged to warn them. He's a
thief . . ."

The moment this conversation was finished, Miss Rainey came
in and stood by his desk. "I'm not going to be able to work for
you any more, Mr. Weed," she said. "I can stay until the seventeenth if you need me, but I've been offered a whirlwind of a job,
and I'd like to leave as soon as possible."

She went out, leaving him to face alone the wickedness of what
he had done to the Thomas boy. His children in their photograph
laughed and laughed, glazed with all the bright colors of summer,
and he remembered that they had met a bagpiper on the beach
that day and he had paid the piper a dollar to play them a battle
song of the Black Watch. The girl would be at the house when he
got home. He would spend another evening among his kind neighbors, picking and choosing dead-end streets, cart tracks, and the
driveways of abandoned houses. There was nothing to mitigate
his feeling—nothing that laughter or a game of softball with the
children would change—and, thinking back over the plane crash,
the Farquarsons' new maid, and Anne Murchison's difficulties
with her drunken father, he wondered how he could have avoided
arriving at just where he was. He was in trouble. He had been
lost once in his life, coming back from a trout stream in the north
woods, and he had now the same bleak realization that no amount
of cheerfulness or hopefulness or valor or perseverance could help
him find, in the gathering dark, the path that he'd lost. He
smelled the forest. The feeling of bleakness was intolerable, and
he saw clearly that he had reached the point where he would have
to make a choice.

He could go to a psychiatrist, like Miss Rainey; he could go to
church and confess his lusts; he could go to a Danish massage
parlor in the West Seventies that had been recommended by a

salesman; he could rape the girl or trust that he would somehow be prevented from doing this; or he could get drunk. It was his life, his boat, and, like every other man, he was made to be the father of thousands, and what harm could there be in a tryst that would make them both feel more kindly toward the world? This was the wrong train of thought, and he came back to the first, the psychiatrist. He had the telephone number of Miss Rainey's doctor, and he called and asked for an immediate appointment. He was insistent with the doctor's secretary—it was his manner in business—and when she said that the doctor's schedule was full for the next few weeks, Francis demanded an appointment that day and was told to come at five.

The psychiatrist's office was in a building that was used mostly by doctors and dentists, and the hallways were filled with the candy smell of mouth-wash and memories of pain. Francis' character had been formed upon a series of private resolves—resolves about cleanliness, about going off the high diving board or repeating any other feat that challenged his courage, about punctuality, honesty, and virtue. To abdicate the perfect loneliness in which he had made his most vital decisions shattered his concept of character and left him now in a condition that felt like shock. He was stupefied. The scene for his *miserere mei Deus* was, like the waiting room of so many doctors' offices, a crude token gesture toward the sweets of domestic bliss: a place arranged with antiques, coffee tables, potted plants, and etchings of snow-covered bridges and geese in flight, although there were no children, no marriage bed, no stove, even, in this travesty of a house, where no one had ever spent the night and where the curtained windows looked straight onto a dark air shaft. Francis gave his name and address to a secretary and then saw, at the side of the room, a policeman moving toward him. "Hold it, hold it," the policeman said. "Don't move. Keep your hands where they are."

"I think it's all right, Officer," the secretary began. "I think it will be—"

"Let's make sure," the policeman said, and he began to slap Francis' clothes, looking for what—pistols, knives, an icepick? Finding nothing, he went off, and the secretary began a nervous apology: "When you called on the telephone, Mr. Weed, you seemed very excited, and one of the doctor's patients has been threatening his life, and we have to be careful. If you want to go in now?" Francis pushed open a door connected to an electrical chime, and in the doctor's lair sat down heavily, blew his nose into a handkerchief, searched in his pockets for cigarettes, for matches, for something, and said hoarsely, with tears in his eyes, "I'm in love, Dr. Herzog."

It is a week or ten days later in Shady Hill. The seven-fourteen has come and gone, and here and there dinner is finished and the dishes are in the dish-washing machine. The village hangs, morally and economically, from a thread; but it hangs by its thread in the evening light. Donald Goslin has begun to worry the "Moonlight Sonata" again. *Marcato ma sempre pianissimo!* He seems to be wringing out a wet bath towel, but the housemaid does not heed him. She is writing a letter to Arthur Godfrey. In the cellar of his house, Francis Weed is building a coffee table. Dr. Herzog recommended woodwork as a therapy, and Francis finds some true consolation in the simple arithmetic involved and in the holy smell of new wood. Francis is happy. Upstairs, little Toby is crying, because he is tired. He puts off his cowboy hat, gloves, and fringed jacket, unbuckles the belt studded with gold and rubies, the silver bullets and holsters, slips off his suspenders, his checked shirt, and Levis, and sits on the edge of his bed to pull off his high boots. Leaving this equipment in a heap, he goes to the closet and takes his space suit off a nail. It is a struggle for him to get into the long tights, but he succeeds. He loops the magic cape over his shoulders and, climbing onto the footboard of his bed, he spreads his arms and flies the short distance to the floor, landing with a thump that is audible to everyone in the house but himself.

"Go home, Gertrude, go home," Mrs. Masterson says. "I told you to go home an hour ago, Gertrude. It's way past your suppertime, and your mother will be worried. Go home!" A door on the Babcocks' terrace flies open, and out comes Mrs. Babcock without any clothes on, pursued by her naked husband. (Their children are away at boarding school, and their terrace is screened by a hedge.) Over the terrace they go in at the kitchen door, as passionate and handsome a nymph and satyr as you will find on any wall in Venice. Cutting the last of the roses in her garden, Julia hears old Mr. Nixon shouting at the squirrels in his bird-feeding station. "Rapscallions! Varmints! Avaunt and quit my sight!" A miserable cat wanders into the garden, sunk in spiritual and physical discomfort. Tied to its head is a small straw hat—a doll's hat—and it is securely buttoned into a doll's dress, from the skirts of which protrudes its long, hairy tail. As it walks, it shakes its feet, as if it had fallen into water.

"Here, pussy, pussy, pussy" Julia calls.

"Here, pussy, here, poor pussy!" But the cat gives her a skeptical look and stumbles away in its skirts. The last to come is Jupiter. He prances through the tomato vines, holding in his generous mouth the remains of an evening slipper. Then it is dark; it is a night where kings in golden suits ride elephants over the mountains.

EDITORS' ANALYSIS

In "The Country Husband," John Cheever presents a suburban man who apparently has everything he wants except the essential—excitement and the joy of being alive. Through a banal passion for a babysitter, a mature man thinks he has found an outlet for his feeling which will recreate his life. However, our Country Husband does not express his momentary but obsessive commitment to the babysitter in any rash act. He rather returns to the bosom of his family, after a brief session with a psychiatrist, to take up wood-working for therapy. He is perhaps sadder, and if not wiser then at least chastened. The babysitter is at first an emblem of his revolt, but is finally, through a series of ironic strategies, reduced to a psychological symptom. What the hero really wants, it seems, is not a romantic passion, is not to wake up to find the day full of bright longings. He wishes only to continue on his way as a "country husband."

QUESTIONS

1. The story at first may seem to be an accumulation of unrelated detail: the husband Francis Weed trying desperately to interest someone in the airplane crash he has survived, the quarreling children, the neat wife primarily concerned with status in suburbia. How does Cheever infuse this detail with rich meaning?

2. The title is abstract and generalized. Is it used to suggest that Francis Weed is both an individual and a type? The final sentence of the story makes it clear that the story is, in part, a fable. Find other instances in the prose of this fabular intention.

3. Compare the appeal to Francis of the two women—the wife and the babysitter. Whose youth and passion is the husband pursuing, his own or that of the babysitter?

4. To what extent does the hero live "underground"? Is he ever fully aware of what he feels? What is the basis of his sense of loss when he decides to consult his secretary's psychiatrist?

5. Describe the nature of Francis Wood's marriage, what he thinks that it means to him, and then compare it with the American ideal of marriage.

A Domestic Dilemma

by CARSON McCULLERS

Carson McCullers (1917-   ) won a place as one of America's most talented writers with her first novel, *The Heart is a Lonely Hunter* (1940), published when she was twenty-two. It was the story of a deaf-mute in a southern town, and carried with it the additional implications of being a parable of fascism. She has maintained her reputation with her subsequent publications, the best known of which is her novel *The Member of the Wedding* (1946). She also turned this novel into a play which was one of the successes of the 1950 season on Broadway, and won the Critics' Award as the best play of the year. *The Ballad of the Sad Café* (1951) is an anthology of her novels and short stories.

"A Domestic Dilemma" is, on its surface, a sketch of a commuting husband, and the problems that confront him at the end of the day, when he gets off the bus and turns into his own yard. Below the surface, the story carries implications concerning larger issues: the institution of marriage itself seems to be in trouble, and the American husband keeps the trouble alive when he competes with his wife in her old domain of running a household and raising children.

On Thursday Martin Meadows left the office early enough to make the first express bus home. It was the hour when the evening lilac glow was fading in the slushy streets, but by the time the bus had left the Mid-town terminal the bright city night had come. On Thursdays the maid had a half-day off and Martin liked to get home as soon as possible, since for the past year his wife had not been—well. This Thursday he was very tired and, hoping that no regular commuter would single him out for conversation, he fastened his attention to the newspaper until the

A Domestic Dilemna. Reprinted from *The Ballad of the Sad Café*. The selection from *The Ballad of the Sad Café*, by Carson McCullers, 1951, is reprinted by permission of and arrangement with Houghton Mifflin Company, the authorized publishers.

bus had crossed the George Washington Bridge. Once on 9-W Highway Martin always felt that the trip was halfway done, he breathed deeply, even in cold weather when only ribbons of draught cut through the smoky air of the bus, confident that he was breathing country air. It used to be that at this point he would relax and begin to think with pleasure of his home. But in this last year nearness brought only a sense of tension and he did not anticipate the journey's end. This evening Martin kept his face close to the window and watched the barren fields and lonely lights of passing townships. There was a moon, pale on the dark earth and areas of late, porous snow; to Martin the countryside seemed vast and somehow desolate that evening. He took his hat from the rack and put his folded newspaper in the pocket of his overcoat a few minutes before time to pull the cord.

The cottage was a block from the bus stop, near the river but not directly on the shore; from the living-room window you could look across the street and opposite yard and see the Hudson. The cottage was modern, almost too white and new on the narrow plot of yard. In summer the grass was soft and bright and Martin carefully tended a flower border and a rose trellis. But during the cold, fallow months the yard was bleak and the cottage seemed naked. Lights were on that evening in all the rooms in the little house and Martin hurried up the front walk. Before the steps he stopped to move a wagon out of the way.

The children were in the living room, so intent on play that the opening of the front door was at first unnoticed. Martin stood looking at his safe, lovely children. They had opened the bottom drawer of the secretary and taken out the Christmas decorations. Andy had managed to plug in the Christmas tree lights and the green and red bulbs glowed with out-of-season festivity on the rug of the living room. At the moment he was trying to trail the bright cord over Marianne's rocking horse. Marianne sat on the floor pulling off an angel's wings. The children wailed a startling welcome. Martin swung the fat little baby girl up to his shoulder and Andy threw himself against his father's legs.

'Daddy, Daddy, Daddy!'

Martin set down the little girl carefully and swung Andy a few times like a pendulum. Then he picked up the Christmas tree cord.

'What's all this stuff doing out? Help me put it back in the drawer. You're not to fool with the light socket. Remember I told you that before. I mean it, Andy.'

The six-year-old child nodded and shut the secretary drawer. Martin stroked his fair soft hair and his hand lingered tenderly on the nape of the child's frail neck.

'Had supper yet, Bumpkin?'

'It hurt. The toast was hot.'

The baby girl stumbled on the rug and, after the first surprise of the fall, began to cry; Martin picked her up and carried her in his arms back to the kitchen.

'See, Daddy,' said Andy. 'The toast——'

Emily had laid the childrens' supper on the uncovered porcelain table. There were two plates with the remains of cream-of-wheat and eggs and silver mugs that had held milk. There was also a platter of cinamon toast, untouched except for one tooth-marked bite. Martin sniffed the bitten piece and nibbled gingerly. Then he put the toast into the garbage pail.

'Hoo—phui—What on earth!'

Emily had mistaken the tin of cayenne for the cinnamon.

'I like to have burnt up,' Andy said. 'Drank water and ran out-doors and opened my mouth. Marianne didn't eat none.'

'Any,' corrected Martin. He stood helpless, looking around the walls of the kitchen. 'Well, that's that, I guess,' he said finally. 'Where is your mother now?'

'She's up in you alls' room.'

Martin left the children in the kitchen and went up to his wife. Outside the door he waited for a moment to still his anger. He did not knock and once inside the room he closed the door behind him.

Emily sat in the rocking chair by the window of the pleasant room. She had been drinking something from a tumbler and as he entered she put the glass hurriedly on the floor behind the chair. In her attitude there was confusion and guilt which she tried to hide by a show of spurious vivacity.

'Oh, Marty! You home already? The time slipped up on me. I was just going down——' She lurched to him and her kiss was strong with sherry. When he stood unresponsive she stepped back a pace and giggled nervously.

'What's the matter with you? Standing there like a barber pole. Is anything wrong with you?'

'Wrong with *me?*" Martin bent over the rocking chair and picked up the tumbler from the floor. 'If you could only realize how sick I am—how bad it is for all of us.'

Emily spoke in a false, airy voice that had become too familiar to him. Often at such times she affected a slight English accent, copying perhaps some actress she admired. 'I haven't the vaguest idea what you mean. Unless you are referring to the glass I used for a spot of sherry. I had a finger of sherry—maybe two. But what is the crime in that, pray tell me? I'm quite all right. Quite all right.'

'So anyone can see.'

As she went into the bathroom Emily walked with careful gravity. She turned on the cold water and dashed some on her face with her cupped hands, then patted herself dry with the corner of a bath towel. Her face was delicately featured and young, unblemished.

'I was just going down to make dinner.' She tottered and balanced herself by holding to the door frame.

'I'll take care of dinner. You stay up here. I'll bring it up.'

'I'll do nothing of the sort. Why, whoever heard of such a thing?'

'Please,' Martin said.

'Leave me alone. I'm quite all right. I was just on the way down——'

'Mind what I say.'

'Mind your grandmother.'

She lurched toward the door, but Martin caught her by the arm. 'I don't want the children to see you in this condition. Be reasonable.'

'Condition!' Emily jerked her arm. Her voice rose angrily. 'Why, because I drink a couple of sherries in the afternoon you're trying to make me out a drunkard. Condition! Why, I don't even touch whiskey. As well you know. *I* don't swill liquor at bars. And that's more than you can say. I don't even have a cocktail at dinnertime. I only sometimes have a glass of sherry. What, I ask you, is the disgrace of that? Condition!'

Martin sought words to calm his wife. 'We'll have a quiet supper by ourselves up here. That's a good girl.' Emily sat on the side of the bed and he opened the door for a quick departure. 'I'll be back in a jiffy.'

As he busied himself with the dinner downstairs he was lost in the familiar question as to how this problem had come upon his home. He himself had always enjoyed a good drink. When they were still living in Alabama they had served long drinks or cocktails as a matter of course. For years they had drunk one or two—possible three drinks before dinner, and at bedtime a long nightcap. Evenings before holidays they might get a buzz on, might even become a little tight. But alcohol had never seemed a problem to him, only a bothersome expense that with the increase in the family they could scarcely afford. It was only after his company had transferred him to New York that Martin was aware that certainly his wife was drinking too much. She was tippling, he noticed, during the day.

The problem acknowledged, he tried to analyze the source. The change from Alabama to New York had somehow disturbed her; accustomed to the idle warmth of a small Southern town, the matrix of the family and cousinship and childhood friends, she had failed to accommodate herself to the stricter, lonelier mores of the North. The duties of motherhood and housekeeping were onerous to her. Homesick for Paris City, she had made no friends in the suburban town. She read only magazines and murder books. Her interior life was insufficient without the artifice of alcohol.

The revelations of incontinence insidiously undermined his previous conceptions of his wife. There were times of unexplainable malevolence, times when the alcoholic fuse caused an explosion of unseemly anger. He encountered a latent coarseness in Emily, inconsistent with her natural simplicity. She lied about drinking and deceived him with unsuspected stratagems.

Then there was an accident. Coming home from work one evening about a year ago, he was greeted with screams from the children's room. He found Emily holding the baby, wet and naked from her bath. The baby had been dropped, her frail, frail skull striking the table edge, so that a thread of blood was soaking into the gossamer hair. Emily was sobbing and intoxicated. As Martin cradled the hurt child, so infinitely precious at that moment, he had an affrighted vision of the future.

The next day Marianne was all right. Emily vowed that never again would she touch liquor, and for a few weeks she was sober, cold and downcast. Then gradually she began—not whiskey or gin—but quantities of beer, or sherry, or outlandish liqueurs; once he had come across a hatbox of empty crème de menthe bottles. Martin found a dependable maid who managed the household competently. Virgie was also from Alabama and Martin had never dared tell Emily the wage scale customary in New York. Emily's drinking was entirely secret now, done before he reached the house. Usually the effects were almost imperceptible —a looseness of movement or the heavy-lidded eyes. The times of irresponsibilities, such as the cayenne-pepper toast, were rare, and Martin could dismiss his worries when Virgie was at the house. But, nevertheless, anxiety was always latent, a threat of indefined disaster that underlaid his days.

'Marianne!' Martin called, for even the recollection of that time brought the need for reassurance. The baby girl, no longer hurt, but no less precious to her father, came into the kitchen with her brother. Martin went on with the preparations for the meal. He opened a can of soup and put two chops in the frying pan. Then he sat down by the table and took his Marianne on his knees for a pony ride. Andy watched them, his fingers wobbling the tooth that had been loose all that week.

'Andy-the-candyman!' Martin said. 'Is that old critter still in your mouth? Come closer, let Daddy have a look.'

'I got a string to pull it with.' The child brought from his pocket a tangled thread. 'Virgie said to tie it to the tooth and tie the other end to the doorknob and shut the door real suddenly.'

Martin took out a clean handkerchief and felt the loose tooth carefully. 'That tooth is coming out of my Andy's mouth tonight. Otherwise I'm awfully afraid we'll have a tooth tree in the family.'

'What?'

'A tooth tree,' Martin said. 'You'll bite into something and swallow that tooth. And the tooth will take root in poor Andy's stomach and grow into a tooth tree with sharp little teeth instead of leaves.'

'Shoo, Daddy,' Andy said. But he held the tooth firmly between his grimy little thumb and forefinger. 'There ain't any tree like that. I never seen one.'

'There *isn't* any tree like that and I never *saw* one.'

Martin tensed suddenly. Emily was coming down the stairs. He listened to her fumbling footsteps, his arm embracing the little boy with dread. When Emily came into the room he saw from her movements and her sullen face that she had again been at the sherry bottle. She began to yank open drawers and set the table.

'Condition!' she said in a furry voice. 'You talk to me like that. Don't think I'll forget. I remember every dirty lie you say to me. Don't you think for a minute that I forget.'

'Emily!' he begged. 'The children——'

'The children—yes! Don't think I don't see through your dirty plots and schemes. Down here trying to turn my own children against me. Don't think I don't see and understand.'

'Emily! I beg you—please go upstairs.'

'So you can turn my children—my very own children——'
Two large tears coursed rapidly down her cheeks. 'Trying to turn
my little boy, my Andy, against his own mother.'

With drunken impulsiveness Emily knelt on the floor before
the startled child. Her hands on his shoulders balanced her.
'Listen, my Andy—you wouldn't listen to any lies your father
tells you? You wouldn't believe what he says? Listen, Andy, what
was your father telling you before I came downstairs?' Uncertain,
the child sought his father's face. 'Tell me. Mama wants to know.'

'About the tooth tree.'

'What?'

The child repeated the words and she echoed them with unbelieving terror. 'The tooth tree!' She swayed and renewed her
grasp on the child's shoulder. 'I don't know what you're talking
about. But listen, Andy, Mama is all right, isn't she?' The tears
were spilling down her face and Andy drew back from her, for he
was afraid. Grasping the table edge, Emily stood up.

'See! You have turned my child against me.'

Marianne began to cry, and Martin took her in his arms.

'That's all right, you can take *your* child. You have always
shown partiality from the very first. I don't mind, but at least you
can leave me my little boy.'

Andy edged close to his father and touched his leg. 'Daddy,' he
wailed.

Martin took the children to the foot of the stairs. 'Andy, you
take up Marianne and Daddy will follow you in a minute.'

'But Mama?' the child asked, whispering.

'Mama will be all right. Don't worry.'

Emily was sobbing at the kitchen table, her face buried in the
crook of her arm. Martin poured a cup of soup and set it before
her. Her rasping sobs unnerved him; the vehemence of her emo-
ton, irrespective of the source, touched in him a strain of tenderness. Unwillingly he laid his hand on her dark hair. 'Sit up and
drink the soup.' Her face as she looked up at him was chastened
and imploring. The boy's withdrawal or the touch of Martin's
hand had turned the tenor of her mood.

'Ma-Martin,' she sobbed. 'I'm so ashamed.'

'Drink the soup.'

Obeying him, she drank between gasping breaths. After a
second cup she allowed him to lead her up to their room. She was
docile now and more restrained. He laid her nightgown on the
bed and was about to leave the room when a fresh round of grief,
the alcoholic tumult, came again.

'He turned away. My Andy looked at me and turned away.'

Impatience and fatigue hardened his voice, but he spoke warily. 'You forget that Andy is still a little child—he can't comprehend the meaning of such scenes.'

'Did I make a scene? Oh, Martin, did I make a scene before the children?'

Her horrified face touched and amused him against his will. 'Forget it. Put on your nightgown and go to sleep.'

'My child turned away from me. Andy looked at his mother and turned away. The children——'

She was caught in the rhythmic sorrow of alcohol. Martin withdrew from the room saying: 'For God's sake go to sleep. The children will forget by tomorrow.'

As he said this he wondered if it was true. Would the scene glide so easily from memory—or would it root in the unconscious to fester in the after-years? Martin did not know, and the last alternative sickened him. He thought of Emily, foresaw the morning-after humiliation: the shards of memory, the lucidities that glared from the obliterating darkness of shame. She would call the New York office twice—possibly three or four times. Martin anticipated his own embarrassment, wondering if the others at the office could possibly suspect. He felt that his secretary had divined the trouble long ago and that she pitied him. He suffered a moment of rebellion against his fate; he hated his wife.

Once in the children's room he closed the door and felt secure for the first time that evening. Marianne fell down on the floor, picked herself up and calling: 'Daddy, watch me,' fell again, got up, and continued the falling-calling routine. Andy sat in the child's low chair, wobbling the tooth. Martin ran the water in the tub, washed his own hands in the lavatory, and called the boy into the bathroom.

'Let's have another look at that tooth.' Martin sat on the toilet, holding Andy between his knees. The child's mouth gaped and Martin grasped the tooth. A wobble, a quick twist and the nacreous milk tooth was free. Andy's face was for the first moment split between terror, astonishment, and delight. He mouthed a swallow of water and spat into the lavatory.

'Look, Daddy! It's blood. Marianne!'

Martin loved to bathe his children, loved inexpressibly the tender, naked bodies as they stood in the water so exposed. It was not fair of Emily to say that he showed partiality. As Martin soaped the delicate boy-body of his son he felt that further love would be impossible. Yet he admitted the difference in the quality of his emotions for the two children. His love for his daughter was graver, touched with a strain of melancholy, a gentleness that was akin to pain. His pet names for the little boy were the absurdities of daily inspiration—he called the little girl always Marianne, and his voice as he spoke it was a caress. Martin patted dry the fat baby stomach and the sweet little genital fold. The washed child faces were radiant as flower petals, equally loved.

'I'm putting the tooth under my pillow. I'm supposed to get a quarter.'

'What for?'

'*You* know, Daddy. Johnny got a quarter for his tooth.'

'Who puts the quarter there?' asked Martin. 'I used to think the fairies left it in the night. It was a dime in my day, though.'

'That's what they say in kindergarden.'

'Who does put it there?'

'Your parents.' Andy said. 'You!'

Martin was pinning the cover on Marianne's bed. His daughter was already asleep. Scarcely breathing, Martin bent over and kissed her forehead, kissed again the tiny hand that lay palm-upward, flung in slumber beside her head.

'Good night, Andy-man.'

The answer was only a drowsy murmur. After a minute Martin took out his change and slid a quarter underneath the pillow. He left a night light in the room.

As Martin prowled about the kitchen making a late meal, it occurred to him that the children had not once mentioned their mother or the scene that must have seemed to them incomprehensible. Absorbed in the instant—the tooth, the bath, the quarter —the fluid passage of child-time had borne these weightless episodes like leaves in the swift current of a shallow stream while the adult enigma was beached and forgotten on the shore. Martin thanked the Lord for that.

But his own anger, repressed and lurking, arose again. His youth was being frittered by a drunkard's waste, his very manhood subtly undermined. And the children, once the immunity of incomprehension passed—what would it be like in a year or so? With his elbows on the table he ate his food brutishly, untasting. There was no hiding the truth—soon there would be gossip in the office and in the town; his wife was a dissolute woman. Dissolute. And he and his children were bound to a future of degradation and slow ruin.

Martin pushed away from the table and stalked into the living room. He followed the lines of a book with his eyes but his mind conjured miserable images: he saw his children drowned in the river, his wife a disgrace on the public street. By bedtime the dull, hard anger was like a weight upon his chest and his feet dragged as he climbed the stairs.

The room was dark except for the shafting light from the half-opened bathroom door. Martin undressed quietly. Little by little, mysteriously, there came in him a change. His wife was asleep, her peaceful respiration sounding gently in the room. Her high-heeled shoes with the carelessly dropped stockings made to him a mute appeal. Her underclothes were flung in disorder on the chair. Martin picked up the girdle and the soft, silk brassière and stood for a moment with them in his hands. For the first time that evening he looked at his wife. His eyes rested on the sweet forehead, the arch of the fine brow. The brow had descended to Marianne, and the tilt at the end of the delicate nose. In his son he could trace the high cheekbones and pointed chin. Her body was full-bosomed, slender and undulant. As Martin watched the tranquil slumber of his wife the ghost of the old anger vanished. All thoughts of blame or blemish were distant from him now. Martin put out the bathroom light and raised the window. Careful not to awaken Emily he slid into the bed. By moonlight he watched his wife for the last time. His hand sought the adjacent flesh and sorrow paralleled desire in the immense complexity of love.

EDITORS' ANALYSIS

In Carson McCuller's "A Domestic Dilemma," it is the wife, raised among the comfortable simplicities of a southern town, who is unable to come up to the expected role of the modern, suburban wife of a New York business man. In her loneliness and isolation, she can focus only on her own feelings of inadequacy, and takes to drink. The story leaves the domestic dilemma unresolved, and its strength, in part, lies in this fact. Yet in the last moments of the story, the husband, aware of "the immense complexity of love," drops his identity as the angry American husband, worried about what his secretary will think of his wife, anxious for his children. We are allowed to see him when, for a little while, he is able to become an unconditional male, filled with a mood of pity and desire.

QUESTIONS

1. Compare Carson McCuller's use of detail in the opening paragraphs of her story with that of John Cheever in "The Country Hus-

band." Do you consider both openings equally appropriate to what follows? One better than the other?

2. Is the wife's trouble really ever explained, or only hinted at? Do we know why she is an obsessive drinker? Does she? Is her unhappiness an exaggeration of that of many American wives, or is it the limited problem of a single woman?

3. The wife accuses her husband of partiality toward his daughter. Is she the victim of too much pseudo-psychology? Reacting naturally? Is there something more deep-seated in her accusation?

4. What motivates the change in the husband, as described in the last paragraph of the story? Is he weak-willed, guilty of surrender to a drunken wife? Or does he suddenly understand something of the human condition of which he had been unaware before?

5. Compare this story of marriage with Cheever's. Could either one be considered an epitome of American marriage? A "concrete universal?"

Sandra

by GEORGE P. ELLIOTT

George P. Elliott (1920-   ) is the author of one novel, *Parktilden Village* (1958), a study of the passive immorality of American intellectuals and their children. It was not a popular success but has been much discussed by literary critics. He has published stories in *Hudson Review, Esquire,* and in other magazines. His short stories have been reprinted in the *O. Henry Prize Stories,* in *Best American Short Stories,* and in other anthologies. He is the editor of *Fifteen Modern American Poets* (1956). His critical writing has appeared most often in *Hudson Review* and in the *Nation.*

"Sandra" is a satirical fantasy on American marriage which, the sociologists assure us, includes ingredients which are unique in history. Modern psychology emphasizes domestic values and a new standard of conjugal responsibility. But we are all aware of trouble. For one thing, the American wife competes with the husband on his own grounds. Women now receive the same education as men, but lip-service is still paid to the traditional division of labor between the sexes. Mr. Elliott's fantasy is set in the midst of our awareness of conjugal trouble.

A few years ago I inherited a handsome neo-Spanish house in a good neighborhood in Oakland. It was much too large for a single man, as I knew perfectly well; if I had behaved sensibly I would have sold it and stayed in my bachelor quarters; I could have got a good price for it. But I was not sensible; I liked the house very much; I was tired of my apartment-house life; I didn't need the money. Within a month I had moved in and set about looking for a housekeeper.

From the moment I began looking, everyone assured me that I should get a domestic slave. I was reluctant to get one, not so much because of the expense as because of my own inexperience.

Sandra. Originally published in *Epoch,* Fall 1953. Copyright, 1953, by George P. Elliott. Reprinted with permission of the author.

No one in my family had ever had one, and among my acquaintances there were not more than three or four who had any. Nevertheless, the arguments in favor of my buying a slave were too great to be ignored. The argument that irritated me most was the one used by the wives of my friends. "When you marry," they would say, "think how happy it will make your wife to have a domestic slave." Then they would offer, zealously, to select one for me. I preferred to do my own selecting. I began watching the classified ads for slaves for sale.

Some days there would be no slaves listed for sale at all; on Sundays there might be as many as ten. There would be a middle-aged Negro woman, 22 years experience, best recommendations, $4500; or a 35-year-old Oriental, speaks English, excellent cook, recommendations, $5000; or a middle-aged woman of German descent, very neat, no pets or vices . . . sensible choices, no doubt, but none of them appealed to me. Somewhere in the back of my mind there was the notion of the slave I wanted. It made me restless, looking; all I knew about it was that I wanted a female. I was hard to satisfy. I took to dropping by the Emeryville stores, near where my plant is located, looking for a slave. What few there were in stock were obviously of inferior quality. I knew that I would have to canvass the large downtown stores to find what I wanted. I saw the ads of Oakland's Own Department Store, announcing their January white sale; by some quirk, they had listed seven white domestic slaves at severely reduced prices. I took off a Wednesday, the first day of the sale, and went to the store at opening time, 9:45, to be sure to have the pick of the lot.

Oakland's Own is much the largest department store in the city. It has seven floors and two basements, and its quality runs from $1498 consoles to factory-reject cotton work socks. It has a good solid merchandising policy, and it stands behind its goods in a reassuring, old fashioned way. The wives of my friends were opposed to my shopping in Oakland's Own, because, they said, secondhand slaves were so much better trained than new, and cost so little more. Nevertheless, I went.

I entered the store the moment the doors were opened, and went straight up to the sixth floor on the elevator. All the same I found a shapeless little woman in the slave alcove ahead of me picking over the goods—looking at their teeth and hair, telling them to bend over, to speak so she could hear the sound of their voices. I was furious at having been nosed out by the woman, but

I could not help admiring the skill and authority with which she inspected her merchandise. She told me something about herself. She maintained a staff of four, but what with bad luck, disease and her husband's violent temper she was always having trouble. The Federal Slave Board had ruled against her twice—against her husband, really, but the slaves were registered in her name —and she had to watch her step. In fact she was on probation from the FSB now. One more adverse decision and she didn't know what she'd do. Well, she picked a strong, stolid-looking female, ordered two sets of conventional domestic costumes for her, signed the charge slip, and left. The saleswoman came to me.

I had made my decision. I had made it almost the moment I had come in, and I had been in agonies for fear the dumpy little shopper would choose my girl. She was not beautiful exactly, though not plain either, nor did she look especially strong. I did not trouble to read her case-history card; I did not even find out her name. I cannot readily explain what there was about her that attracted me. A certain air of insouciance as she stood waiting to be looked over—the bored way she looked at her fingernails and yet the fearful glance she cast from time to time at us shoppers— the vulgarity of her make-up and the soft charm of her voice—I do not know. Put it down to the line of her hip as she stood waiting, a line girlish and womanly at once, dainty and strong, at ease but not indolent. It's what I remember of her best from that day, the long pure line from her knee to her waist as she stood staring at her nails, cocky and scared and humming to herself.

I knew I should pretend impartiality and indifference about my choice. Even Oakland's Own permits haggling over the price of slaves; I might knock the price down as much as $300, particularly since I was paying for her cash on the line. But it wasn't worth the trouble to me. After three weeks of dreary looking I had found what I wanted, and I didn't feel like waiting to get it. For form's sake, I asked the saleswoman for the card on my slave. She was the sixth child of a carpenter in Chico. Chico is a miserable town in the plains of the San Joaquin Valley; much money is spent each year teaching the people of Chico how to read and write; *chico* means greasewood. Her father had put her her up for sale, with her own consent, at the earliest legal age, eighteen, the year of graduation from high school. The wholesaler had taught her the rudiments of cooking, etiquette, and house-cleaning. She was listed as above average in cleanliness, intelligence and personality, superb in copulation, and fair in versatility and sewing. But I had known as much from just looking at her, and I didn't care. Her name was Sandra, and in a way I had known that too. She had been marked down from $3850 to $3299. As the saleswoman said, how could I afford to pass up such a bargain? I got her to knock the price down the amount of the sales taxes, wrote out my check, filled out the FSB forms, and took my slave Sandra over to be fitted with clothes.

And right there I had my first trouble as a master, right on the fifth floor of Oakland's Own in the Women's Wear department. As a master, I was supposed to say to Sandra, or even better to the saleswoman about Sandra, "Plain cotton underwear, heavy-weight nylon stockings, two dark-blue maid's uniforms and one street dress of conservative cut," and so on and so on. *The slave submits to the master:* I had read it in the FSB manual for domestic slave owners. Now I find it's all very well dominating slaves in my office or my factory. I am chief engineer for the Jergen Calculating Machine Corp., and I have had no trouble with my industrial and white-collar slaves. They come into the plant knowing precisely where they are, and I know precisely where I am. It's all cut and dried. I prefer the amenities when dealing with, say, the PBX operator. I prefer to say, "Miss Persons, will you please call Hoskins of McKee Steel?" rather than "Persons, get me Hoskins of McKee." But this is merely a preference of mine, a personal matter, and I know it and Persons knows it. No, all that is well set, but this business of Sandra's clothes quite threw me.

I made the blunder of asking her her opinion. She was quick to use the advantage I gave her, but she was very careful not to go too far. "Would you like a pair of high heels for street wear?" I asked her. "If it is agreeable with you, sir." "Well, now, let's see what they have in your size.—Those seem sturdy enough and not too expensive. Are they comfortable?" "Quite comfortable, sir." "There aren't any others you'd rather have?" "These are very nice, sir." "Well, I guess these will do quite well, for the time being at least." "I agree with you, sir."

I agree with you: that's a very different matter from *I submit to you.* And though I didn't perceive the difference at the moment, still I was anything but easy in my mind by the time I had got Sandra installed in my house. Oh, I had no trouble preserving the proper reserve and distance with her, and I could not in the slightest detail complain of her behavior. It was just that I was not to the manner bred; that I was alone in the house with her, knowing certain external things to do, but supported by no customs and precedents as I was at the plant; that I found it very uncomfortable to order a woman, with whom I would not eat dinner at the same table, to come to my bed for an hour or so after she had finished washing the dishes. Sandra was delighted with the house and with her quarters, with the television set I had had installed for her and with the subscription to *Cosmopolitan* magazine that I had ordered in her name. She was delighted. That was the bad thing about it—I was glad. I should have provided these facilities only as a heavy industry provides half-hour breaks and free coffee for its workers—to keep her content and to get more work out of her. Instead I was as glad at her pleasure in them as though she were an actual person. She was so delighted that tears came to her eyes and she kissed my feet; then she asked me where the foot basin was kept. I told her I had none. She said that the dishpan would do until we got one. I told her to order a foot basin from Oakland's Own the next day, along with any other utensils or supplies she felt we needed. She thanked me, fetched the dishpan and washed my feet. It embarrassed me to have her do it; I knew it was often done, I enjoyed the sensuous pleasure of it, I admired the grace and care with which she bent over my feet like a shoeshine, but all the same I was embarrased. Yet she did it every day when I came home.

I do not think I could describe more economically the earlier stages of my connection to Sandra than by giving an account of the foot washing.

At first, as I have said, I was uneasy about it, though I liked it too. I was not sure that as a slave she had to do it, but she seemed to think she had to and she certainly wanted to. Now this was all wrong of me. It is true that domestic slaves usually wash their master's feet, but this is not in any sense one of the slave's rights. It is a matter about which the master decides, entirely at his own discretion. Yet, by treating it as a set duty, a duty like serving me food in which she had so profound an interest as to amount to a right, Sandra had from the outset made it impossible for me to will not to have her wash my feet. She did it every day when I came home; even when I was irritable and told her to leave me alone, she did it. Of course, I came to depend upon it as one of the pleasures and necessary routines of the day. It was, in fact, very soothing; she spent a long time at it and the water was always just lukewarm, except in cold weather when it was quite warm; she always floated a slice of lemon in the water.

The curve of her back, the gesture with which she would shake the hair out of her eyes, the happy, private smile she wore as she did it, these were beautiful to me. She would always kiss, very lightly, the instep of each foot after she had dried them—always, that is, when we were alone.

If I brought a friend home with me, she would wash our feet all right, but matter-of-factly, efficiently, with no little intimacies as when I was alone. But if it was a woman who came with me, or a man and wife, Sandra would wash none of our feet. Nor did she wash the feet of any callers. I thought this was probably proper etiquette. I had not read my *Etiquette for Slaves* as well as Sandra obviously had. I let it go. During the first few weeks, all my friends, and particularly all my women friends, had to come to observe Sandra. She behaved surely and with complete consistency towards them all. I was proud of her. None of the women told me that Sandra was anything less than perfect, not even Helen who would have been most likely to, being an old friend and sharp-tongued. After the novelty had worn off, I settled down with her into what seemed to be a fine routine. To be sure, it was not long before I would think twice about bringing someone home for dinner with me; if there was much doubt in my mind about it, the difference in Sandra's foot washing alone would sway me not to bring my friend along, especially if my friend was a woman.

When I would come home late at night she would be waiting for me, with a smile and downcast eyes. I went, in October, to a convention in St. Louis for a week. When I came back, I think she spent an hour washing my feet, asking me to tell her about the physical conditions of my trip, nothing personal or intimate but just what I had eaten and what I had seen and how I had slept; but the voice in which she asked it—One night I came home very late, somewhat high, after a party. I did not want to disturb her, so I tried to go to my room noiselessly. But she heard me and came in in her robe to wash my feet; she helped me to bed, most gently. Not by a glance did she reproach me for having disturbed her sleep. But then, she never reproached me.

I did not realize fully how much I had come to depend on her until she fell sick. She was in the hospital with pneumonia for three days and spent six days convalescing. It was at Thanksgiving time. I declined invitations out to dinner, in order to keep Sandra company—to tend to her, I said to myself, though she tended to herself very nicely. I was so glad to have her well again that the first time she could come to me I kept her in my bed all night—so that she might not chill herself going back to her own bed, I told myself. That was the first time, yet by Christmas we were sleeping together regularly, though she kept her clothes in her own room. She still called me sir, she still washed my feet; according to the bill of sale I owned her: I thought her a perfect slave. I was uneasy no longer.

In fact, of course, I was making a fool of myself, and it took Helen to tell me so.

"Dell," she said over the edge of her cocktail glass, "you're in love with this creature."

"In love with Sandra!" I cried. "What do you mean?"

And I was about to expostulate hotly against the notion when I bethought me that too much heat on my part would only confirm her in her opinion. Therefore, seeming to study the problem, I relapsed into a brown study—under Helen's watchful eye—and tried to calculate the best out for myself.

I rang for Sandra.

"More manhattans," I told her.

She bowed, took the shaker on her tray, and left. She was impeccable.

"No, Helen," I said finally, "she does not make my pulses race. The truth is, I come a lot closer to being in love with you than with Sandra."

This threw her considerably off balance, as I had hoped it would.

"How absurd. You've never even made a pass at me."

"True."

But Sandra returned with the drinks, and after she had left we talked about indifferent matters.

As I was seeing Helen to the door, she said to me, "All the same, Dell, watch out. You'll be marrying this creature next. And who will drop by to see you then?"

"If I ever marry Sandra," I said, "it will not be for love. If I have never made a pass at you, my dear, it has not been for lack of love."

I looked at her rather yearningly, squeezed her hand rather tightly, and with a sudden little push closed the door behind her. I leaned against the wall for a moment and offered up a short prayer that Helen would never lose her present husband and come looking in my part of the world for another. I could have managed to love her all right, but she scared me to death.

I thought about what she had told me. I knew that I was not in love with Sandra—there were a thousand remnants of Chico in her that I could not abide—but I could not deny that I needed her very much. What Helen had made me see clearly was the extent to which I had failed to keep Sandra a slave. I did not know whether it was her scheming that had brought it about or my slackness, or whether, as I suspected, it was something of both. Some of the more liberal writers on the subject say, of course, that such development is intrinsic in the situation for anyone in our cultural milieu. It is a problem recognized by the FSB in its handbook. But the handbook advises the master who finds himself in my predicament to trade his slave for another, preferably some stodgy, uninteresting number or one who is deficient in the proper qualities—in my case, as I thought, copulating. The trouble with this sound advice was that I didn't want to get rid of Sandra. She made me comfortable.

In fact, she made me so comfortable that I thought I was happy. I wanted to show my gratitude to her. After she had straightened up the kitchen that evening I called her into the living room where I was sitting over the paper.

"Yes, sir?" she said, standing demurely on the other side of the coffee table.

"Sandra," I began, "I'm very fond of you. I would like to do something for you."

"Yes, sir."

"Sit down."

"Thank you, sir."

As she sat, she took a cigarette from the box, without asking my permission, and lighted it. The way she arched her lips to smoke it, taking care not to spoil her lipstick, annoyed me, and the coy way she batted her eyelids made me regret I had called her in. "Still," I thought, "the Chico in her can be trained out. She's sound."

"What can I give you, Sandra?"

She did not answer for a moment. Every slave knows the answer to that question, and knows it is the one answer for which he won't be thanked.

"Whatever you wish to give me, sir, would be deeply appreciated."

I couldn't think of a thing to buy for her. Magazines, movies, television, clothes, jewelry, book club books, popular records, a permanent wave every four months, what else could I get her?

Yet I had started this offer; I had to follow up with something. In my uneasiness and annoyance with myself, and knowing so well what it was she wanted, I went too far.

"Would you like freedom, Sandra?"

She dropped her eyes and seemed to droop a little. Then tears rolled down her cheeks, real mascara-stained tears of sadness.

"Oh yes, sir," she said. "Oh, my God, yes. Don't tease me about it. Please don't tease me."

So I promised her her freedom. I myself was moved, but I did not want to show it.

"I'm going for a short walk," I said. "You may go to your room."

I went for my walk, and when I came back she had prepared my foot bath. She had burned two pine boughs in the fireplace so that the room smelled wonderful. She had put on her loveliest dress, and had brushed her hair down as I liked it best. She did not speak as she washed my feet, nor even look up at my face. All her gratitude she expressed in the tenderness with which she caressed my feet and ankles. When she had finished drying them, she kissed them and then pressed them for a time against her breast. I do not think either of us, during these past years, has ever been happier than at that moment.

Well, I had my lawyer draw up a writ of substantial manumission, and Sandra took the brass ring out of her left ear, and that was that. And that was about all of that, so far as I could see. She was free to go as she wanted, but she didn't want. She got wages now, it is true, but all she did with them was to buy clothes and geegaws. She continued to take care of my house and me, to sleep in my bed and keep her own possessions in her own room, and to wash my feet as before. The manumission was nothing in itself, only a signpost that there had been some changes made. Continually and slowly changes kept being made.

For one thing, we began to eat together, unless I had guests in to dinner. For another, she began to call me Mr. Oakes. It seemed strange to have her go where she wanted, without asking me about it, on her nights out. I became so curious about what she could be doing that finally I asked her where she went. To night school, she said, learning how to type. I was delighted to hear that she had not been wasting her time at public dances, but I could not imagine why she wanted to learn typing. She had even bought a portable typewriter which she practiced on in her room when I was away. "Why?" she said. "My mother always said to me, 'Sandra, they can't fire slaves.' Well, I'm not a slave any longer. That was one nice thing about it, I wasn't ever afraid you'd fire me." "But my darling," I cried, "I'm never going to fire you. I couldn't possibly get along without you." "I know it," she replied, "and I never want to leave either. All the same, I'm going to learn how to type." She had her own friends in to visit her; she even gave a bridge party one evening when I was not at home. But she never called me by my first name, she never checked up on me, she never asked me the sort of intrusive, prying question which a man hates answering. She kept her place.

Then she discovered she was pregnant. I immediately said I would assume all the financial responsibilities of her pregnancy and of rearing the child. She thanked me, and did not mention the subject again. But she took to sleeping in her own bed most of the time. She would serve breakfast while still in her robe and slippers. Her eyes were often red and swollen, though she always kept some sort of smile on her face. She mentioned something about going back to Chico. She began serving me canned soup at dinner. I drove her off to Reno and married her.

Helen had been right, I had married Sandra; but I had been right too, it wasn't for love. Oh, I loved her, some way or other, I don't know just how. But I had married her simply because it was the next thing to do; it was just another milestone.

Nothing much happened for a while after we were married, except that she called me Dell and didn't even take the curlers out of her hair at breakfast. But she hadn't got to be free and equal overnight. That was to take some months of doing.

First of all, as a wife, she was much frailer than she had been as a slave. I had to buy all sorts of things for her, automatic machines to wash the clothes and the dishes, a cooking stove with nine dials and two clocks, an electric ironer that could iron a shirt in two minutes, a vacuum cleaner, one machine to grind the garbage up and another to mix pancake batter, a thermostatic furnace, an electric floor waxer, and a town coupe for her to drive about to do her errands in. She had to get other people to wash her hair now, and shave her legs and armpits, and polish her toenails and fingernails for her. She took out subscriptions to five ladies' magazines, which printed among them half a million words a month for her to read, and she had her very bathrobe designed in Paris. She moved the television set into the living room and had a tear-drop chandelier hung from the center of the ceiling. When she had a miscarriage in her sixth month, she had a daily bouquet of blue orchids brought to her room; she had to rest, and pale blue orchids are so restful. She became allergic to the substances of which my mattress and pillows were composed, and I had to get a foam rubber mattress and foam rubber pillows. She finally insisted that we go to visit her family in Chico, so we finally did, and that we go visit my family in Boston, so we finally did. The visits were equally painful. We began to go to musical comedies and night clubs. Helen had been right: my friends did not drop by to see us, and they were apt to be sick when I invited them to dinner. Still we weren't all the way.

One night I came home late from work, tired and hungry. Dinner was not yet started, because Sandra had been delayed by her hairdresser. She fixed pork chops, frozen green beans, and bread and butter, with canned apricots for dessert. I could have done better myself. After dinner, after the machine had washed the dishes, I asked her if she would bathe my feet. I was so tired, I told her, my feet were so tired; it would be very soothing to me. But she said, in an annoyed voice, that she was feeling nervous herself. She was going to go to bed early. Besides, the silence she left behind her said, besides I am your wife now. She went to bed and I went to bed. She was restless; she twisted and turned. Every time I would shift my position or start to snore a little, she would sigh or poke me. Finally she woke me clear up and said it was impossible for her to sleep like this. Why didn't I go to sleep in her former room? She couldn't because of her allergy, she had to stay in the foam rubber bed. So I moved into her room. And then I knew that she was equal, for most of the equal wives of my friends lived like this.

Another night, I came home wanting very much to make love to her. She had avoided my embrace for a long while. She was always too nervous, or too tired, for the less she worked the tireder she became; or she was busy, or simply not in the mood. But tonight I would admit of no evasion. She was beautiful and desirable, and I knew how well she had once made love with me. Finally, I held her in my arms. She knew I wanted her, and in a way as odd as mine she loved me too. But there was no sensuous pressure of her body against mine, no passion in her kiss. She put her arms about my neck not to caress me but to hang like an albatross against me. She pressed her head against my shoulder not for amorous affection but to hide her face, to shelter it, in loneliness and fear and doubt. She did not resist me, or yield to me, or respond to me, or try to overcome me. She only went away and left me her body to do with as I pleased. And then I knew that she was free, for most of the free wives of my friends were like this with their husbands.

I had four choices, as I saw it: divorce her, have her psychoanalyzed, kill her, or return her to slavery. I was strongly tempted to kill her, but I was an optimist, I thought she was salvageable. Besides, who would do my housework for me? I made her a slave again.

It is a wise provision of the law that says no slave may be completely manumitted. Even substantial manumission provides for a five-year probationary period. Sandra had not passed probation. I had the necessary papers drawn up, told her, an hour before the men came, what was happening, and had her sent to the FSB Rehabilitation School in Colorado for a month.

She came back with the ring in her ear saying sir to me, and the very first night she washed my feet. Furthermore she made love better than she had done for a year. I thought we were to be happy again, and for a week we seemed to be. But the machines are still there to do most of the work, and she still has her allergy. She does what a slave is supposed to do, but she is depressed about it. She has tasted the fruit of freedom; though it is a bitter fruit it is habit-forming. She does what she is supposed to do, but it is an effort, she has to will it, it exhausts her.

One evening six months ago, I came home to find no dinner cooking, no foot bath waiting for me, no sign of Sandra in her room. I found her lying on my bed reading *McCall's* and smoking with a jewel-studded holder I had given her when she was my wife. She flicked an ash onto the rug when I entered the room, waved a langorous *Hi!* at me, and kept on reading. I had my choice; she had clearly set it up for me. I hesitated only a moment. I went down to the basement where I had stored away the three-thonged lash which had been provided along with the manual of instructions when I had first bought her, and I beat her on the bed where she lay.

I think I was more upset by the beating than Sandra was. But I knew I had had to do it. I knew I had neglected my duty as a master not to have done it long ago. I think, now, that all this trouble could have been avoided if formerly I had only kept a firm hand, that is to say, had beaten her when she had risen too presumptuously. For the truth is, Sandra is happiest as a slave.

But the beatings I should have given her formerly would simply have hurt; she would simply have avoided them. Now, I am not so sure.

For she repeated the offense, exactly, within a month, and I repeated the punishment. It wasn't so bad for me the second time. She began seeing just how far she could go before I would bring out the lash. She cooked more and more badly till I gave her warning one evening. When I had finished speaking, she sank to the floor, pressed her forehead against my foot looked at me, and said, "Your wish is my command." The irony was all in the act and words, if irony there was, for there was none in the voice or face. The truth was, as she discovered the next evening when she served me corned beef hash and raw carrots for dinner, my lash is her command. She seems happier, in a way, after these distasteful blow-ups, comes to my bed voluntarily and with the welts still on her back, does her work well, hums sometimes. Yet she falls back into her old stubborn mood, again and again. There seems to be nothing else for me to do but beat her. The FSB manual supports me. Yet I find it repugnant, and it cannot be good for Sandra's skin. I had to lash her a week ago, and already, from the dirt she is allowing to collect on the living room rug, it looks as though I'll have to do it again.

It seems a pity to have to resort to this, when it was all quite unnecessary. It's my own fault of course; I lacked the training, the matter-of-fact experience of being a master, and I did not set about my duties as a master so conscientiously as I should have. I know all this, but knowing it doesn't help matters a bit. Sometimes I think I should have killed her: it would have been better for both of us; but then she will do some little act of spontaneous love, as now bringing me a cup of hot chocolate and kissing me lightly on the back of the neck, which makes me glad to have her around. Yet tomorrow I shall have to beat her again. This is not what I had wanted, and it cannot be what she wants, not really. We were uneasy and felt something lacking when she was a slave before, though we were happy too. We were altogether miserable when she was free. Yet, this is not what either of us had ever wanted, though we are both of us doing what we must.

EDITORS' ANALYSIS

Elliott's "Sandra" presents a simplified solution to an American problem. Oppressed by the "new woman," rejecting the terms of the challenge set down by her, his hero buys a slave—who then turns out to be the "new woman." Why? Because his hero cannot understand love in any way but the American way, and gradually makes his Sandra into a "good" American wife. He abdicates his control in her favor. Is it the American woman's fault that American marriage has so many flaws?

QUESTIONS

1. Does the author's freewheeling style give him advantages over the tighter styles of "The Country Husband" and of "A Domestic Dilemma?" Or do you think that Elliott's style makes for confusion? Discuss.

2. How easily do you accept the half real, half fantastic events of the story? Does Elliott's crossing the line away from realism make his story merely a tour-de-force for you? A kind of well-played game of ideas?

3. Is Sandra a slave or a wife? Is there irony in calling her a slave?

4. Analyze the four choices which the author envisages when he finds his life with Sandra becoming more complicated than he can bear.

5. Do all three husbands, in the three stories in this section, have a good deal in common? Is it that they are simply American husbands?

5.

AMBITION

"How the Devil Came Down Division Street,"
by Nelson Algren

"The Battler," *by Ernest Hemingway*

"The Walls of Ávila," *by Evan S. Connell, Jr.*

How the Devil Came Down Division Street

by NELSON ALGREN

Nelson Algren (1909-   ) achieved fame with his novel *The Man With the Golden Arm* (1949), largely a study of its central character, Frankie Machine, a dealer in a gambling club on Chicago's West Side, an area of wretched poverty and crime. This novel won the National Book Award in 1950. Earlier fiction of Algren's included *Somebody in Boots* (1935), a documentary novel of social protest, and *Never Come Morning* (1942), another portrait of Chicago's West Side. His most recent novel, *A Walk on the Wild Side* (1956) is set in the slums of New Orleans during the depression and is told with corrosive humor. *The Neon Wilderness* (1947) is a collection of his short stories, and *Chicago: City on the Make* (1951) is a bitter eulogy, in poetic prose. Algren has often been identified as an American realist. But the curiously surrealistic atmosphere of his best-known work, *The Man With the Golden Arm*, belies this easy identification.

Fictional studies of ambition, its quality, its direction, are peculiarly appealing to the American reader, conscious of the urgency of his own hopes of success. In our relatively classless society in which the ultimate sin is to lose faith in such hopes, Algren's story presents a strange world: one in which hopelessness is a condition of survival. In tone and attitude, this story is an epitome of the world as viewed by Algren.

Last Saturday evening there was a great argument in the Polonia Bar. All the biggest drunks on Division were there, trying to decide who the biggest drunk of them all was. Symanski said he was, and Oljiec said he was, and Koncel said he was, and Czechowski said he was.

Then Roman Orlov came in and the argument was decided.

How the Devil Came Down Division Street. First published in *Harper's Bazaar*, May, 1944. Reprinted by permission of the author and *Harper's Bazaar*.

For Poor Roman has been drunk so long, night and day, that when we remember living men we almost forget Poor Roman, as though he were no longer really among the living at all.

'The devil lives in a double-shot,' Roman explains himself obscurely. 'I got a great worm inside. Gnaws and gnaws. Every day I drown him and every day he gnaws. Help me drown the worm, fellas.'

So I bought Poor Roman a double-shot and asked him frankly how, before he was thirty, he had become the biggest drunk on Division.

It took a long time, and many double-shots, for him to tell. But tell it he did, between curses and sobs, and I tell it now as closely to what he told as I can. Without the sobs, of course. And of course without any cursing.

When Roman was thirteen, it seems, the Orlovs moved into three stove-heated rooms in the rear of a lopsided tenement on Noble Street. Mama O. cooked in a Division Street restaurant by day and cooked in her own home by night.

Papa O. played an accordion for pennies in Division Street taverns by night and slept alone in the room by day.

There were two beds in the tiny flat, so nobody encouraged Papa O. to come home at all.

Because he was the oldest, Roman slept between the twins, on the bed set up in the front room, to keep the pair from fighting during the night as they did during the day. Every day, Teresa, who was eleven and could not learn her lessons as well as some of her classmates, slept with Mama O. in the windowless back bedroom; under a bleeding heart in a gilded oval frame.

If Papa O. got in before light, as happened occasionally early in the week, he crawled uncomplaining under Roman's bed until Roman rose and got the twins, who were seven, up with him in time for Mass.

If Udo, who was something between a collie and a St. Bernard and as big as both, was already curled up beneath the front-room bed, Papa O. slugged him with the accordion in friendly reproach —and went on into the back bedroom to crawl under Mama O.'s bed. In such an event he slept under a bed all day. For he never crawled, even with daylight, into Mama O.'s bed. Empty or not. As though he did not feel himself worthy to sleep there even when she was gone.

It was as though, having given himself all night to his accordion, he must remain true to it during the day.

For all manner of strange things went on in Papa O.'s head, as even the twins had become aware. Things so strange that Teresa was made ashamed of them by her school mates, whenever they wanted someone to tease.

This, too, was why no one, not even the twins, paid Papa O. any heed when the family returned from Mass one Sunday forenoon and he told them someone had been knocking while they were away.

'Some*body* was by door,' he insisted. 'I say "Hallo." Was no*body*.' He looked slyly about him at the children. 'Who plays tricks by Papa?' he asked.

'Maybe was the Zolewitzes,' Mama O. suggested indifferently. 'Mama Z. comes perhaps to borrow.'

That Sunday night it was cold in all the corners. Papa O. was gone to play for pennies and drinks, Mama O. was frying *pierogi*, the twins were in bed and Teresa was studying her catechism across the table from Roman, when someone knocked lightly twice.

To Roman it sounded like someone at the clothes-closet door; but that was foolish to think, since the twins were in bed. Yet, when he opened the hall door, only a cold wind came into the room from the long gaslit passage.

Roman, being only thirteen, did not dare look behind the door. Far less to speak of the clothes closet.

All that night a light snow fell, while Roman O. lay wakeful, fancying he saw it falling on darkened streets all over the mysterious earth, on the pointing rooftops of old world cities, on mountain-high waves of the mid-Atlantic, and in the leaning eaves of Noble Street. He was just falling off to sleep when the knocking came again. Three times, like a measured warning. The boy stiffened under the covers, listening with his fear. Heard the hall door squeak softly, as though Papa O. were sneaking in. But Papa O. never knocked, and Papa O. never sneaked. Papa O. came with the accordion banging against buildings all down Noble Street, jingling his pennies proudly, singing off-key bravely, mumbling and laughing and stumbling. Papa O. never knocked. He kicked the door in happily and shouted cheerfully, 'What you say, all peoples? How's t'ings, ever-body?' Papa O. pulled people out of bed and rattled pans and laughed at nothing and argued with unseen bartenders until somebody gave him sausage and eggs and coffee and bread and hung the accordion safely away.

Roman crept, barefooted, in the long underwear Mama O. had sewed on him in the early fall, to the hallway door.

The whole house slept. The windows were frosted and a thin line of ice had edged up under the front window and along the pane. The family slept. Roman shoved the door open gently. The tenement slept. Down the hall the single gas jet flickered feebly. No one. Nothing. The people slept.

Roman looked behind the door, shivering now with more than cold.

No one. Nothing. All night long.

He returned to bed and prayed quietly, until he heard Mama O. rise; waited till he knew she had the fire going in the big kitchen stove. Then, dressing with his back to the heat, he told Mama O. what he had heard. Mama O. said nothing.

Two mornings later, Papa O. came home without the accordion. It did not matter then to Mama O. whether he had sold it or lost it or loaned it: she knew it at last for a sign, she had felt the change coming, she said, in her blood. For she had dreamed a dream, all night, of a stranger waiting in the hall: a young man, drunken, leaning against the gaslit wall for support, with blood down the front of his shirt and on his hands. She knew, as all the Orlovs knew, that the unhappy dead return to warn or comfort, to plead or repent, to gain peace or to avenge.

That day, standing over steaming kettles, Mama O. went back in her mind to all those dear to her of earth who had died: the cousin drowned at sea, the brother returned from the war to die, the mother and father gone from their fields before she had married.

That night she knocked on Mama Zolewitz's door. Mama Z. sat silently, as though she had been expecting Mama O. for many evenings.

'Landlord doesn't like we should tell new tenants too soon,' Mama Z. explained even before being told of the knocking, 'so you shouldn't say it, I told. It was a young man lived in this place, in your very rooms. A strong young man, and good to look at. But sick, sick in the head from the drink. A sinner certainly. For here he lived with his lady without being wed, and she worked and he did not. That he did not work had little to do with what happened, and the drink had little to do. For it was being unwed that brought it on, at night, on the New Year. He returned from the taverns that night and beat her till her screams were a whimpering. Till her whimpering became nothing. A strong young man, like a bull, made violent by the drink. When the whimpering ceased, there was no sound at all. No sound until noon, when the police came with shouting.

'What was there to shout about? I could have told them before they came. The young man had hanged himself in the bedroom closet. Thus it is that one sin leads to another and both were buried together. In unsanctified ground, with no priest near.'

Mama O. grew pale. Her very clothes closet.

'It is nothing to worry,' Mama Z. told her neighbor sagely, 'he does not knock to do harm. He comes only to gain a little peace that good Christian prayer for him may give. Pray for the young man, Mama O. He wishes peace.'

That night after supper the Orlovs gathered in prayer about the front-room stove, and Papa O. prayed also. For now that the accordion was gone, the taverns must do without him. When the prayer was done, he went to bed with Mama O. like a good husband, and the knocking did not come again.

Each night the Orlovs prayed for the poor young man. And each night Papa O. went to bed with Mama O. for lack of his accordion.

Mama O. knew then that the knocking had been a sign of good omen, and told the priest, and the priest blessed her for a Christian. He said it was the will of God that the Orlovs should redeem the young man by prayer and that Papa O. should have no accordion.

Papa O. stayed at home until, for lack of music, he became the best janitor in the 800 block of Noble Street. Mama Z. went to the priest and told of her part in the miracle of the poor young man, and the priest blessed Mama Z. also.

When the landlord learned that his house was no longer haunted, he brought the Orlovs gifts; and when the rent was late, he said nothing. So the priest blessed him equally, and in time the Orlovs paid no rent at all, but prayed for the landlord instead.

Teresa became the most important person in her class, for it became known that a miracle had been done in the Orlov home. Sister Mary Ursula said the child looked more like a little saint every day. And no other child in the room ever had her lessons as well as Teresa thereafter.

The twins sensed the miracle, and grew up to be fast friends, doing all things together, even to wearing the same clothes and reading the same catechism. Udo, too, knew that the home was blessed. For he received no more blows from the accordion.

Only one sad aspect shadowed this great and happy change:

Poor Roman was left bedless. For with Papa O. home every night like a good husband, Teresa must sleep between the twins.

Thus it came about that the nights of Roman Orlov became fitful and restless, first under the front-room bed and then under the back-room bed. With the springs overhead squeaking half the night as likely as not. The nights of Roman's boyhood were thereafter passed beneath one bed or the other, with no bed of his own at all. Until, reaching his young manhood and his seventeenth year, he took at last to sleeping during the day in order to have no need for sleep at night.

And at night, as everyone knows, there is no place to go but the taverns.

So it was, being abroad with no place to go and the whole night to kill, that Roman took his father's place. He had no accordion for excuse—only lack of a bed. He came to think of the dawn, when the taverns closed and he must go home, as the bitterest hour of the day.

This is why he still calls the dawn the bitterest hour: he must go home though he has no home. Nor wife, nor family, nor hope, nor joy.

Is this a drunkard's tale or sober truth? I can only say he told it like the truth, drinking double-shots all the while. I only know that no one argues about who the biggest drunk on Division is if Roman O. is around.

I only know what Mama O. now tells, after many years and Papa O. in his grave and the twins scattered: that the young man who knocked was in truth the devil. For did she not give, without knowing what she did, a son in return for a husband?

'I'm drownin' the worm t'night,' Poor Roman explains, talking to his double-shot. 'Help me drown the worm t'night, fellas.'

Does the devil live in a double-shot? Or is he the one who gnaws, all night, within?

EDITORS' ANALYSIS

In Algren's story, it is not frustrated ambition but lack of a bed which drives Roman Orlov into becoming the greatest drunk of the Polonia Bar. But why does this scion of the immigrant's dream not have a bed? Consoled by faith, the Orlovs have nevertheless remained poor. Just when the family thinks that it is saved, the devil of poverty takes it. Religion has blinded them to the real danger, the chance to grapple with the real issues of their lives; and by giving them a specious satisfaction, has made it impossible for them to search out the lasting solutions which life in an ambitious society demands. The story stands, perhaps as purely as any in this collection, as the objectification of a thesis: Within the degradation of poverty, the consolations of faith offer only a blindness which disarms us.

QUESTIONS

1. Comment on Algren's way of telling his story as if it were Orlov's drunken autobiography. Does this method give the story a meaning larger than Orlov's view of himself and his family?

2. Does the "truth" of the story depend upon your acceptance of Algren's attitudes toward poverty and religion? His acquiescence in Orlov's failure?

3. Who is the devil in the title, and in the last paragraph?

4. Why do not the Orlovs resist the powers which are ruining their lives? Do you believe that Roman Orlov is simply stupid?

5. Judging by your own experience of the American dream of personal success, what other possibilities lay before Roman Orlov besides following his father's unsteady footsteps? Is he the kind of man who could have found a job in a diner, for example, and then worked his way through college?

The Battler

by ERNEST HEMINGWAY

Ernest Hemingway (1899-   ), with the publication of his first important novel, *The Sun Also Rises* (1926), became a literary spokesman for the "lost generation." He created a style in which events are recorded with a minimum of detail and in a highly understated dialogue. He also helped set the attitude of rebellion of his generation toward conventional sexual morality and toward an easy optimism in assessing the nature of existence. His most successful novels, after *The Sun Also Rises*, have been *A Farewell to Arms* (1929), *For Whom the Bell Tolls* (1940), and *The Old Man and the Sea* (1952), a short novel on which (in part) his award of the Nobel Prize (1954) was based. Hemingway's fiction has been mainly concerned with an expatriate society in which powerful or desperate individuals seek justification for their lives through personal courage and dignity. Hemingway has created a public image of himself almost in imitation of characters in his novels. A sardonic sketch of this public personality may be found in Lillian Ross's "Profile" of Hemingway, published in *The New Yorker*, May 13, 1950.

"The Battler" carries a double meaning, suggesting the beginning struggles of the young Nick Adams of the story, and the final holding on to existence by the ex-fighter. In laconic style and in "tough" point of view, "The Battler" is pure Hemingway. The story also includes a touch of subdued sentiment in its depiction of the care with which the Negro watches over the battered, half-crazy ex-champ.

Nick stood up. He was all right. He looked up the track at the lights of the caboose going out of sight around the curve. There was water on both sides of the track, then tamarack swamp.

He felt of his knee. The pants were torn and the skin was barked. His hands were scraped and there were sand and cinders driven up under his nails. He went over to the edge of the track down the little slope to the water and washed his hands. He washed them carefully in the cold water, getting the dirt out from the nails. He squatted down and bathed his knee.

That lousy crut of a brakeman. He would get him some day. He would know him again. That was a fine way to act.

"Come here, kid," he said. "I got something for you."

He had fallen for it. What a lousy kid thing to have done. They would never suck him in that way again.

"Come here kid, I got something for you." Then *wham* and he lit on his hands and knees beside the track.

Nick rubbed his eye. There was a big bump coming up. He would have a black eye, all right. It ached already. That son of a crutting brakeman.

He touched the bump over his eye with his finger. Oh, well, it was only a black eye. That was all he had gotten out of it. Cheap at the price. He wished he could see it. Could not see it looking into the water, though. It was dark and he was a long way from anywhere. He wiped his hands on his trousers and stood up, then climbed the embankment to the rails.

He started up the track. It was well ballasted and made easy walking, sand and gravel packed between the ties, solid walking. The smooth roadbed like a causeway went on ahead through the swamp. Nick walked along. He must get to somewhere.

Nick had swung on to the freight train when it slowed down for the yards outside of Walton Junction. The train, with Nick on it, had passed through Kalkaska as it started to get dark. Now he must be nearly to Mancelona. Three or four miles of swamp. He stepped along the track, walking so he kept on the ballast between the ties, the swamp ghostly in the rising mist. His eye ached and he was hungry. He kept on hiking, putting the miles of track back of him. The swamp was all the same on both sides of the track.

Ahead there was a bridge. Nick crossed it, his boots ringing hollow on the iron. Down below the water showed black between the slits of ties. Nick kicked a loose spike and it dropped into the water. Beyond the bridge were hills. It was high and dark on both sides of the track. Up the track Nick saw a fire.

He came up the track toward the fire carefully. It was off to one side of the track, below the railway embankment. He had only seen the light from it. The track came out through a cut and where the fire was burning the country opened out and fell away into woods. Nick dropped carefully down the embankment and cut into the woods to come up to the fire through the trees. It was a beechwood forest and the fallen beechnut burrs were under his shoes as he walked between the trees. The fire was bright now, just at the edge of the trees. There was a man sitting by it. Nick waited behind the tree and watched. The man looked to be alone. He was sitting there with his head in his hands looking at the fire. Nick stepped out and walked into the firelight.

The man sat there looking into the fire. When Nick stopped quite close to him he did not move.

"Hello!" Nick said.

The man looked up.

"Where did you get the shiner?" he said.

"A brakeman busted me."

"Off the through freight?"

"Yes."

"I saw the bastard," the man said. "He went through here 'bout an hour and a half ago. He was walking along the top of the cars slapping his arms and singing."

"The bastard!"

"It must have made him feel good to bust you," the man said seriously.

"I'll bust him."

"Get him with a rock sometime when he's going through," the man advised.

"I'll get him."

"You're a tough one, aren't you?"

"No," Nick answerd.

"All you kids are tough."

"You got to be tough," Nick said.

"That's what I said."

The man looked at Nick and smiled. In the firelight Nick saw that his face was misshapen. His nose was sunken, his eyes were slits, he had queer-shaped lips. Nick did not perceive all this at once, he only saw the man's face was queerly formed and mutilated. It was like putty in color. Dead looking in the firelight.

"Don't you like my pan?" the man asked.

Nick was embarrassed.

"Sure," he said.

"Look here!" the man took off his cap.

He had only one ear. It was thickened and tight against the side of his head. Where the other ear should have been there was a stump.

"Ever see one like that?"

"No," said Nick. It made him a little sick.

"I could take it," the man said. "Don't you think I could take it, kid?"

"You bet!"

"They all bust their hands on me," the little man said. "They couldn't hurt me."

He looked at Nick. "Sit down," he said. "Want to eat?"

"Don't bother," Nick said. "I'm going on to the town."

"Listen!" the man said. "Call me Ad."

"Sure!"

"Listen," the little man said. "I'm not quite right."

"What's the matter?"

"I'm crazy."

He put on his cap. Nick felt like laughing.

"You're all right," he said.

"No, I'm not. I'm crazy. Listen, you ever been crazy?"

"No," Nick said. "How does it get you?"

"I don't know," Ad said. "When you got it you don't know about it. You know me, don't you?"

"No."

"I'm Ad Francis."

"Honest to God?"

"Don't you believe it?"

"Yes."

Nick knew it must be true.

"You know how I beat them?"

"No," Nick said.

"My heart's slow. It only beats forty a minute. Feel it."

Nick hesitated.

"Come on," the man took hold of his hand. "Take hold of my wrist. Put your fingers there."

The little man's wrist was thick and the muscles bulged above the bone. Nick felt the slow pumping under his fingers.

"Got a watch?"

"No."

"Neither have I," Ad said. "It ain't any good if you haven't got a watch."

Nick dropped his wrist.

"Listen," Ad Francis said. "Take ahold again. You count and I'll count up to sixty."

Feeling the slow hard throb under his fingers Nick started to count. He heard the little man counting slowly, one, two, three, four, five, and on—aloud.

"Sixty," Ad finished. "That's a minute. What did you make it?"

"Forty," Nick said.

"That's right," Ad said happily. "She never speeds up."

A man dropped down the railroad embankment and came across the clearing to the fire.

"Hello, Bugs!" Ad said.

"Hello!" Bugs answered. It was a negro's voice. Nick knew from the way he walked that he was a negro. He stood with his back to them, bending over the fire. He straightened up.

"This is my pal Bugs," Ad said. "He's crazy, too."

"Glad to meet you," Bugs said. "Where you say you're from?"

"Chicago," Nick said.

"That's a fine town," the negro said. "I didn't catch your name."

"Adams. Nick Adams."

"He says he's never been crazy, Bugs," Ad said.

"He's got a lot coming to him," the negro said. He was unwrapping a package by the fire.

"When are we going to eat, Bugs?" the prizefighter asked.

"Right away."

"Are you hungry, Nick?"

"Hungry as hell."

"Hear that, Bugs?"

"I hear most of what goes on."

"That ain't what I asked you."

"Yes. I heard what the gentleman said."

Into a skillet he was laying slices of ham. As the skillet grew hot the grease sputtered and Bugs, crouching on long nigger legs over the fire, turned the ham and broke eggs into the skillet, tipping it from side to side to baste the eggs with the hot fat.

"Will you cut some bread out of that bag, Mister Adams?" Bugs turned from the fire.

"Sure."

Nick reached in the bag and brought out a loaf of bread. He cut six slices. Ad watched him and leaned forward.

"Let me take your knife, Nick," he said.

"No, you don't," the negro said. "Hang onto your knife, Mister Adams."

The prizefighter sat back.

"Will you bring me the bread, Mister Adams?" Bugs asked. Nick brought it over.

"Do you like to dip your bread in the ham fat?" the negro asked.

"You bet!"

"Perhaps we'd better wait until later. It's better at the finish of the meal. Here."

The negro picked up a slice of ham and laid it on one of the pieces of bread, then slid an egg on top of it.

"Just close that sandwich, will you, please, and give it to Mister Francis."

Ad took the sandwich and started eating.

"Watch out how that egg runs," the negro warned. "This is for you, Mister Adams. The remainder for myself."

Nick bit into the sandwich. The negro was sitting opposite him beside Ad. The hot fried ham and eggs tasted wonderful.

"Mister Adams is right hungry," the negro said. The little man whom Nick knew by name as a former champion fighter was silent. He had said nothing since the negro had spoken about the knife.

"May I offer you a slice of bread dipped right in the hot ham fat?" Bugs said.

"Thanks a lot."

The little white man looked at Nick.

"Will you have some, Mister Adolph Francis?" Bugs offered from the skillet.

Ad did not answer. He was looking at Nick.

"Mister Francis?" came the nigger's soft voice.

Ad did not answer. He was looking at Nick.

"I spoke to you, Mister Francis," the nigger said softly.

Ad kept on looking at Nick. He had his cap down over his eyes. Nick felt nervous.

"How the hell do you get that way?" came out from under the cap sharply at Nick.

"Who the hell do you think you are? You're a snotty bastard. You come in here where nobody asks you and eat a man's food and when he asks to borrow a knife you get snotty."

He glared at Nick, his face was white and his eyes almost out of sight under the cap.

"You're a hot sketch. Who the hell asked you to butt in here?"

"Nobody."

"You're damn right nobody did. Nobody asked you to stay either. You come in here and act snotty about my face and smoke my cigars and drink my liquor and then talk snotty. Where the hell do you think you get off?"

Nick said nothing. Ad stood up.

"I'll tell you, you yellow-livered Chicago bastard. You're going to get your can knocked off. Do you get that?"

Nick stepped back. The little man came toward him slowly, stepping flat-footed forward, his left foot stepping forward, his right dragging up to it.

"Hit me," he moved his head. "Try and hit me."

"I don't want to hit you."

"You won't get out of it that way. You're going to take a beating, see? Come on and lead at me."

"Cut it out," Nick said.

"All right, then, you bastard."

The little man looked down at Nick's feet. As he looked down the negro, who had followed behind him as he moved away from the fire, set himself and tapped him across the base of the skull. He fell forward and Bugs dropped the cloth-wrapped blackjack on the grass. The little man lay there, his face in the grass. The negro picked him up, his head hanging, and carried him to the fire. His face looked bad, the eyes open. Bugs laid him down gently.

"Will you bring me the water in the bucket, Mister Adams," he said. "I'm afraid I hit him just a little hard."

The negro splashed water with his hand on the man's face and pulled his ears gently. The eyes closed.

Bugs stood up.

"He's all right," he said. "There's nothing to worry about. I'm sorry, Mister Adams."

"It's all right." Nick was looking down at the little man. He saw the blackjack on the grass and picked it up. It had a flexible handle and was limber in his hand. It was made of worn black leather with a handkerchief wrapped around the heavy end.

"That's a whalebone handle," the negro smiled. "They don't make them any more. I didn't know how well you could take care of yourself and, anyway, I didn't want you to hurt him or mark him up no more than he is."

The negro smiled again.

"You hurt him yourself."

"I know how to do it. He won't remember nothing of it. I have to do it to change him when he gets that way."

Nick was still looking down at the little man, lying, his eyes closed in the firelight. Bugs put some wood on the fire.

"Don't you worry about him none, Mister Adams. I seen him like this plenty of times before."

"What made him crazy?" Nick asked.

"Oh, a lot of things," the negro answered from the fire. "Would you like a cup of this coffee, Mister Adams?"

He handed Nick the cup and smoothed the coat he had placed under the unconscious man's head.

"He took too many beatings, for one thing," the negro sipped the coffee. "But that just made him sort of simple. Then his sister was his manager and they was always being written up in the papers all about brothers and sisters and how she loved her brother and how he loved his sister, and then they got married in New York and that made a lot of unpleasantness."

"I remember about it."

"Sure. Of course they wasn't brother and sister no more than a rabbit, but there was a lot of people didn't like it either way and they commenced to have disagreements, and one day she just went off and never come back."

He drank the coffee and wiped his lips with the pink palm of his hand.

"He just went crazy. Will you have some more coffee, Mister Adams?"

"Thanks."

"I seen her a couple of times," the negro went on. "She was an awful good-looking woman. Looked enough like him to be twins. He wouldn't be bad-looking without his face all busted."

He stopped. The story seemed to be over.

"Where did you meet him?" asked Nick.

"I met him in jail," the negro said. "He was busting people all the time after she went away and they put him in jail. I was in for cuttin' a man."

He smiled, and went on soft-voiced:

"Right away I liked him and when I got out I looked him up. He likes to think I'm crazy and I don't mind. I like to be with him and I like seeing the country and I don't have to commit no larceny to do it. I like living like a gentleman."

"What do you all do?" Nick asked.

"Oh, nothing. Just move around. He's got money."

"He must have made a lot of money."

"Sure. He spent all his money, though. Or they took it away from him. She sends him money."

He poked up the fire.

"She's a mighty fine woman," he said. "She looks enough like him to be his own twin."

The negro looked over at the little man, lying breathing heavily. His blond hair was down over his forehead. His mutilated face looked childish in repose.

"I can wake him up any time now, Mister Adams. If you don't mind I wish you'd sort of pull out. I don't like to not be hospitable, but it might disturb him back again to see you. I hate to have to thump him and it's the only thing to do when he gets started. I have to sort of keep him away from people. You don't mind, do you, Mister Adams? No, don't thank me, Mister Adams. I'd have warned you about him but he seemed to have taken such a liking to you and I thought things were going to be all right. You'll hit a town about two miles up the track. Mancelona they call it. Good-bye. I wish we could ask you to stay the night but it's just out of the question. Would you like to take some of that ham and some bread with you? No? You better take a sandwich," all this in a low, smooth, polite nigger voice.

"Good. Well, good-bye, Mister Adams. Good-bye and good-luck!"

Nick walked away from the fire across the clearing to the railway tracks. Out of the range of the fire he listened. The low soft voice of the negro was talking. Nick could not hear the words. Then he heard the little man say, "I got an awful headache, Bugs."

"You'll feel better, Mister Francis," the negro's voice soothed. "Just you drink a cup of this hot coffee."

Nick climbed the embankment and started up the track. He found he had a ham sandwich in his hand and put it in his pocket. Looking back from the mounting grade before the track curved into the hills he could see the firelight in the clearing.

EDITORS' ANALYSIS

"The Battler," as far as its simply related events are concerned, may seem a slight story. Actually, its sketchy details are, as Hemingway himself has suggested of all good writing, the visible tip of the iceberg. We sense, underneath, a vast weight of implication. The man who has lost one ear in the ring, whose wife has left him, and who has truly gone crazy, clings to a kind of existence, doggedly, admirably. Nick Adams, who has been tossed off a freight train as a bum, has as yet no need for holding on. He is full of young and healthy anger at the brakeman, and full of young, expendable energy as he moves out into the night, down the track, seeking only the shelter of the nearest town. In the meeting of these two men we sense both exaltation at the rough beginnings of undefined adventure and ambition, and a stoic resignation at the meaninglessness of most fulfilled ambitions.

QUESTIONS

1. Do you find it difficult to get into the story because of Hemingway's great economy in his use of detail, his unwillingness to "talk" much about his characters?

2. Does the story explain why Ad Francis suddenly turns on Nick Adams? Has it something to do with his youth? Other things?

3. Why does the Negro take such pride in serving Ad Francis as caretaker? Is his comment on Ad's wife "She's a mighty fine woman" meant to be ironic? A simple moral evaluation?

4. Is Ad Francis's pleasure in his slow heart beat an element in his craziness? Something to which he clings, out of his past? Discuss.

5. What mood in Nick, and in you as reader, is suggested by the details in the last paragraph? Resignation? Indifference? Something less tangible?

The Walls of Ávila

by EVAN S. CONNELL, JR.

Evan S. Connell, Jr., is the author of a number of highly praised stories, many collected in the volume *The Anatomy Lesson* (1957), and of two novels, *Mrs. Bridge* (1959) and *The Patriot* (1960). He studied at a number of universities, served in the Navy, and now practices the trade of writing in San Francisco.

> *Thou shalt make castels in Spayne,*
> *And dreme of joye, al but in vayne.*
> —ROMAUNT OF THE ROSE

Ávila lies only a few kilometers west and a little north of Madrid, and is surrounded by a grim stone wall that was old when Isabella was born. Life in this town has not changed very much from the days when the earth was flat; somehow it is as though news of the passing centuries has never arrived in Ávila. Up the cobbled street saunters a donkey with a wicker basket slung on each flank, and on the donkey's bony rump sits a boy nodding drowsily in the early morning sun. The boy's dark face looks medieval. He is delivering bread. At night the stars are metallic, with a bluish tint, and the Spaniards stroll gravely back and forth beside the high stone wall. There are not so many gypsies, or *gitanos*, in this town as there are in, say, Valencia or Seville. Ávila is northerly and was not impressed by these passionate Asiatic people, at least not the way Córdoba was, or Granada.

These were things we learned about Avila when J. D. returned. He came home after living abroad for almost ten years. He was thinner and taller than any of us remembered, and his crew-cut hair had turned completely gray although he was just thirty-eight. It made him look very distinguished, even a little dramatic. His skin was now as brown as coffee, and there were wind wrinkles about his restless cerulean blue eyes, as though the light of strange beaches and exotic plazas had stamped him like a visa to prove he had been there. He smiled a good deal, perhaps because he did not feel at ease with his old friends any more. Ten years did not seem long to us, not really long, and we were disconcerted by the great change in him. Only his voice was familiar. At the bus station where three of us had gone to meet him only Dave Zobrowski recognized him.

Apparently this town of Ávila meant a great deal to J. D., although he could not get across to us its significance. He said that one night he was surprised to hear music and laughter coming from outside the walls, so he hurried through the nearest gate, which was set between two gigantic watch towers, and followed the wall around until he came to a carnival. There were concessions where you could fire corks at cardboard boxes, each containing a chocolate bar, or dip for celluloid fishes with numbered bellies, and naturally there was a carousel, the same as in America. It rotated quite slowly, he said, with mirrors flashing from its peak while enameled stallions gracefully rose and descended on their gilded poles. But nothing was so well attended as a curious swing in which two people stood, facing each other, grasping a handle, and propelled themselves so high that at the summit they were nearly upside down. The shadow of this swing raced up the wall and down again. "Like this!" J. D. exclaimed, gesturing, and he stared at each of us in turn to see if we understood. He said it was like the shadow of some grotesque instrument from the days of the Inquisition, and he insisted that if you gazed up into the darkness long enough you could make out, among the serrated ramparts of the ancient wall, the forms of helmeted men leaning on pikes and gazing somberly down while their black beards moved in the night wind.

He had tales of the Casbah in Tangiers and he had souvenirs from the ruins of Carthage. On his key chain was a fragment of polished stone, drilled through the center, that he had picked up from the hillside just beyond Tunis. And he spoke familiarly of the beauty of Istanbul, and of Giotto's tower, and the Seine, and the golden doors of Ghiberti. He explained how the Portuguese are fuller through the cheeks than are the Spaniards, their eyes more indolent and mischievous, and how their songs—*fados*, he called them—were no more than lazy cousins of the fierce flamenco one heard throughout Andalusia.

When Zobrowski asked in what year the walls of Ávila were built J. D. thought for quite a while, his lean face sober while he gently rocked a tumbler of iced rum, but at last he said the fortifications were probably begun seven or eight hundred years ago. They had been repaired occasionally and were still impregnable to primitive force. It was queer, he added, to come upon such a place, indestructible when assaulted on its own terms, yet obsolete.

He had postal cards of things that had interested him. He had not carried a camera because he thought it bad manners. We did not completely understand what he meant by this but we had no time to discuss it because he was running on, wanting to know if we were familiar with Giambologna, saying, as he displayed a card, "In a grotto of the Boboli Gardens not far from the Uffizi—" He stopped abruptly. It had occurred to him that he might be embarrassed. No one said anything. None of us had ever heard of the Boboli Gardens, or of the sculptor Giambologna, or of the Venus that J. D. had wanted to describe.

"Here's the Sistine Chapel, of course," he said, taking another card from his envelope. "That's the Libyan sybil."

"Yes," said Zobrowski. "I remember this. There was a print of it in one of our high-school textbooks. Good God, how time does pass."

"Those damn textbooks," J. D. answered. "They ruin everything. They've ruined Shakespeare and the Acropolis and half the things on earth that are really worth seeing. Just like the Lord's Prayer—I can't hear it. I don't know what it says. Why wasn't I left to discover it for myself? Or the Venus de Milo. I sat in front of it for an hour but I couldn't see it."

He brought out a postal card of a church tower. At the apex was a snail-like structure covered with what appeared to be huge tile baseballs.

"That's the *Sagrada Familia*," he explained. "It's not far from the bull ring in Barcelona."

The *Sagrada Familia* was unfinished; in fact it consisted of nothing but a façade with four tremendous towers rising far above the apartment buildings surrounding it. He said it was a landmark of Barcelona, that if you should get lost in the city you had only to get to a clearing and look around for this weird church. On the front of it was a cement Christmas tree, painted green and hung with cement ornaments, while the tiled spires were purple and yellow. And down each spire ran vertical lettering that could be read a kilometer away. Zobrowski asked what was written on the towers.

"There's one word on each tower," said J. D. "The only one I recall is 'Ecstasy.'"

Dave Zobrowski listened with a patient, critical air, as though wondering how a man could spend ten years in such idle traveling. Russ Lyman, who had once been J. D.'s closest friend, listened in silence with his head bowed. When we were children together it had been Russ who intended to go around the world some day, but he had not, for a number of reasons. He seemed to hold a monopoly on bad luck. The girl he loved married somebody else, then his business failed, and so on and on through the years. Now he worked as a drugstore clerk and invested his pitiful savings in gold mines or wildcat oil wells. He had been thirty-two when the girl he loved told him good-by, tapping the ash from her cigarette onto his wrist to emphasize that she meant it; he promptly got drunk, because he could not imagine anything else to do, and a few days later he began going around with a stout, amiable girl named Eunice who had grown up on a nearby farm. One October day when the two of them were walking through an abandoned orchard they paused to rest in the shade of an old stone wall in which some ivy and small flowers were growing. Eunice was full of the delicate awkwardness of certain large girls, and while Russell was looking at her a leaf came fluttering down to rest on her shoulder. He became aware of the sound of honeybees flickering through the noonday sun, and of the uncommonly sweet odor of apples moldering among the clover, and he was seized with such passion that he immediately took the willing girl. She became pregnant, so they got married, although he did not want to, and before much longer he stopped talking about going around the world.

J. D., handing Russell a card of a little street in some North African town, remarked that on this particular street he had bought a tasseled red fez. And Russell nodded a bit sadly.

"Now, this is Lisbon," J. D. said. "Right over here on the far side of this rectangular plaza is where I lived. I used to walk down to the river that you see at the edge of the card, and on the way back I'd wander through some little shops where you can buy miniature galleons of filigreed gold."

"I suppose you bought one," said Zobrowski.

"I couldn't resist," said J. D. with a smile. "Here's a view of Barcelona at night, and right here by this statue of Columbus I liked to sit and watch the tide come sweeping in. An exact copy of the *Santa Maria* is tied up at the dock near the statue. And whenever the wind blew down from the hills I could hear the butter-pat clap of the gypsies dancing on the Ramblas." He looked at us anxiously to see if we were interested. It was clear that he loved Spain. He wanted us to love it, too.

"One time in Galicia," he said, "at some little town where the train stopped I bought a drink of water from a wrinkled old woman who was holding up an earthen jug and calling, '*Agua! Agua fria!*" He drew a picture of the jug—it was called a *porrón* —and he demonstrated how it was to be held above your head while you drank. Your lips were never supposed to touch the spout. The Spaniards could drink without swallowing, simply letting the stream of water pour down their throats, and after much dribbling and choking J. D. had learned the trick. But what he most wanted to describe was the old woman who sold him the water. She could have been sixty or ninety. She was toothless, barefoot, and with a rank odor, but somehow, in some way he could not get across to us, they had meant a great deal to each other. He tried to depict a quality of arrogance or ferocity about her, which in the days when she was young, must have caused old men to murmur and young men to fall silent whenever she passed by. He could not forget an instant when he reached out the train window to give her back the clay jug and met her deep, unwavering eyes.

"The train was leaving," he said, leaning forward. "It was leaving forever. And I heard her scream at me. I didn't know what she said, but there was a Spaniard in the same compartment who told me that this old Galician woman had screamed at me, 'Get off the train! Stay in my land!'" He paused, apparently remembering, and slowly shook his head.

It was in Spain, too, in a cheap water-front night club called *El Hidalgo*—and he answered Russell's question by saying that Don Quixote, for example, was an *hidalgo*—it was here that he fell in love for the only time in his life. The cabaret was in an alley of the Gothic quarter where tourists seldom ventured. J. D. often spent his evenings there, buying lottery tickets and brown paper cigarettes and drinking a yellowish wine called *manzanilla*. One night the flamenco dancers were in a furious mood—he said he could feel the tension gathering the way electricity will sometimes gather on a midwestern afternoon until it splits the air. An enormously fat gypsy woman was dancing by herself, dancing the symbols of fertility that have survived a thousand generations. She was dressed in what he likened to a bedspread covered with orange polka dots. Raising and lowering her vast arms she snapped her fingers and angrily danced alone; then all at once a savage little man in high-heeled boots sprang out of the crowd and began leaping around her. The staccato of his boots made the floor tremble and caused the manzanilla to sway inside the bottles.

"Everybody was howling and clapping," said J. D., and he clapped once as the gypsies clap, not with the entire hand but with three fingers flat against the palm. It sounded like a pistol shot. "Somebody was looking at me," he went on. "I could feel someone's eyes on me. I looked into the shadows and saw her. She was about nineteen, very tall and imperial, with her hair in braids. She began walking toward me, and she was singing. She sang to me that her name was Paquita—"

"She was improvising a song," said Zobrowski.

J. D. nodded. "It had the sound of a lament. Those old tragedies you hear in Spain, they're paralyzing."

"Just what do you mean?" Zobrowski asked.

"I don't know," said J. D. "It's as if a dagger was still plunged to the hilt in her breast."

Zobrowski smiled. "Go on. No doubt this young woman was beautiful."

"Yes. And she never stopped looking at me. I don't remember what happened, but she must have walked across the room because I realized I was standing up and she was standing directly in front of me, touching my lips with one finger."

"I have had similar dreams," said Zobrowski.

Russell was listening avidly. "I didn't think Spanish women could ever get away from their chaperons."

"*Dueña*, I believe, is the word," Zobrowski said.

"There was no *dueña* for that girl," answered J. D. He was silent for a little while and then concluded his story. "Later that night I saw her walking the streets."

"Well, that explains everything," Zobrowski smiled. "You simply mistook her professional interest in you for some sort of transcendental love."

J. D. looked at Dave Zobrowski for a long time, and finally said, "I didn't think I could make you understand." To Russell he said, "I find myself repeating her name. In the night I see her everywhere. In Paris, or in Rome, or even in this town, I see a girl turning away and my heart hesitates as it did that night in Barcelona."

"You should have married her," said Russell.

"I think he has done enough foolish things as it is," Zobrowski replied, and that seemed to end the matter. At least J.D. never referred to Paquita again. He spoke of the Andalusian gypsies, saying that they are a mixture of Arab and Indian, while the Catalonians are almost pure Sudra Indian. He gave this information as though it were important; he seemed to value knowledge for itself alone. But, looking into our faces, he saw that we could not greatly care about Spanish gypsies one way or another.

He had a pale gray cardboard folder with a drawing of St. George on the cover. Inside was a map of the geographical limits of the Catalan language, and this inscription: "With the best wishes for all the friends of the Catalan speaking countries once free in the past they will be free and whole again thanks to the will and strength of the Catalan people."

This was a folder of the resistance movement; it had been given to him, at the risk of imprisonment and perhaps at the risk of life itself, by a charwoman of Valencia. Zobrowski inquired if these were the people who opposed Franco. J. D. said that was correct. In Algiers he had met a waiter who had fought against Franco and barely escaped the country; this waiter had been in Algiers since 1938 and had no hope of seeing his family again, though he believed, as the charwoman believed, that one day Spain would be free.

After inspecting the pathetic little folder Zobrowski suggested, "I can easily appreciate your concern for these people. However you might also spend some time considering your own situation. Frankly, time is getting on, while you elect to dawdle about the water fronts of the world."

J. D. shrugged.

"I've been meaning to ask," said Zobrowski. "Did you ever receive the letter I addressed to you in Vienna?"

"I don't remember it," said J. D.

"It concerned an executive position with the Pratt Hanover Company. They manufacture farm implements. I spoke to Donald Pratt about you and he was very much interested."

"No, I never got the letter," said J. D. and he grinned. "I was traveling quite a bit and I guess a lot of letters never caught up with me."

"Would you have come back if you had received the offer from Pratt?"

"No, I guess not," said J. D., rather apologetically.

"We've known each other a long time, haven't we?"

J. D. nodded. "Since we were kids, Dave."

"Exactly. I would like to know how you manage to live."

"Oh, I work here and there. I had a job at the American embassy in Switzerland for a while, and to be honest about it, I've done some black marketing. I've learned how to get along, how to pull the levers that operate the world."

Then he began to describe Lucerne. It seemed far distant, in every dimension, from the days when we were children and used to bicycle down the river road to the hickory woods and hunt for squirrels. Each of us had a .22 rifle, except J. D., who went hunting with a lemonwood bow. He had made it himself, and he had braided and waxed the string, and sewn a quiver, and planed his arrows. He did not hit many squirrels with his equipment and we would often taunt him about losing the arrows among the high weeds and underbrush, but he never seemed to mind; he would go home to his father's tool chest in the basement and calmly set about planing another batch of sticks. We would watch him clip turkey feathers into crisp rhomboids and carefully glue them into place, bracing each feather with matchsticks until the glue hardened. We would sit on the wash tub, or on his father's work bench, and smoke pieces of grapevine while we studied the new arrows. When he fitted on the bronze tip and banded each arrow with hunter's green and white Russell would watch with an almost hypnotized expression. But Dave Zobrowski, even in those days, was puzzled and a trifle impatient with J. D.

Remembering such things as J. D.'s bow and arrow we could see that it was he, and not Russell, who was destined to go away. We thought he had left a good deal of value here in the midwest of America. Our town is not exotic, but it is comprehensible and it is clean. This is partly due to Dave Zobrowski, who has always been vehement about cleanliness. That he grew up to become a physician and a member of the sanitary commission surprised no one. He likes to tell of disgusting conditions he has seen in other cities. While he was in Chicago at a medical convention he investigated a hotel charging the same price as the Pioneer House here in town, and he reported, all too graphically, how the ceiling was stained from leakage, how there was pencil writing on the walls, together with the husks of smashed roaches, and how he found a red hair embedded in the soap. Even the towel was rancid. Looking out the smoky window he saw wine bottles and decaying fruit in the gutter.

Visitors to this town often wonder how it is possible to exist without ballet, opera, and so forth, but it usually turns out that they themselves attend only once or twice each season, if at all. Then, too, if you are not accustomed to a certain entertainment you do not miss it. Russell, for example, grew up in a home devoid of music but cheerful and harmonious all the same. To his parents music was pointless, unless at Christmas time, when the phonograph would be wound up, the needle replaced, and the carols dusted off; consequently Mozart means nothing to him.

A Brooklyn police captain named Lehmbruck drove out here to spend his vacation but went back east after a week, saying it was too quiet to sleep. However he seemed to be interested in the sunset, remarking that he had never seen the sun go down anywhere except behind some buildings. And he had never eaten old ham—he studied the white specks very dubiously, and with some embarrassment asked if the ham was spoiled. The Chamber of Commerce later received a wistful little note from Captain Lehmbruck, hinting that he might have another try at the prairie next summer.

Christmas here is still made instead of bought, even if we think no more of Christ than anyone else. And during the summer months the sidewalks are overhung with white or lavender spirea, and we can watch the rain approaching, darkening the farmland. Life here is reasonable and tradition not discounted, as evidenced by the new public library which is a modified Parthenon of Tennessee marble. There was a long and bitter argument about the inscription for its façade. One group wanted the so-called living letter, while the majority sought reassurance in the Doric past. At last we chiseled it with "Pvblic," "Covnty," "Strvctvre," and so forth.

J. D. knew about all these things, but he must have wanted more, and as he talked to us about his travels we could read in his restless blue eyes that he was not through searching. We thought he would come home when his father died, at least for a little while. Of course he was six thousand miles away, but most men would have returned from any distance. We did not know what he thought of us, the friends who had been closest to him, and this was altogether strange because our opinions about him were no secret—the fact that Russell envied him and that Zobrowski thought his life was going to rot.

Russell, to be sure, envied everybody. For a time after the marriage we believed Russell would collect himself, whatever it was needed collecting, because he went around looking very pleased with himself, although Eunice seemed a bit confused. He began to go shooting in the hickory woods again, firing his old .22 more to exult in its noise than to kill a squirrel. Yet something within him had been destroyed. Whether it could have been an insufferable jealousy of J. D.—who was then in Finland—or love that was lost, or the hard core of another sickness unknown to anyone on earth, no one could say, but it was to be only a few years after J. D.'s visit that we would find Russell lying in the garage with his head almost torn off and a black .45 service automatic in his hand.

"Here is where Dante first met Beatrice," said J. D. adding with a smile that several locations in Florence claimed this distinction, even as half the apartments in Toledo insist El Greco painted there. And he had a picture of Cala Ratjada where he had lived with a Danish girl named Vivian. We had forgotten, if indeed we had ever realized it, that in other countries people are not required to be so furtive about their affairs. We learned that Cala Ratjada was a fishing village on the eastern end of Majorca. Majorca we had heard of because the vacation magazines were publicizing it.

"I understand there's a splendid cathedral in the capital," Zobrowski said. "Palma, isn't it?"

J. D. agreed rather vaguely. It was plain he did not care much for cathedrals, unless there was something queer about them as there was about the *Sagrada Familia*. He preferred to tell about the windmills on Majorca, and about his bus ride across the island with a crate of chickens on the seat beside him. We had not known there was a bus across the island; the travel magazines always advised tourists to hire a car with an English-speaking driver. So we listened, because there is a subtle yet basic difference between one who travels and one who does not.

He had lived with this Danish girl all of one summer in a boarding house—a *pension* he called it—and every afternoon they walked through some scrubby little trees to a white sandy beach and went swimming nude. They took along a leather bag full of heavy amber wine and drank this and did some fancy diving off the rocks. He said the Mediterranean there at Cala Ratjada was more translucent even than the harbor of Monte Carlo. When their wine was finished and the sand had become cool and the shadows of the trees were touching the water they walked back to the village. For a while they stopped on the embarcadero to watch the Balearic fishermen spreading their nets to dry. Then J. D. and the Danish girl returned to the *pension* for dinner. They ate such things as fried octopus, or baby squid, or a huge seafood casserole called a *paella*.

"Where is she now?" Russell asked.

"Vivian?" said J. D. "Oh, I don't know. She sent me a card from Frederikshavn a year or so ago. She'd been wanting to go to India, so maybe that's where she is now."

"Didn't she expect you to marry her?"

J. D. looked at Russell and then laughed out loud; it was the first time he had laughed all evening.

"Neither of us wanted to get married," he said. "We had a good summer. Why should we ruin it?"

This was a kind of reasoning we were aware of, via novels more impressive for poundage than content; otherwise it bore no relation to us. What bound them together was as elementary as a hyphen, and we suspected they could meet each other years later without embarrassment. They had loved without aim or sense, as young poets do. We could imagine this, to be sure, but we could not imagine it actually happening. There were women in our town, matrons now, with whom we had been intimate to some degree a decade or so ago, but now when we met them, or were entertained in their homes, we were restrained by the memory of the delicate past. Each of us must carry, as it were, a balloon inked with names and dates.

So far as we knew, J. D. looked up only one of the women he used to know here in town. He called on Helen Louise Sawyer who used to win the local beauty contests. When we were young most of us were afraid of her, because there is something annihilating about too much beauty; only J. D. was not intimidated. Perhaps he could see then what we learned to see years later— that she was lonely, and that she did not want to be coveted for the perfection of her skin or for the truly magnificent explosion of her bosom. When Helen Louise and J. D. began going around together we were astonished and insulted because Russell, in those days, was much more handsome than J. D., and Dave Zobrowski was twice as smart. All the same she looked at no one else. Then he began leaving town on longer and longer expeditions. He would return wearing a southern California sport shirt, or with a stuffed grouper he had caught off Key West. Helen Louise eventually went into the real-estate business.

He telephoned her at the office and they went to dinner at the Wigwam, which is now the swank place to eat. It is decorated with buffalo skins and tomahawks and there are displays of flint arrowheads that have been picked up by farmers in neighboring counties. The only incongruities are the pink jade ashtrays that, by midnight, seem to have been planted with white, magenta-tipped stalks to remind the diners that a frontier has vanished. And well it has. The scouts are buried, the warriors mummified. Nothing but trophies remain: a coup stick hung by the Wigwam's flagstone hearth, a pipe smoked by Satanta, a cavalry saber and a set of moldering blue gloves crossed on the mantel, a tan robe laced to the western wall, a dry Pawnee scalp behind the bar. The wind still sweeps east from the lofty Colorado plains, but carries with it now only the clank of machinery in the wheat fields. The Mandans have gone, like the minor chords of an Iowa death song, with Dull Knife and Little Wolf whose three hundred wretched squaws and starving men set out to fight their way a thousands miles to the fecund Powder River that had been their home.

There is a gratification to the feel of history behind the places one has known, and the Wigwam's historical display is extensive. In addition, the food is good. There is hot biscuit with clover honey, and the old ham so mistrusted by Captain Lehmbruck of Brooklyn. There are Missouri fried chicken, spare ribs, venison with mushrooms, catfish, beef you can cut with a fork, wild rice and duck buried under pineapple sauce, as well as various European dishes. That evening J. D. asked for a certain Madeira wine and apparently was a little taken aback to find that the Wigwam had it. Travelers, real travelers, come to think of their homes as provincial and are often surprised.

Helen Louise had metamorphosed, as even we could see, and we knew J. D. was in for a shock. Through the years she had acquired that faintly resentful expression that comes from being stared at, and she seemed to be trying to compensate for her beauty. Although there was nothing wrong with her eyes she wore glasses; she had cropped her beautiful golden hair to a Lesbian style; and somehow she did not even walk the way she used to. The pleasing undulations had mysteriously given way to a militant stride. Her concern in life was over such items as acreage and location. At the business she was quite good; every real-estate man in town hated her, no doubt thinking she should have become a housewife instead of the demon that she was. But apparently she had lost her desire to marry, or sublimated it. At the lunch hour she could be seen in an expensive suit, speaking in low tones to another businesswoman, and her conversation when overheard would be, ". . . referred the order to me . . . Mrs. Pabst's opinion . . . second mortgage . . . bought six apartments . . ."

We guessed that J. D.'s evening with Helen Louise might be an indication that he had grown tired of wandering around the earth, and that he wanted to come home for good. Helen Louise, if no longer as voluptuous as she had been at twenty or twenty-five, was still provocative, and if she married was it not possible she might come to look very much as she had looked ten years before? But J. D. had very little to say about his evening with her; and after he was gone Helen Louise never mentioned him.

"Did you know that in Cadiz," he said—because it was to him a fact worth noting, like that fact that in Lisbon he had lived on a certain plaza—"Did you know that in Cadiz you can buy a woman for three *pesetas*?" Whether or not he might have been referring to Helen Louise we did not know, nor did anyone ask.

"Once I talked with Manolete," he said, as though it were the first line of a poem.

"I've heard that name," Zobrowski answered. "He's a toreador, is he not?"

"I think 'toreador' was invented by Bizet," J. D. replied. "Manolete was a matador. But he's dead. It was in Linares that he was *cogido*. On the twenty-seventh of August in nineteen-forty-seven. At five in the afternoon, as the saying goes." And he continued, telling us that the real name of this bullfighter had been Manuel Rodriguez, and that after he was gored in Linares the ambulance which was taking him to a hospital started off in the wrong direction, and there was a feeling of bitterness in Spain when the news was broadcast that he was dead of his wounds.

"What you are trying to express," Zobrowski suggested, "is that this fellow was a national hero."

"Yes," said J. D.

"Like Babe Ruth."

"No," said J. D. instantly and with a vexed expression. He gestured helplessly and then shrugged. He went on to say that he happened to be in Heidelberg when death came for Manolete in the town of Linares. He looked around at us as if this circumstance were very strange. As he spoke he gestured excitedly and often skipped from one topic to another because there was so little time and he had so much to tell us. In a way he created a landscape of chiaroscuro, illuminating first one of his adventures and now another, but leaving his canvas mostly in shadow.

"One morning in Basle," he said, "it began to snow while I was having breakfast. Snow was falling on the Rhine." He was sitting by a window in a tea shop overlooking the river. He described the sunless, blue-gray atmosphere with large white flakes of snow piling up on the window ledge, and the dark swath of the river. Several waitresses in immaculate uniforms served his breakfast from a heavy silver tray. There was coffee in a silver pitcher, warm breads wrapped in thick linen napkins, and several kinds of jam and preserves; all the while the snow kept mounting on the ledge just outside the window, and the waitresses murmured in German. He returned to Basle on the same morning of the following year—all the way from Palermo—just to have his breakfast there.

Most of his ten years abroad had been spent on the borders of the Mediterranean, and he agreed with Zobrowski's comment that the countries in that area must be the dirtiest in Europe. He told about a servant girl in one of his *pensions* who always seemed to be on her knees scrubbing the floor, but who never bathed herself. She had such a pervasive odor that he could tell whenever she had recently been in a room.

He said that Pompeii was his biggest disappointment. He had expected to find the city practically buried under a cliff of lava. But there was no lava. Pompeii was like any city abandoned and overgrown with weeds. He had visited the Roman ruins of North Africa, but the names he mentioned did not mean anything to us. Carthage did, but if we had ever read about the others in school we had long since stored their names and dates back in the dusty bins alongside algebra and Beowulf. Capri was the only celebrated spot he visited that surpassed all pictures of it, and he liked Sorrento too, saying that he had returned to the mainland about sundown when the cliffs of Sorrento become red and porous like the cliffs of the Grand Canyon. And in a town called Amalfi he had been poisoned—he thought it was the eggs.

All this was delivered by a person we had known since childhood, yet it might as well have come from a foreign lecturer. J. D. was not trying to flaunt his adventures; he described them because we were his friends and he could not conceive of the fact that the ruins of Pompeii would mean less to us than gossip on the women's page. He wanted to tell us about the ballet in Cannes, where the audience was so quiet that he had heard the squeak of the dancer's slippers. But none of us had ever been to a ballet, or especially wanted to go. There was to us something faintly absurd about men and women in tights. When Zobrowski suggested as much, J. D. looked at him curiously and seemed to be struggling to remember what it was like to live in our town.

A number of things he said did not agree with our concept. According to him the Swedish girls are not in the least as they appear on calendars, which invariably depict them driving some cows down a pea-green mountainside. J. D. said the Swedes were long and gaunt with cadaverous features and gloomy dispositions, and their suicide rate was among the highest on earth.

Snails, he said, though no one had inquired, have very little taste. You eat them with a tiny two-pronged fork and some tongs that resemble a surgeon's forceps. The garlic-butter sauce is excellent, good enough to drink, but snail meat tasted to him rubbery like squid.

About the taxi drivers of Paris: they were incredibly avaricious. If you were not careful they would give you a gilded two-franc piece instead of a genuine fifty-franc piece for change, and if you caught them at it they became furious. But he did say that the French were the most urbane people to be found.

He had traveled as far east as Teheran and as far north as Trondheim. He had been to Lithuania and to Poland, and to Egypt and to the edge of the Sahara, and from his gestures as well as the animation of his voice we could tell he was no through yet. While he was telling us about his plans as we sat comfortably in the cocktail lounge of the Pioneer House, a bellboy came in and respectfully said to Dave, "Dr. Zobrowski, the hospital is calling."

Without a word Zobrowski stood up and followed the boy. A few minutes later he returned wearing his overcoat and carrying his gray Homburg. "I'm sorry, but it's an emergency," he said to us all, and then to J. D., "Since you are not to be in town much longer I suppose this is goodby."

J. D. uncrossed his long legs and casually stood up.

"No doubt you lead an entertaining life," Zobrowski observed, not bothering to conceal his disapproval. "But a man cannot wander the face of the earth forever."

"That's what everybody tells me," J. D. answered with a grin. "It doesn't bother me much any more."

Zobrowski pulled on his yellow pigskin gloves and with a severe expression he began to settle the fingers as carefully as though he had put on surgical gloves. "In my opinion," he said suddenly, and lifted his eyes, "you are a damn fool."

They stared at each other for perhaps a minute, not with hostility, nor exactly with surprise, but as though they had never quite seen each other until that instant. Yet these were the two men who, about thirty years previously, had chipped in equal shares to buy a dog, a squat little beast with peculiar teeth that made it look like a beaver.

"From birth we carry the final straw," said Zobrowski at last. J. D. only smiled.

Zobrowski's normally hard features contracted until he looked cruel, and he inclined his head, saying by this gesture, "As you wish." He had always known how to use silence with devastating force, yet J. D. was undismayed and did nothing but shrug like a Frenchman.

Zobrowski turned to Russell. "I had lunch with my broker the other day. He has some information on that Hudson's Bay mining stock of yours that makes me feel we should have a talk. Stop by my office tomorrow morning at eight-thirty. I have had my receptionist cancel an appointment because of this matter."

Russell's mouth slowly began to drop open as he gazed at Zobrowski. He never made reasonable investments and several times had been saved from worse ones only because he confided his financial plans, along with everything else, to anybody who would listen. Then, too, the making of money necessitates a callousness he had never possessed.

"That stock's all right," he said weakly. "I'm positive it's all right. Really it is, Dave. You should have bought some."

"Yes," Zobrowski said, looking down on him with disgust. And turning to J. D. he said, "Let us hear from you. Good-by." Then he went striding across the lounge.

"Oh, God!" mumbled Russell, taking another drink. He was ready to weep from humiliation and from anxiety over the investment. In the past few years he had become quite bald and flabby, and had taken to wearing suspenders because a belt disturbed his intestines. He rubbed his jowls and looked around with a vague, desperate air.

"Whatever happened to little Willie Grant?" J. D. asked, though Grant had never meant a thing to him.

"He's—he's in Denver," Russell said, gasping for breath.

"What about Martha Mathews?"

This was the girl who rejected Russell, but J. D. was abroad when it happened and may never have heard. He looked astonished when Russell groaned. Economically speaking, she was a great deal better off than if she had married Russell. She had accepted a housing contractor with more ambition than conscience, and now spent most of her time playing cards on the terrace of the country club.

J. D. had been in love, moderately, in the abstract, with a long-legged sloe-eyed girl named Minnette whose voice should have been poured into a glass and drunk. Her mother owned a bakery. We usually saw Minnette's mother when we came trotting home from school at the noon hour; she would be standing at the door with arms rolled in her apron while she talked to the delivery man, or, in winter time, we would often see her as she bent over, pendulous, tranquil, somehow everlasting, to place chocolate éclairs in the bakery window while sleet bounced indignantly off the steaming glass. At such moments she looked the way we always wanted our own harried mothers to look. If the truth were known it might be that we found her more stimulating than her daughter, although this may have been because we were famished when we passed the bakery. In any event he inquired about Minnette, so we told him her eyes still had that look, and that she was married to the mortician, an extremely tall man named Knopf who liked to underline trenchant phrases in the little books on Success that you buy for a quarter.

Answering these somehow anachronistic questions stirred us the way an old snapshot will do when you come upon it while hunting for something else. Later on Russell was to say that when J. D. mentioned the yellow brick building where the four of us began our schooling he remembered for the first time in possibly a decade how we used to sit around a midget table and wield those short, blunt, red-handled scissors. We had a paste pot and sheets of colored paper, and when our labors were done the kindergarten windows displayed pumpkins, Christmas trees, owls, eggs, rabbits, or whatever was appropriate to the season. J. D. could always draw better than anyone else. When visiting night for parents came around it would be his work they admired. David Zobrowski, of course, was the scholar; we were proud to be Dave's best friends. Russell managed to remain undistinguished in any way until time for the singing class. Here no one could match him. Not that anyone wanted to. He sang worse than anyone who ever attended our school. It was as if his voice operated by a pulley, and its tenor was remotely canine. The class consisted of bluebirds and robins, with the exception of Russ who was placed at a separate desk and given no designation at all. Usually he gazed out the window at the interminable fields, but when it came to him that he, too, could sing, and his jaw began to work and his throat to contract, he would be warned into silence by the waving baton. It hurt his feelings very much.

Going to and from the business district ordinarily meant passing this musty little building, which had long since been converted into headquarters for the Boy Scout troop, and which now related to us no more than the Wizard of Oz, but until J. D. spoke of it we had not realized that the swings and the slide were gone, and crab grass was growing between the bricks of the front walk.

When we were in high school J. D. occasionally returned to wander through the corridors of the elementary school. The rest of us had been glad enough to move on and we considered his visits a bit queer, but otherwise never paused to think about them.

These were the streets where we had lived, these the houses, during a period of time when today could not influence tomorrow, and we possessed the confidence to argue about things we did not understand. Though, of course, we still did that. On winter nights we dropped away to sleep while watching the snow come drifting by the street light, and in summer we could see the moths outside the screens fluttering desperately, as though to tell us something. Our childhood came and went before we were ready to grasp it. Things were different now. The winged seeds that gyrate down from the trees now mean nothing else but that we must sweep them from the automobile hood because stains on the finish lower the trade-in value. Now, in short, it was impractical to live as we used to live with the abandon of a mule rolling in the dust.

In those days our incipient manhood had seemed a unique power, and our single worry that some girl might become pregnant. We danced with our eyes closed and our noses thrust into the gardenias all the girls wore in their hair, meanwhile estimating our chances, And, upon discovering literature, thanks to the solemn pedantry of a sophomore English teacher, we affected bow ties and cigarette holders and were able to quote contemporary poets with a faintly cynical tone.

On a postcard of a Rotterdam chocolate factory, sent to Russell but addressed to us all, J. D. scribbled, "I see nothing but the noon dust a-blowing and the green grass a-growing." If not con-

temporary it was at least familiar, and caused Zobrowski to remark, with a certain unconscious measure, "As fond as I am
of him I sometimes lose patience. In a furrow he has found a
feather of Pegasus and what should have been a blessing has
become a curse."

Now J. D. was inquiring after one or two we had forgotten,
or who had moved away, leaving no more trace than a cloud,
and about a piano teacher who had died one sultry August afternoon on the streetcar. Yet his interest was superficial. He was
being polite. He could not really care or he would not have gone
away for ten years. He wondered whatever became of the
bearded old man who used to stand on a street corner with a
stack of Bibles and a placard promising a free copy of the New
Testament to any Jew who would renounce the faith. We did
not know what happened to the old man; somehow he had just
vanished. Quite a few things were vanishing.

J. D. cared very little for the men who had once been our
fraternity brothers, which was odd because in our hearts we
still believed that those days and those men had been so extraordinary that people were still talking about them. Yet we could
recall that he took no pride in being associated with them. The
militant friendship of fraternity life made him surly. He refused
to shake hands as often as he was expected to. We had been
warned that, as pledges, we would be thrown into the river some
night. This was part of learning to become a finer man. When the
brothers came for us about three o'clock one morning, snatching
away our blankets and singing the good fellowship song, we put
up the traditional fight—all of us except J. D. He refused to
struggle. He slumped in the arms of his captors as limp as an
empty sack. This puzzled and annoyed the brothers, who held
him aloft by his ankles and who bounced his head on the floor.
He would not even open his eyes. They jabbed him stiffly in the
ribs, they twisted his arms behind his back, they kicked him in
the pants, they called him names, and finally, very angry, they
dragged him to the river and flung him in. But even when he
went sailing over the bullrushes he was silent as a corpse.
Strangely, he did not hit the water with a loud splash. Years
later he told us that he twisted at the last moment and dove
through the river scum, instead of landing flat on his back as
Russell did. They vanished together, as roommates should, but
Russell was again audible in a few seconds—thrashing back to
shore, where the brothers helped him out and gave him a towel
and a bathrobe and a drink of brandy.

J. D., however, did not reappear. Even before Russell had reached the shore we were beginning to worry about J. D. There was no moon that night and the river had an evil look. We stood in a row at the edge of the water. We heard the bullfrogs, and the dark bubbling and plopping of whatever calls the river home, but nothing more. And all at once the structure of the fraternity collapsed. The last vestige of unity disappeared. We were guilty individuals. Some people began lighting matches and peering into the river, while other called his name. But there was no answer, except in the form of rotten, half-submerged driftwood floating by, revolving in the sluggish current, and, beyond the confused whispering, the brief, crying shadows of night birds dipping in wild alarm over the slimy rushes.

When we saw him again we asked what happened, but several years passed before he told anyone. Then he said—and only then was his revenge complete—"Oh, I just swam under water as far as I could. After that I let the river carry me out of sight." He swam ashore a mile or two downstream, and by a back road he returned to the fraternity house. Nobody was there; everbody was at the river searching for his body. The fraternity was almost ruined because of J. D.

Now he had climbed the Matterhorn, and we were not surprised. He knew what it was like in Venice, or in Copenhagen, and as we reflected on his past we came to understand that his future was inevitable. We knew he would leave us again, perhaps forever.

Russell, tamping out a cheap cigar, said boldly, "Eunice and I have been thinking about a trip to the Bahamas next year, or year after." He considered the nicotine on his fingertips, and after a pause, because his boast was empty, and because he knew that we knew how empty it was, he added, "Though it depends." He began picking helplessly at his fingertips. He would never go anywhere.

"You'll like the Bahamas," J. D. said.

"We consider other places," Russell said unexpectedly, and there were tears in his eyes.

J. D. was watching him with a blank, pitiless gaze.

"I think I'll go to Byzantium," Russell said.

"That doesn't exist any more."

Russell took a deep breath to hush the panic that was on him, and at last he said, "Well, gentlemen, I guess I'd better get some shut-eye if I'm going to talk business with Dave in the morning."

"It's late," J. D. agreed.

Then we asked when he would be coming home for good, although it was a foolish question, and J. D. laughed at it. Later, in talking about him, we would recall his reason for not wanting to live here. He had explained that the difference between our town and these other places he had been was that when you go walking down a boulevard in some strange land and you see a tree burgeoning you understand that this is beautiful, and there comes with the knowledge a moment of indescribable poignance in the realization that as this tree must die, so will you die. But when, in the home you have always known, you find a tree in bud you think only that spring has come again. Here he stopped. It did not make much sense to us, but for him it had meaning of some kind.

So we asked when he would be coming back for another visit. He said he didn't know. We asked what was next. He replied that as soon as he could scrape together a few more dollars he thought he might like to see the Orient.

"They say that in Malaya . . ." he began, with glowing eyes. But we did not listen closely. He was not speaking to us anyway, only to himself, to the matrix which had spawned him and to the private god who guided him. His voice reached us faintly, as if from beyond the walls of Ávila.

EDITORS' ANALYSIS

The *Romaunt of the Rose* which is cited at the beginning of "The Walls of Ávila" is often given as one of the sources of romantic love, defined as the longing for the unattainable. Romantic love, aspiring toward what cannot be possessed, often self-destroying, certainly unearthly and uninterested in the humdrum and conjugal, exists strangely in our society alongside the urge to form stable family units.

The need to find a way of loving is not the major subject of this story, but exists as a powerfully felt theme under another poignant effort—how to find a style of life suitable for a man? The traveller, known with a peculiar dryness as "J.D.," has rebelled against all the traditional ways of growing up in his town. He has not taken any of the usual money-making or career or marriage exits into "reality;" he has behaved like a storybook wanderer; and now he has returned to rub his friends' noses in his private joys and memories. Clearly he has an ambition to set himself off from everyone, though toward what purpose is not clear. He is one of a gallery of American isolates, like those of Sherwood Anderson, but there is a curious new *intention* in his career of wandering the earth. He means to show something to himself and others; he means to prove something; his eyes glow and he builds dreams of joy and his old friends twist with reproach, discomfort, revulsion. In a way quite different from Anderson's compulsive eccentrics, Connell's protagonist means to be special.

QUESTIONS

1. What purpose is served by the succession of comments on places visited? Are J.D.'s comments original and personal? How interested does he seem to be in the places he visited? Or is he interested more in his own vision of freedom? Or in his picture of himself as a traveller?

2. Discuss the differing reactions of Dave Zobrowski and Russ Lyman to their old friend. How do their judgments reflect their own paths of life?

3. Contrast the vision of loveliness that the traveller has found with the reality of Helen Sawyer, once the local belle and now a garrulous real estate agent. Is she totally unsympathetic now? Or does the withdrawn purity of J.D. seem partly to be judged as smug?

4. What is the point of the flashback anecdote about swimming in the river? Does this adventure have anything in common with J.D.'s travels? Is there a pattern of "utility" in his adventures?

5. Does the author mean to hold up J.D., a man ambitious to build his life in an exceptional way, as a moral example? How? Are his old friends correct in their judgment of his failure? Is he correct in his apparent judgment of theirs? To what extent are personal failures responsible for the "all but in vayne" retreats from aspiration dissected in this story?

6·

OUTSIDERS

Hands

by SHERWOOD ANDERSON

Sherwood Anderson, one of the most seriously dedicated writers of his generation, was largely concerned with exploring the "lives of quiet desperation" led by men and women in the small towns and industrial cities of America. His first novel, *Windy McPherson's Son* (1916) was laid in a bleak Iowa town, and his second novel, *Marching Men* (1917), concerned the Pennsylvania coal mining region. His first work to attract national attention was the collection of related stories, *Winesburg, Ohio* (1919), portraying the sterility and the heartbreak of small-town life in America. *Dark Laughter* (1925), a novel contrasting the simple pleasure of Negroes with the repressed lives of whites, is often considered his best work. In *A Story Teller's Story* (1924), Anderson discusses the consciously autobiographical elements in his fiction, and his major concern over the role of the literary artist in twentieth-century America.

Anderson's "Hands" is told as if it were the author's personal reminiscence, and its central character, Wing Biddlebaum, as is typical of Anderson's fiction, is presented as an unwitting victim. The story's emphasis on the cruelty of men and women toward anyone who varies from the arbitrary norms of society represents one of Anderson's deep-seated, personal convictions.

Upon the half decayed veranda of a small frame house that stood near the edge of a ravine near the town of Winesburg, Ohio, a fat little old man walked nervously up and down. Across a long field that had been seeded for clover but that had produced only a dense crop of yellow mustard weeds, he could see the public highway along which went a wagon filled with berry pickers returning from the fields. The berry pickers, youths and maidens, laughed and shouted boisterously. A boy clad in a blue shirt leaped from the wagon and attempted to drag after him one of the maidens who screamed and protested shrilly. The feet of the

Hands. Reprinted from *Winesburg, Ohio*, 1919, with the permission of Eleanor Anderson.

boy in the road kicked up a cloud of dust that floated across the face of the departing sun. Over the long field came a thin girlish voice. "Oh, you Wing Biddlebaum, comb your hair, it's falling into your eyes," commanded the voice to the man, who was bald and whose nervous little hands fiddled about the bare white forehead as though arranging a mass of tangled locks.

Wing Biddlebaum, forever frightened and beset by a ghostly band of doubts, did not think of himself as in any way a part of the life of the town where he had lived for twenty years. Among all the people of Winesburg but one had come close to him. With George Willard, son of Tom Willard, the proprietor of the new Willard House, he had formed something like a friendship. George Willard was the reporter on the *Winesburg Eagle* and sometimes in the evenings he walked out along the highway to Wing Biddlebaum's house. Now as the old man walked up and down on the veranda, his hands moving nervously about, he was hoping that George Willard would come and spend the evening with him. After the wagon containing the berry pickers had passed, he went across the field through the tall mustard weeds and climbing a rail fence peered anxiously along the road to the town. For a moment he stood thus, rubbing his hands together and looking up and down the road, and then, fear overcoming him, ran back to walk again upon the porch on his own house.

In the presence of George Willard, Wing Biddlebaum, who for twenty years had been the town mystery, lost something of his timidity, and his shadowy personality, submerged in a sea of doubts, came forth to look at the world. With the young reporter at his side, he ventured in the light of day into Main Street or strode up and down on the rickety front porch of his own house, talking excitedly. The voice that had been low and trembling became shrill and loud. The bent figure straightened. With a kind of wriggle, like a fish returned to the brook by the fisherman, Biddlebaum the silent began to talk, striving to put into words the ideas that had been accumulated by his mind during long years of silence.

Wing Biddlebaum talked much with his hands. The slender expressive fingers, forever active, forever striving to conceal themselves in his pockets or behind his back, came forth and became the piston rods of his machinery of expression.

The story of Wing Biddlebaum is a story of hands. Their restless activity, like unto the beating of the wings of an imprisoned bird, had given him his name. Some obscure poet of the town had thought of it. The hands alarmed their owner. He wanted to keep them hidden away and looked with amazement at the quiet inexpressive hands of other men who worked beside him in the fields, or passed, driving sleepy teams on country roads.

When he talked to George Willard, Wing Biddlebaum closed his fists and beat with them upon a table or on the walls of his house. The action made him more comfortable. If the desire to talk came to him when the two were walking in the fields, he sought out a stump or the top board of a fence and with his hands pounding busily talked with renewed ease.

The story of Wing Biddlebaum's hands is worth a book in itself. Sympathetically set forth it would tap many strange, beautiful qualities in obscure men. It's a job for a poet. In Winesburg the hands had attracted attention merely because of their activity. With them Wing Biddlebaum had picked as high as a hundred and forty quarts of strawberries in a day. They became his distinguishing feature, the source of his fame. Also they made more grotesque an already grotesque and elusive individuality. Winesburg was proud of the hands of Wing Biddlebaum in the same spirit in which it was proud of Banker White's new stone house and Wesley Moyer's bay stallion, Tony Tip, that had won the two-fifteen trot at the fall races in Cleveland.

As for George Willard, he had many times wanted to ask about the hands. At times an almost overwhelming curiosity had taken hold of him. He felt that there must be a reason for their strange activity and their inclination to keep hidden away and only a growing respect for Wing Biddlebaum kept him from blurting out the questions that were often in his mind.

Once he had been on the point of asking. The two were walking in the fields on a summer afternoon and had stopped to sit upon a grassy bank. All afternoon Wing Biddlebaum had talked as one inspired. By a fence he had stopped and beating like a giant woodpecker upon the top board had shouted at George Willard, condemning his tendency to be too much influenced by the people about him. "You are destroying yourself," he cried. "You have the inclination to be alone and to dream and you are afraid of dreams. You want to be like others in town here. You hear them talk and you try to imitate them."

On the grassy bank Wing Biddlebaum had tried again to drive his point home. His voice became soft and reminiscent, and with a sigh of contentment he launched into a long rambling talk, speaking as one lost in a dream.

Out of the dream Wing Biddlebaum made a picture for George Willard. In the picture men lived again in a kind of pastoral golden age. Across a green open country came clean-limbed young men, some afoot, some mounted upon horses. In crowds the young men came to gather about the feet of an old man who sat beneath a tree in a tiny garden and who talked to them.

Wing Biddlebaum became wholly inspired. For once he forgot the hands. Slowly they stole forth and lay upon George Willard's shoulders. Something new and bold came into the voice that talked. "You must try to forget all you have learned," said the old man. "You must begin to dream. From this time on you must shut your ears to the roaring of voices."

Pausing in his speech, Wing Biddlebaum looked long and earnestly at George Willard. His eyes glowed. Again he raised the hands to caress the boy and then a look of horror swept over his face.

With a convulsive movement of his body, Wing Biddlebaum sprang to his feet and thrust his hands deep into his trousers pockets. Tears came to his eyes. "I must be getting along home. I can talk no more with you," he said nervously.

Without looking back, the old man had hurried down the hillside and across a meadow, leaving George Willard perplexed and frightened upon the grassy slope. With a shiver of dread the boy arose and went along the road toward town. "I'll not ask him about his hands," he thought, touched by the memory of the terror he had seen in the man's eyes. "There's something wrong, but I don't want to know what it is. His hands have something to do with his fear of me and of everyone."

And George Willard was right. Let us look briefly into the story of the hands. Perhaps our talking of them will arouse the poet who will tell the hidden wonder story of the influence for which the hands were but fluttering pennants of promise.

In his youth Wing Biddlebaum had been a school teacher in a town in Pennsylvania. He was not then known as Wing Biddlebaum, but went by the less euphonic name of Adolph Myers. As Adolph Myers he was much loved by the boys of his school.

Adolph Myers was meant by nature to be a teacher of youth. He was one of the those rare, little-understood men who rule by a power so gentle that it passes as a lovable weakness. In their feeling for the boys under their charge such men are not unlike the finer sort of women in their love of men.

And yet that is but crudely stated. It needs the poet there.

With the boys of his school Adolph Myers had walked in the evening or had sat talking until dusk upon the school house steps lost in a kind of dream. Here and there went his hands, caressing the shoulders of the boys, playing about the tousled heads. As he talked his voice became soft and musical. There was a caress in that also. In a way the voice and the hands, the stroking of the shoulders and the touching of the hair was a part of the schoolmaster's effort to carry a dream into the young minds. By the caress that was in his fingers he expressed himself. He was one of those men in whom the force that creates life is diffused, not centralized. Under the caress of his hands doubt and disbelief went out of the minds of the boys and they began also to dream.

And then the tragedy. A half-witted boy of the school became enamored of the young master. In his bed at night he imagined unspeakable things and in the morning went forth to tell his dreams as facts. Strange, hideous accusations fell from his loose-hung lips. Through the Pennsylvania town went a shiver. Hidden, shadowy doubts that had been in men's minds concerning Adolph Myers were galvanized into beliefs.

The tragedy did not linger. Trembling lads were jerked out of bed and questioned. "He put his arms about me," said one. "His fingers were always playing in my hair," said another.

One afternoon a man of the town, Henry Bradford, who kept a saloon, came to the schoolhouse door. Calling Adolph Myers into the school yard he began to beat him with his fists. As his hard knuckles beat down into the frightened face of the schoolmaster, his wrath became more and more terrible. Screaming with dismay, the children ran here and there like disturbed insects. "I'll teach you to put your hands on my boy, you beast," roared the saloon keeper, who, tired of beating the master, had begun to kick him about the yard.

Adolph Myers was driven from the Pennsylvania town in the night. With lanterns in their hands a dozen men came to the door of the house where he lived alone and commanded that he dress and come forth. It was raining and one of the men had a rope in his hands. They had intended to hang the schoolmaster, but something in his figure, so small, white, and pitiful, touched their hearts and they let him escape. As he ran away into the darkness they repented of their weakness and ran after him, swearing and throwing sticks and great balls of soft mud at the figure that screamed and ran faster and faster into the darkness.

For twenty years Adolph Myers had lived alone in Wines-burg. He was but forty but looked sixty-five. The name of Biddlebaum he got from a box of goods seen at a freight station as he hurried through an eastern Ohio town. He had an aunt in Winesburg, a black-toothed old woman who raised chickens, and with her he lived until she died. He had been ill for a year after the experience in Pennsylvania, and after his recovery worked as a day laborer in the fields, going timidly about and striving to conceal his hands. Although he did not understand what had happened he felt that the hands must be to blame. Again and again the fathers of the boys had talked of the hands. "Keep your hands to yourself," the saloon keeper had roared, dancing with fury in the schoolhouse yard.

Upon the veranda of his house by the ravine, Wing Biddlebaum continued to walk up and down until the sun had disappeared and the road beyond the field was lost in the grey shadows. Going into his house he cut slices of bread and spread honey upon them. When the rumble of the evening train that took away the express cars loaded with the day's harvest of berries had passed and restored the silence of the summer night, he went again to walk upon the veranda. In the darkness he could not see the hands and they became quiet. Although he still hungered for the presence of the boy, who was the medium through which he expressed his love of man, the hunger became again a part of his loneliness and his waiting. Lighting a lamp, Wing Biddle-baum washed the few dishes soiled by his simple meal and, setting up a folding cot by the screen door that led to the porch, prepared to undress for the night. A few stray white bread crumbs lay on the cleanly washed floor by the table; putting the lamp upon a low stool he began to pick up the crumbs, carry-ing them to his mouth one by one with unbelievable rapidity. In the dense blotch of light beneath the table, the kneeling figure looked like a priest engaged in some service of his church. The nervous expressive fingers, flashing in and out of the light, might well have been mistaken for the fingers of the devotee going swiftly through decade after decade of his rosary.

EDITORS' ANALYSIS

Sherwood Anderson's "Hands" is a story of an individual tragically isolated from society by his deviations from accepted behavior. The special fascination this kind of person holds for us has been reinforced by our contemporary interest in psychology and its emphasis upon extreme variation in human conduct. The power of Anderson's story, however, comes from the fact that it has stirred into uneasy consciousness our own private attitudes toward sex and toward love. Wing Biddlebaum may not be wholly innocent; yet it is his unwary and compulsive behavior which forces from us our sympathetic awareness that every individual in society has only a narrow margin of safety.

QUESTIONS

1. Do you find the presentation of the events of this story flat, and somewhat too matter-of-fact, in comparison to the presentation found in younger writers, closer to you in time? Is there some dating of style in Anderson?

2. What evidence does the story give that Wing Biddlebaum knows that he has violated the moral code of his society? Do you think that Anderson passes over Wing's own awareness of himself too lightly?

3. Is the degree of Wing's innocence important in the total effect of the story? Could you accept him if he were truly depraved, even if for good reason?

4. Does Anderson describe the mob attacking Wing Biddlebaum as in any way fearful? If so, why? Is Henry Bradford's rage the outcome of fear? Of moral courage?

5. What is the effect on you, as reader, of the last four sentences in which Anderson describes Wing Biddlebaum in "the dense blotch of light beneath the table?"

Three Players of a Summer Game

by TENNESSEE WILLIAMS

Tennessee Williams (1914-   ) established himself at the age of thirty-one, with the production of his play *The Glass Menagerie* (1945), as a significant figure in the American theater. Since this time, he has produced a play on Broadway at the rate of about one every two years. Among those most widely discussed are *A Streetcar Named Desire* (1947), *Summer and Smoke* (1948), *Camino Real* (1953), *Cat on a Hot Tin Roof* (1954), *Orpheus Descending* (1957). He has published a volume of short stories and one novel, *The Roman Spring of Mrs. Stone* (1950). Both in his plays and in his fiction, William's main concern is with the sicknesses and failures in love which isolate men and women from each other, or from the normal and comfortable routines of living. We all inhabit a new world of awareness, bounded by Freudian swamps. Williams attempts to illuminate small corners of this new world.

The story "Three Players of a Summer Game" presents its characters almost as if they were intellectual abstractions, or as if they were part of some elaborate charade which we were invited to view with a minimum of emotional response. However, as a story of outsiders, afraid to love or of being unable to love, and surrounded by people with whom they cannot communicate, it is a fictional portrait which is central to Williams's view of things.

Croquet is a summer game that seems, in a curious way, to be composed of images, very much as a painter's abstraction of summer or one of its games would be composed of them. The delicate wire wickets set in a lawn of smooth emerald that flickers fierily at some points and rests under violet shadow in others; the wooden poles gaudily painted and like moments that stand out in a season that was a struggle for something of unspeakable importance to someone passing through it; the clean and hard wooden spheres of different colors and the strong, rigid shape of the mallets that drive the balls through the wickets; the formal design of those wickets and poles upon the croquet lawn—all this is like a painter's abstraction of a summer and a game played in it. And I cannot think of croquet without hearing a sound like the faraway booming of a cannon fired to announce a white ship coming into a harbor. The faraway booming sound is that of a green-and-white striped awning coming down over a gallery of a white frame house in Meridian, Mississippi. The house is of Victorian design carried to an extreme of improvisation, an almost grotesque pile of galleries and turrets and cupolas and eaves, all freshly painted white—so white and so fresh that it has the blue-white glitter of a block of ice in the sun. The house is like a new resolution not yet tainted by any defection from it. And I associate the summer game with players coming out of this house with the buoyant air of persons just released from a suffocating enclosure. Their clothes are as light in weight and color as the flattering clothes of dancers. There are three players—a woman, a man, and a little girl.

The voice of the woman player is not at all loud, yet it has a pleasantly resonant quality; it carries farther than most voices, and it is interspersed with peals of treble laughter. The woman player, even more than her male opponent in the game, has the grateful quickness of motion of someone let out of a suffocating enclosure; her motion has the quickness of breath released just after a moment of terror, of fingers unclenched when panic is suddenly past, or of a cry that subsides into laughter. She seems unable to speak or move about moderately; she moves convulsively in rushes, whipping her white skirts with long strides that quicken to running. Her skirts make a faint crackling sound as her pumping thighs whip them open—the sound that comes to you, greatly diminished by distance, when fitful fair-weather gusts belly out and slacken the faraway sails of a yawl. This agreeably cool summer sound is accompanied by another, which is even cooler—the ceaseless tiny chatter of beads hung in long loops from her throat. They are not pearls but they have a milky lustre; they are small, faintly speckled white ovals—polished bird eggs turned solid and strung upon glittery filaments of silver. The woman player is never still for a moment; sometimes she exhausts herself and collapses on the grass in the conscious attitudes of a dancer. She is a thin woman, with long bones and skin of a silky sheen, and her eyes are only a shade or two darker than the blue-tinted bird's-egg beads about her long throat. She is never still—not even when she has fallen in exhaustion on the grass. The neighbors think she's gone mad, but they feel no pity for her, and that, of course, is because of her male opponent in the game. This player is Brick Pollitt, a young Delta planter, a man so tall, with such a fiery thatch of hair, that to see a flagpole on an expanse of green lawn or even a particularly brilliant weather vane or cross on a steeple is sufficient to recall that long-ago summer which his legend belongs to.

This male player of the summer game is a drinker who has not yet fallen beneath the savage axe blows of his liquor. He is not so young any more, but he has not yet lost the slim grace of his youth. He is a head taller than the tall woman player. He is such a tall man that even in those sections of the lawn dimmed under violet shadow his head continues to catch fiery rays of the descending sun, the way the heavenward-pointing index finger of a huge gilded hand atop a Protestant steeple in Meridian goes on drawing the sun's flame for a good while after the lower surfaces of the town have sunk into lingering dusk.

The third player of the summer game is the woman's daughter, a plump twelve-year-old child named Mary Louise. This little girl has made herself distinctly unpopular among the children of the neighborhood by imitating too perfectly the elegant manners and cultivated Eastern voice of her mother. She sits in an electric automobile, on the sort of fat silk pillow that expensive lap dogs sit on, uttering treble peals of ladylike laughter, tossing her copper curls, using grown-up expressions such as "Oh, how delightful!" and "Isn't that just lovely!" She sits in the electric automobile sometimes all afternoon, by herself, as if she were on display in a glass box, only now and then raising a plaintive voice to call her mother and ask if it is all right for her to come in now, or if she can drive the electric around the block, which she is sometimes then permitted to do.

Our house was on the opposite corner, and I was the only child close to her age (I was a boy of fourteen) who could put up with her precocious refinements. For a very short time, she had had another friend, a little girl named Dorothea, and the two of them would get into their mothers' castoff finery and have tea parties on the lawn, but one afternoon Dorothea took umbrage at something, overturned the tea table, and stalked off, chanting a horrid little verse: "Smarty, Smarty, gave a party, Nobody came but a sad old darky!" "Common!" Mary Louise shrieked after her, and they didn't play together any more. Sometimes she called me over to play croquet with her, but that was only when her mother and Brick Pollitt had disappeared into the house too early to play the game. Mary Louise had a passion for croquet. She played it purely for itself; it did not have for her any shadowy connotations.

What the game meant to Brick Pollitt calls for some further account of Brick's life before that summer. He had been a celebrated athlete at Sewanee, and had married a New Orleans débutante who was a Mardi Gras queen and whose father owned a fleet of banana boats. It had seemed a brilliant marriage, with lots of wealth and prestige on both sides, but only two years later Brick started falling in love with his liquor, and Margaret, his wife, began to be praised for her patience and loyalty to him. Brick seemed to be throwing his life away, as if it were something disgusting that he had suddenly found in his hands. This self-disgust came upon him with the abruptness and violence of a crash on a highway. But what had Brick crashed into? Nothing that anybody was able to surmise, for he seemed to have everything that young men like Brick might hope or desire to have. What else is there? There must have been something that he wanted and lacked, or what reason was there for his dropping his life and taking hold of a glass that he never let go of for more than one waking hour? His wife, Margaret, took hold of Brick's ten-thousand-acre plantation. She had Brick's power of attorney, and she managed all his business affairs with astuteness. "He'll come out of it," she would say. "Brick is passing through something that he'll come out of." She always said the right thing, took the conventionally right attitude, and expressed it to the world which admired her for it. Everybody admired her as a remarkably fine and brave little woman who had much to put up with. Two sections of an hourglass could not drain and fill more evenly than Brick and Margaret after he took to drink. It was as though she had her lips fastened to some invisible wound in his body through which drained out of him and flowed into her the assurance and vitality that had been his before his marriage. Margaret Pollitt lost her pale, feminine prettiness and assumed in its place something more impressive—a firm and rough-textured sort of handsomeness. Once very pretty but indistinct, a graceful sketch that was done with a very light pencil, she became vivid as Brick disappeared behind the veil of his liquor. She abruptly stopped being quiet and dainty. She was now apt to have dirty fingernails, which she covered with scarlet enamel. When the enamel chipped off, the gray showed underneath. Her hair was now cut short, so that she didn't have to "mess with it." It was wind-blown and full of sparkle; she jerked a comb through it, making it crackle. She had white teeth that were a little too large for her thin lips, and when she threw her head back in laughter, strong cords stood out in her smooth brown throat .She had a booming laugh that she might have stolen from Brick while he was drunk or asleep beside her at night. She had a way of releasing the clutch on a car at the exact instant that her laughter boomed out, and of not calling goodbye but of thrusting one bare, strong arm straight out with the fingers clenched as the car shot off in high gear and disappear into a cloud of yellow dust. She didn't drive her own little runabout nowaways as much as she did Brick's Pierce-Arrow touring car, for Brick's driver's license had been revoked. She frequently broke the speed limit on the highway. The patrolmen would stop her, but she had such an affability, such a disarming way with her, that they would have a good laugh together and there would be no question of a ticket.

Somebody in her family died in Memphis that spring, and she went there to attend the funeral and collect her inheritance, and while she was away, Brick Pollitt slipped out from under her thumb a bit. Another death occurred during her absence. That nice young doctor who took care of Brick when he had to be carried to the hospital took sick in a shocking way. An awful flower grew in his brain, like a fierce geranium—grew and grew and one day shattered its pot. All of a sudden, the wrong words came out of his mouth; he seemed to be speaking in an unknown tongue; he couldn't find things with his hands; he made troubled signs over his forehead. His wife led him about the house by one hand, yet he stumbled and fell flat; the breath was knocked out of him, and he had to be put to bed by his wife and the Negro yardman; and he lay there laughing weakly, incredulously, trying to find his wife's hand with both of his while she looked at him with eyes that she couldn't keep from blazing with terror. He lived on under drugs for a week, and it was during that time that Brick Pollitt came and sat with Isabel Grey by her dying husband's bed. She couldn't speak; she could only shake her head incessantly, like a metronome, with no lips visible in her white face but two pressed-narrow bands of a dimmer whiteness that shook as if some white liquid flowed beneath them with a rapidity and violence that made them quiver.

"*God*" was the only word she was able to say, but Brick Pollitt somehow understood what she meant by that word, as if it were in a language that she and he, alone of all people, could speak and understand. And when the dying man's eyes opened, as if they were being forced, on something they couldn't bear to look at, it was Brick, his hands suddenly quite sure and steady, who filled the hypodermic needle for her and pumped its contents fiercely into her husband's hard young arm. And it was over.

There was another bed at the back of the house, and he and Isabel lay beside each other on that bed for a couple of hours before they let the town know that her husband's agony was completed, and the only movement between them was the intermittent, spasmodic digging of their fingernails into each other's clenched palm while their bodies lay stiffly separate, deliberately not touching at any other points, as if they abhorred any other contact with each other.

And so you see what the summer game on the violet-shadowed lawn was—it was a running together out of something unbearably hot and bright into something obscure and cool.

The young widow was left with nothing in the way of material possessions except the house and an electric automobile. By the time Brick's wife, Margaret, had returned from her journey to Memphis, Brick had taken over the various details of the widow's life that a brother or a relative, if she had had one, would have seen to. For a week or two, people thought it was very kind of him, and then all at once they decided that Brick's reason for kindness was by no means noble. It appeared that the widow was now his mistress, and this was true. It was true in the limited way that most such opinions are true. She was his mistress, but that was not Brick's reason. His reason had something to do with that chaste interlocking of hands their first time together, after the hypodermic. It had to do with those hours, now receding and fading behind them, as all such hours must, but neither of them could have said what it was, aside from that. Neither of them was able to think very clearly. But Brick was able to pull himself together for a while and take command of the young widow's affairs.

The daughter, Mary Louise, was a plump child of twelve. She was my friend that summer. Mary Louise and I caught lightning bugs and put them in Mason jars, and we played croquet when her mother and Brick Pollitt were not inclined to play. It was Mary Louise that summer who taught me how to deal with mosquito bites. She was plagued by mosquitoes and so was I. She warned me that scratching the bites would leave scars on my skin, which was as tender as hers. I said that I didn't care. Someday you will, she told me. She carried with her constantly that summer a lump of ice in a handkerchief. Whenever a mosquito bit her, instead of scratching the bite she rubbed it gently with the handkerchief-wrapped lump of ice until the sting was frozen to numbness. Of course, in five minutes it would come back and have to be frozen again, but eventually it would disappear and leave no scar. Mary Louise's skin, where it was not temporarily mutilated by a mosquito bite or a slight rash that sometimes appeared after she ate strawberry ice cream, was ravishingly smooth and tender.

The Greys' house was very run down, but soon after Brick Pollitt started coming over to see the young widow, the house was painted. It was painted so white that it was almost a very pale blue; it had the blue-white glitter of a block of ice in the sun. In spite of his red hair, Brick Pollitt, too, had a cool appearance, because he was still young and thin, as thin as the widow, and he dressed, as she did, in clothes of light weight and color. His white shirts looked faintly pink because of his skin underneath them. Once, I saw him at an upstairs window of the widow's house just a moment before he pulled the shade down. I was in an upstairs room of my house, and I saw that Brick Pollitt was divided into two colors as distinct as two stripes of a flag, the upper part of him, which had been exposed to the sun, almost crimson and the lower part of him white as this piece of paper.

While the widow's house was being repainted, at Brick Pollitt's expense, she and her daughter lived at the Alcazar Hotel, also at Brick's expense. Brick drove in from his plantation every morning to watch the house painters at work. His driving license had been restored to him, and this was an important step forward in his personal renovation—being able to drive his own car again. He drove with elaborate caution and formality, coming to a dead stop at every cross street in the town, sounding the silver trumpet at every corner, with smiles and bows and great circular gestures of his hands inviting pedestrians to precede him. But people did not approve of what Brick Pollitt was doing. They sympathized with Margaret, that brave little woman who had to put up with so much. As for Dr. Grey's widow, she had not been very long in the town; the Doctor had married her while he was an interne at a big hospital in Baltimore. Nobody had formed a definite opinion of her before the Doctor died, so it was no effort now simply to condemn her, without any qualification, as a common strumpet.

Brick Pollitt, when he talked to the house painters, shouted to them as if they were deaf, so that all the neighbors could hear what he had to say. He was explaining things to the world, especially the matter of his drinking.

"It's something that you can't cut out completely right away," he would yell up at them. "That's the big mistake that most drinkers make—they try to cut it out completely, and you can't do that. You can do it for maybe a month or two months, but all at once you go back on it worse than before you went off it, and then the discouragement is awful—you lose all faith in yourself and just give up. The thing to do, the way to handle the problem is like a bullfigher handles a bull in a ring. Wear it down little by little, get control of it gradually. That's how I'm handling this thing! Yep. Now, let's say that you get up wanting a drink in the morning. Say it's ten o'clock, maybe. Well, you say to yourself, 'Just wait half an hour, old boy, and then you can have one.' . . . Well, at half past ten you still want that drink and you want it a little bit worse than you did at ten, but you say to yourself, 'Boy, you could do without it half an hour ago, so you can do without it now.' You see, that's how you got to argue about it with yourself, because a drinking man is not one person. A man that drinks is two people, one grabbing the bottle, the other one fighting him off it—not one but two people fighting each other to get control of a bottle. Well, sir. If you talk yourself out of a drink at ten, you can still talk yourself out of a drink at *half past* ten! But at *eleven* o'clock the need for the drink is greater. Now here's the important thing to remember about this struggle. You got to watch those scales, and when they tip too far against your power to resist, you got to give a little. That's not weakness. *That's strategy!* Because don't forget what I told you. A drinking man is not one person but two, and it's a battle of wits going on between them. And so I say at eleven, 'Well, *have* your drink. *Go on* and *have* it! One drink at eleven won't hurt you!'

"What time is it now? . . . Yep! Eleven . . . All right, I'm going to have me that one drink. I could do without it, I don't crave it. But the important thing is . . ."

His voice would trail off as he entered the widow's house. He would stay in there longer than it took to have one drink, and when he came out, there would be a change in his voice as definite as a change of weather or season. The strong and vigorous tone would be a bit filmed over.

Then he would usually begin to talk about his wife. "I don't say my wife Margaret's not an intelligent woman. She is, and both of us know it, but she don't have a good head for property values. Now, you know Dr. Grey, who used to live here before that brain thing killed him. Well, he was my physician, he pulled me through some bad times when I had that liquor problem. I felt I owed him a lot. Now, that was a terrible thing the way he went, but it was terrible for his widow, too; she was left with this house and that electric automobile and that's all, and this house was put up for sale to pay off her debts, and—well, I bought it. I bought it, and now I'm giving it back to her. Now, my wife Margaret, she. And a lot of other folks, too. Don't understand about this. . . . What time is it? Twelve? High noon! . . . This ice is melted . . ."

He'd drift back into the house and stay there half an hour, and when he'd come back out, it would be rather shyly, with a sad and uncertain creaking of the screen door pushed by the hand not holding the tall glass. But after resting a little while on the steps, he would resume his talk to the house painters.

"Yes," he would say, as if he had paused only a moment before, "it's the most precious thing that a woman can give to a man—his lost respect for himself—and the meanest thing one human being can do to another human being is take his respect for himself away from him. I. I had it took away from me."

The glass would tilt slowly up and jerkily down, and he'd have to wipe his chin.

"I had it took away from me! I won't tell you how, but maybe, being men about my age, you're able to guess it. That was how. Some of them don't want it. They cut it off. They cut it right off a man, and half the time he don't even know when they cut it off him. Well, I knew it all right. I could feel it being cut off me. Do you know what I mean? . . . That's right.

"But once in a while there's one—and they don't come often— that wants for a man to keep it, and those are the women that God made and put on this earth. The other kind come out of Hell, or

out of . . . I don't know what. I'm talking too much. Sure. I know
I'm talking too much about private matters. But that's all right.
This property is mine. I'm talking on my own property and I don't
give a hoot who hears me or what they think! I'm not going to try
to fool anybody about it. Whatever I do is nothing to be ashamed
of. I've been through things that I would rather not mention. But
I'm coming out of it now, God damn it, yes, I am! I can't take all
the credit. And yet I'm proud. I'm goddam proud of myself, because I was in a pitiful condition with that liquor problem of
mine, but now the worst is over I've got it just about licked.
That's my car out there and I drove it up here myself. It's no short
drive, it's almost a hundred miles, and I drive it each morning and
drive it back each night. I've got back my driver's license, and I
fired the man that was working for my wife, looking after our
place. I fired that man and not only fired him but give him a kick
in the britches that made him eat standing up for the next week
or two. It wasn't because I thought he was fooling around. It
wasn't that. But him and her both took about the same attitude
toward me, and I didn't like the attitude they took. They would
talk about me right in front of me, as if I wasn't there. 'Is it time
for his medicine?' Yes, they were giving me dope! So one day I
played possum. I was lying out there on the sofa and she said to
him, 'I guess he's passed out now.' And he said, 'Jesus, dead drunk
at half past one in the afternoon!' Well. I got up slowly. I wasn't
drunk at that hour, I wasn't even half drunk. I stood up straight
and walked slowly toward him. I walked straight up to them both,
and you should of seen the eyes of them both bug out! 'Yes, Jesus,'
I said, 'at half past one!' And I grabbed him by his collar and by
the seat of his britches and turkey-trotted him right on out of the
house and pitched him on his face in a big mud puddle at the
foot of the steps to the front veranda. And as far as I know or
care, maybe he's still laying there and she's still screaming, 'Stop,
Brick!' But I believe I did hit her. Yes, I did. I did hit her. There's
times when you got to hit them, and that was one of those times. I
ain't been to the house since. I moved in the little place we lived
in before the big one was built, on the other side of the bayou,
and ain't crossed over there since.

"Well, sir, that's all over with now. I got back my power of
attorney which I'd give to that woman and I got back my driver's
license and I bought this piece of property in town and signed my
own check for it and I'm having it completely done over to make
it as handsome a piece of residential property as you can find in

this town and I'm having that lawn out there prepared for the game of croquet."

Then he'd look at the glass in his hand as if he just then noticed, that he was holding it. He'd give it a look of slightly pained surprise, as if he had cut his hand and just now noticed that it was cut and bleeding. Then he would sigh like an old-time actor in a tragic role. He would put the tall glass down on the balustrade with great, great care, look back at it to make sure that it wasn't going to fall over, and walk, very straight and steady, to the porch steps and, just as steady but with more concentration, down them. When he arrived at the foot of the steps, he would laugh as if someone had made a comical remark. He would duck his head genially and shout to the house painters something like this: "Well, I'm not making any predictions, because I'm no fortune-teller, but I've got a strong idea that I'm going to lick my liquor problem this summer, ha-ha, I'm going to lick it this summer! I'm not going to take no cure and I'm not going to take no pledge. I'm just going to prove I'm a man again! I'm going to do it step by little step, the way that people play the game of croquet. You know how you play that game. You hit the ball through one wicket and then you drive it through the next one. You hit it through that wicket and then you drive on to another. You go from wicket to wicket, and it's a game of precision —it's a game that takes concentration and precision, and that's what makes it a wonderful game for a drinker. It takes a sober man to play a game of precision. It's better than shooting pool, because a pool hall is always next door to a gin mill, and you never see a pool player that don't have his liquor glass on the edge of the table or somewhere pretty near it, and croquet is also a better game than golf, because in golf you've always got that nineteenth hole waiting for you. Nope, for a man with a liquor problem croquet may seem a little bit sissy, but let me tell you it's a game of precision. You go from wicket to wicket until you arrive at that big final pole, and then, bang, you've hit it, the game is finished, you're there! And then, and not until then, you can go up here to the porch and have you a cool gin drink, a buck or a Collins. Hey! Where did I leave that glass? Aw! Yeah, hand it down to me, will you? Ha-ha. Thanks."

He would take a birdlike sip, make a fiercely wry face, and shake his head violently as if somebody had drenched it with water. *This God-damned stuff!*"

He would look around to find a safe place to set the glass down again. He would select a bare spot of earth between the hydrangea bushes and deposit the glass there as carefully as if he were planting a memorial tree, and then he would straighten up with a great air of relief and expand his chest and flex his arms. "Ha-ha, yep, croquet is a summer game for widows and drinkers, ha-ha!"

For a few moments, standing there in the sun, he would seem as sure and powerful as the sun itself, but then some little shadow of uncertainty would touch him again, get through the wall of his liquor; some tricky little shadow of a thought, as sly as a mouse, quick, dark, too sly to be caught, and without his moving enough for it to be noticed his still fine body would fall as violently as a giant tree crashes down beneath a final axe stroke, taking with it all the wheeling seasons of sun and stars, whole centuries of them, crashing suddenly into oblivion and rot. He would make this enormous fall without a perceptible movement of his body. At the most, it would show in the faint flicker of something across his face, whose color gave him the name people knew him by. Possibly one knee sagged a little forward. Then slowly, slowly, he would fasten one hand over his belt and raise the other one hesitantly to his head, feel the scalp and the hard round bowl of the skull underneath it, as if he dimly imagined that by feeling that dome he might be able to guess what was hidden inside it—facing now the intricate wickets of the summer to come.

For one reason or another, Mary Louise Grey was locked out of the house a great deal of the time that summer, and since she was a lonely child with little or no imagination, apparently unable to amuse herself with solitary games—except the endless one of copying her mother—the afternoons when she was excluded from the house because her mother had a headache were periods of great affliction. There were several galleries with outside stairs between them, and she would patrol the galleries and wander forlornly about the lawn or go down the front walk and sit in the glass box of the electric. She would vary her steps, sometimes walking sedately, sometimes skipping, sometimes hopping and humming, one plump hand always clutching a handkerchief that contained the lump of ice. This lump of ice to rub her mosquito bites had to be replaced at frequent intervals. "Oh, iceman!" the widow would call sweetly from an upstairs window. "Don't forget to leave some extra pieces for little Mary Louise to rub her mosquito bites with!"

From time to time, Mary Louise would utter a soft cry, and, in a voice that had her mother's trick of carrying a great distance without being loud, call, "Oh, Mother, I'm simply being devoured by mosquitoes!"

"Darling," her mother would answer from the upstairs window, "that's dreadful, but you know that Mother can't help it; she didn't create the mosquitoes and she can't destroy them for you!"

"You could let me come in the house, Mama."

"No, I can't let you come in, precious. Not yet."

"Why not, Mother?"

"Because Mother has a sick headache."

"I will be quiet."

"You say that you will, but you won't. You must learn to amuse yourself, precious; you mustn't depend on Mother to amuse you. Nobody can depend on anyone else forever. I'll tell you what you can do till Mother's headache is better. You can drive the electric out of the garage. You can drive it around the block, but don't go into the business district with it, and then you can stop in the shady part of the drive and sit there perfectly comfortably till Mother feels better and can get dressed and come out. And then I think Mr. Pollitt may come over for a game of croquet. Won't that be lovely?"

"Do you think he will get here in time to play?"

"I hope so, precious. It does him so much good to play croquet."

"Oh, I think it does all of us good to play croquet," Mary Louise would say, in a voice that trembled just at the vision of it.

Before Brick Pollitt arrived—sometimes half an hour before his coming, as though she could hear his automobile on the highway twenty miles from the house—Mary Louise would bound plumply off the gallery and begin setting up the poles and wickets. While she was doing this, her plump little buttocks and her beginning breasts and her shoulder-length copper curls would all bob up and down in unison. I would watch her from our front steps. She worked feverishly against time, for experience had taught her that the sooner she completed the preparations for the game, the greater would be the chance of getting her mother and Mr. Pollitt to play it. Frequently she was not fast enough, or they were too fast for her; by the time she had finished her perspiring job, the veranda would be deserted. Her wailing cries would begin, punctuating the dusk at intervals only a little less frequent than the passing of cars of people going out for evening drives to cool off.

"Mama! Mama! The croquet set is ready!"

Usually there would be a long, long wait for any response to come from the upstairs window toward which the calls were directed. But one time there wasn't. Almost immediately after the wailing voice was lifted, begging for the commencement of the game, Mary Louise's thin, pretty mother showed herself at the window. That was the time when I saw, between the dividing gauze of the bedroom curtains, her naked breasts, small and beautiful, shaken like two angry fists by her violent motion. She leaned between the curtains to answer Mary Louise not in her usual tone of gentle remonstrance but in a shocking cry of rage: "Oh, be still, for God's sake, you fat little monster!"

Mary Louise was shocked into a silence that must have lasted for a quarter of an hour. It was probably the word "fat" that struck her so overwhelmingly, for Mary Louise had once told me, when we were circling the block in the electric, that her mother had told her that she was *not* fat, that she was only plump, and that these cushions of flesh were going to dissolve in two or three more years and then she would be just as thin and pretty as her mother.

Though Mary Louise would call me over to play croquet with her, she was not at all satisfied with my game. I had had so little practice and she so much, and, besides, it was the company of the grown-up people she wanted. She would call me over only when they had disappeared irretrievably into the lightless house or when the game had collapsed owing to Mr. Brick Pollitt's refusal to take it seriously. When he played seriously, he was even better at it than Mary Louise, who practiced sometimes all afternoon in preparation for a game. But there were evenings when he would not leave his drink on the porch but would carry it down onto the lawn with him and play with one hand, more and more capriciously, while in the other hand he carried a tall glass. Then the lawn would become a great stage on which he performed all the immemorial antics of the clown, to the exasperation of Mary Louise and her thin, pretty mother, both of whom would become very severe and dignified on these occasions. They would retire from the croquet lawn and stand off at a little distance, calling softly, like a pair of complaining doves, both in the same ladylike tones of remonstrance. He was not a middle-aged-looking man—that is, he was not at all big around the middle—and he could leap and run like a boy. He could turn cartwheels and walk on his hands, and sometimes he would grunt and lunge like a wrestler or make long, crouching runs like a football player, weaving in and out among the wickets and gaudily painted poles of the cricket lawn. The acrobatics and sports of his youth seemed to haunt him. He would call out hoarsely to invisible teammates and adversaries—muffled shouts of defiance and anger and triumph, to which an incongruous counterpart was continually provided by the faint, cooing voice of the widow: "Brick! Brick! Stop now, please stop! The child is crying! People will think you've gone crazy!" For Mary Louise's mother knew why the lights had gone out on all the screened porches up and down the street and why the automobiles drove past the house at the speed of a funeral procession while Mr. Brick Pollitt was making a circus ring of the croquet lawn.

Late one evening when he was making one of his crazy dashes across the lawn with an imaginary football hugged against his belly, he tripped over a wicket and sprawled on the lawn, and he pretended to be too gravely injured to get back on his feet. His groans brought Mary Louise and her mother running from behind the vine-screened end of the veranda and out upon the lawn to assist him. They took him by the hands and tried to haul him up, but with a sudden shout of laughter he pulled them both down on top of him and held them there till both of them were sobbing. He got up, finally, to replenish his glass of iced gin, and then returned to the lawn. That evening was a fearfully hot one, and Brick decided to cool and refresh himself with the sprinkler while he enjoyed his drink. He turned it on and pulled it out to the center of the lawn. There he rolled about on the grass under its leisurely revolving arch of water, and as he rolled about, he began to wriggle out of his clothes. He kicked off his white shoes and one of his pale-green socks, tore off his drenched white shirt and grass-stained linen pants, but he never succeeded in getting off his necktie. Finally, he was sprawled, like some grotesque fountain figure, in underwear and necktie and the one remaining pale-green sock while the revolving arch of water moved with cool whispers about him. The arch of water had a faint crystalline iridescence, a mist of delicate colors, as it wheeled under the moon, for the moon had by that time begun to poke with an air of slow astonishment over the roof of the little building that housed the electric. And still the complaining doves cooed at him from various windows of the house, and you could tell their voices apart only by the fact that the mother murmured "Brick? Brick?" and Mary Louise called him Mr. Pollitt. "Oh, Mr. Pollitt, Mother is so unhappy! Mother is crying!"

That night, he talked to himself or to invisible figures on the lawn. One of them was his wife, Margaret. He kept saying, "I'm sorry, Margaret, I'm sorry, Margaret, I'm so sorry, so sorry, Margaret. I'm sorry I'm no good, I'm sorry, Margaret, I'm so sorry, so sorry I'm no good, sorry I'm drunk, sorry I'm no good, I'm so sorry it all had to turn out like this . . ."

Later on, much later, after the remarkably slow procession of touring cars had stopped passing the house, a little black sedan that belonged to the police drew up in front of the Greys' and sat there for a while. In it was the chief of police himself. He called "Brick! Brick!" almost as gently and softly as Mary Louise's mother had called from the lightless windows. "Brick! Brick, old boy! Brick, fellow?" he called, till finally the inert fountain figure in underwear and green socks and unremovable necktie staggered out from under the rotating arch of water and stumbled down to the walk and stood there negligently and quietly conversing with the chief of police, under the no longer at all astonished, now quite large and indifferent great yellow stare of the August moon. They began to laugh softly together, Mr. Brick Pollitt and the chief of police, and finally the door of the little black car opened and Mr. Brick Pollitt got in beside the chief of police while the common officer got out to collect the clothes, flabby as drenched towels, on the croquet lawn. Then they drove away, and the summer night's show was over.

It was not quite over for me, for I had been watching it all that time with unabated interest. And about an hour afterward I saw Mary Louise's mother come out onto the lawn; she stood there with an air of desolation for a while. Then she went into the garage and backed the electric out. The electric went sedately off into the summer night, with its buzzing no louder than an insect's, and perhaps an hour later it came back again, containing in its glass show box not only the thin, pretty widow but a quiet and chastened Mr. Pollitt. She curved an arm about his immensely tall figure as they went up the front walk, and I heard him say only one word distinctly. It was the name of his wife.

Early that autumn, which was different from summer in nothing except the quicker coming of dusk, the visits of Mr. Brick Pollitt began to take on a spasmodic irregularity. That faraway boom of a cannon at five o'clock was now the announcement that two ladies in white dresses were waiting on a white gallery for someone who was each time a little more likely to disappoint them than the time before. Disappointment was not a thing that Mary

Louise was inured to; it was a country that she was passing through not as an old inhabitant but as a bewildered explorer, and each afternoon she lugged the oblong box out of the garage, ceremonially opened it upon the center of the lawn, and began to arrange the wickets in their formal pattern between the two gaudily painted poles that meant beginning, middle, and end. And the widow talked to her from the gallery, under the awning, as if there had been no important alteration in their lives or their prospects. Their almost duplicate voices as they talked back and forth between gallery and lawn rang out as clearly as if the enormous corner lot were enclosed at this hour by a still more enormous and perfectly transparent glass bell that picked up and carried through space whatever was uttered beneath it. This was true not only when they were talking to each other across the lawn but when they were seated side by side in the white wicker chairs on the gallery. Phrases from these conversations became catchwords, repeated and mocked by the neighbors, for whom the widow and her daughter and Mr. Brick Pollitt had been three players in a sensational drama. It had shocked and angered them for two acts, but now as it approached a conclusion it was declining into unintentional farce, which they could laugh at. It was not difficult to find something ludicrous in the talks between the two ladies or the high-pitched elegance of their voices.

Mary Louise would ask, "Will Mr. Pollitt get here in time for croquet?"

"I hope so, precious. It does him so much good."

"He'll have to come soon or it will be too dark to see the wickets."

"That's true, precious."

"Mother, why is it dark so early now?"

"Honey, you know why. The sun goes South."

"But why does it go South?"

"Precious, Mother cannot explain the movements of the heavenly bodies, you know that as well as Mother knows it. Those things are controlled by certain mysterious laws that people on earth don't know or understand."

"Mother, are we going East?"

"When, precious?"

"Before school starts."

"Honey, you know it's impossible for Mother to make any definite plans."

"I hope we do. I don't want to go to school here."

"Why not, precious? Are you afraid of the children?"

"No, Mother, but they don't like me. They make fun of me."

"How do they make fun of you?"

"They mimic the way I talk and they walk in front of me with their stomachs pushed out and giggle."

"That's because they're children and children are cruel."

"Will they stop being cruel when they grow up?"

"Why, I suppose some of them will and some of them won't."

"Well, I hope we go East before school opens."

"Mother can't make any plans or promises, honey."

"No, but Mr. Brick Pollitt—"

"Honey, lower your voice! Ladies talk softly."

"Oh, my goodness!"

"What is it, precious?"

"A mosquito just bit me!"

"That's too bad, but don't scratch it. Scratching can leave a permanent scar on the skin."

"I'm not scratching it. I'm just sucking it, Mother."

"Honey, Mother has told you time and again that the thing to do when you have a mosquito bite is to get a small piece of ice and wrap it up in a handkerchief and rub the bite gently with it until the sting is removed."

"That's what I do, but my lump of ice is melted!"

"Get you another piece, honey. You know where the icebox is!"

"There's not much left. You put so much in the ice bag for your headache."

"There must be some left, honey."

"There's just enough left for Mr. Pollitt's drinks."

"Never mind that."

"He needs it for his drinks, Mother."

"Yes, Mother knows what he wants the ice for, precious."

"There's only a little piece left. It's hardly enough to rub a mosquito bite with."

"Well, use it for that purpose, that purpose is better, and anyhow when Mr. Pollitt comes over as late as this, he doesn't deserve to have any ice saved for him."

"Mother?"

"Yes, precious?"

"I love ice and sugar!"

"What did you say, precious?"

"I said I loved ice and sugar!"

"Ice and sugar, precious?"

"Yes, I love the ice and sugar in the bottom of Mr. Pollitt's glass when he's through with it."

"Honey, you mustn't eat the ice in the bottom of Mr. Pollitt's glass!"

"Why not, Mother?"

"Because it's got liquor in it!"

"Oh, no, Mother. It's just ice and sugar when Mr. Pollitt's through with it."

"Honey, there's always a little liquor left in it."

"Oh, no. Not a drop's left when Mr. Pollitt's through with it!"

"But you say there's sugar left in it, and, honey you know that sugar is very absorbent."

"It's what, Mummy?"

"It absorbs some liquor, and that's a good way to cultivate a taste for it. And, honey, you know what dreadful consequences a taste for liquor can have. It's bad enough for a man, but for a woman it's fatal. So when you want ice and sugar, let Mother know and she'll prepare some for you, but don't ever let me catch you eating what's left in Mr. Pollitt's glass!"

"Mama?"

"Yes, precious?"

"Its almost completely dark now. Everybody is turning on their lights or driving out on the river road to cool off. Can't we go out riding in the electric?"

"No, honey, we can't till we know Mr. Pollitt's not—"

"Do you still think he will come?"

"Precious, how can I say? Is Mother a fortune-teller?"

"*Oh, here comes the Pierce, Mummy, here comes the Pierce!*"

"*Is it? Is it the Pierce?*"

"Oh, no. No, it isn't. It's a Hudson Super Six. Mummy, I'm going to pull up the wickets now and water the lawn, because if Mr. Pollitt does come, he'll have people with him or won't be in a condition to play croquet. And when I've finished, I want to drive the electric around the block."

"Drive it around the block, honey, but don't go into the business district with it."

"Are you going with me, Mummy?"

"No, precious, I'm going to sit here."

"It's cooler in the electric."

"I don't think so. The electric goes too slowly to make much breeze."

If Mr. Pollitt did finally arrive those evenings, it was likely to be with a caravan of cars that came from Memphis, and then Mrs. Grey would have to receive a raffish assortment of strangers as if she herself had invited them to a party. The party would not confine itself to the downstairs rooms and galleries but would explode quickly and brilliantly in all directions, filling both floors of the house, spilling out upon the lawn, and sometimes even penetrating the little building that housed the electric automobile and the oblong box that held the packed-away croquet set. On those party nights, the fantastically balustraded and gabled and turreted white building would glitter all over, like one of those huge night-excursion boats that came downriver from Memphis, and it woud be full of ragtime music and laughter. But at some point in the evening there would be, almost invariably, a disturbance. Some male guest would start cursing loudly, a woman would scream, you would hear a shattering of glass. Almost immediately afterward, the lights would go out in the house, as if it really were a boat and had run aground. From all the doors and galleries and stairs, people would come rushing forth, and the dispersion would be more rapid than the arrival had been. A little later, the police car would pull up in front of the house. The thin, pretty widow would come out on the front gallery to receive the chief of police, and you could hear her light voice tinkling like glass chimes. "Why, it was nothing, it was nothing at all, just somebody who drank a little too much and lost his temper. You know how that Memphis crowd is, Mr. Duggan, there's always one gentleman in it who can't hold his liquor. I know it's late, but we have such a huge lawn—it occupies half the block—that I shouldn't think anybody who wasn't overcome with curiosity would have to know that a party had been going on!"

And then something happened that made no sound at all.

It wasn't an actual death, but it had nearly all the external indications of one. When there is a death in a house, the house is unnaturally quiet for a day or two. During that interval, the space that separates a house from those who watch it seems to become a translucent thickness of glass behind which whatever activity is visible goes on with the startling hush of a film when the sound track is broken. So it had been five months ago, when the pleasant young Doctor had died of that fierce flower grown in his skull. There had been an unnatural quiet for several days, and then a peculiar gray car with frosted windows had crashed through the bell of silence and the young Doctor, identifiable by the bronze gleam of hair at one end of the strapped and sheeted figure on the cot, had emerged from the house as if he were giving a public demonstration of how to go to sleep soundly in jolting motion under a blaze of lights.

That was five months ago, and it was now early October.

Mr. Pollitt had not been seen at the Greys' for more than a week when, one day, a truck pulled up before the house and a workman planted a square wooden sign at the front of the lawn. Mrs. Grey came out of the house as if it had caught fire. She ran down the steps, her white skirts making the crackling noise of flame, calling out as she descended, "You, man! What are you doing! What are you putting up there!"

"A 'For Sale' sign," he told her.

"Who told you to put that up? This house isn't for sale"

"Yes, ma'am, it is!"

"Who said so?"

"Mrs. Pollitt, *she* said so."

He stared at Mrs. Grey and she came no closer. Then he gave the pole of the red-lettered sign a final blow with the back of a shovel and tossed the implement crashing into the truck and drove off. The back of the sign said nothing, so presently Mrs. Grey continued her running advance to the front of the lawn, where the great red letters were visible. She stood in front it it, rapidly shaking her head, finally gasping aloud as if the import of it had just then struck her, and then she turned and went slowly and thoughtfully back to the radiant fantasy of a house just as Mary Louise appeared from behind it with the hose.

"Mother!" she called, "I'm going to water the lawn!"

"Don't!" said Mrs. Grey.

The next afternoon, a fat and pleasantly smiling man, whom I had seen times without number loitering around in front of the used-car lot next to the Paramount movie, came up the front walk of the Greys' house with the excessive nonchalance of a man who is about to commit a robbery. He pushed the bell, waited awhile, pushed it again, and then was admitted through an opening that seemed to be hardly wide enough for his figure. He came back out almost immediately with something in his closed fist. It was the key to the little building that contained the croquet set and the electric automobile. He drew its folding doors all the way open, and disclosed the electric sitting there with its usual manner of a lady putting on or taking off her gloves at the entrance to a reception. He stared at it, as if its elegance were momentarily baffling. Then he got in and drove it out of the garage, holding the polished black pilot stick with a look on his round face that was like the look of an adult who is a little embarrassed to find himself being amused by a game that was meant for children. He drove it serenely out into the wide, shady street, and at an upstairs window of the house there was some kind of quick movement, as if a figure looking out had been startled by something and then had retreated in haste.

Later, after the Greys had left town, I saw the elegant square vehicle, which appeared to be made out of glass and patent leather, standing with an air of haughty self-consciousness among a dozen or so other cars for sale in the lot next door to the Paramount movie theatre, and as far as I know, it may be still sitting there, but many degrees less glittering by now.

The Greys had come and gone all in one quick season: the young Doctor, with his understanding eyes and quiet voice, whom everyone liked in a hesitant, early way and had said would do well in the town; the thin, pretty woman, whom no one had really known except Brick Pollitt; and the plump little girl, who might someday be as pretty and slender as her mother. They had come and gone in one season, yes, like one of these tent shows that suddenly appear in a vacant lot in a Southern town and cross the sky at night with mysteriously wheeling lights and unearthly music, and then are gone, and the summer goes on without them, as if they had never come there.

As for Mr. Brick Pollitt, I can remember seeing him only once after the Greys left town, for my time there was also coming to an end. This last time that I saw him was a brilliant fall morning. It was a Saturday morning in October. Brick's driver's license had been revoked again, and his wife, Margaret, sat in the driver's seat of the Pierce-Arrow touring car. Brick did not sit beside her. He was on the back seat of the car, pitching this way and that way with the car's jolting motion, like a loosely wrapped package being delivered somewhere. Margaret Pollitt handled the car with a wonderful male assurance, her bare arms brown and muscular, and the car's canvas top had been lowered, the better to expose on its back seat the sheepishly grinning and nodding figure of Brick Pollitt. He was immaculately clothed and barbered. The knot of his polka-dot tie was drawn as tight as strong and eager fingers could knot a tie for an important occasion. One of his large red hands protruded, clasping the door to steady his motion, and two bands of gold glittered, a small one about a finger, a large one about the wrist. His cream-colored coat was neatly folded on the seat beside him and he wore a shirt of thin white material. He was a man who had been, and even at that time still was, the handsomest you were likely to remember.

Margaret blew the car's silver trumpet at every intersection. She leaned this way and that way, elevating or thrusting out an arm as she greeted people on porches, merchants beside store entrances, people she barely knew along the walks, calling them all by their familiar names, as if she were running for office in the town, while Brick nodded and grinned with senseless amiability behind her. It was exactly the way that some ancient conqueror, such as Caesar, or Alexander the Great, or Hannibal, might have led in chains through a capital city the prince of a state newly conquered.

EDITORS' ANALYSIS

This is essentially a simple story of a dominating wife who has withheld her love from her gay young husband, and has turned him into a drunk. He plays the role of intimidated child with his wife, personally assuming the guilt for the breakdown of their marriage. His love affair with the young doctor's widow, which is the central incident of the story, cannot make up for his sense of failure with his own wife. So he returns to her, to live the life of one wholly defeated in love. Williams gives this series of events a somber, emotionally moving tone, partly by his resources of eccentric imagery, partly by the irony of telling it from the point of view of a fourteen-year-old boy, himself not yet old enough to understand clearly what he is witnessing.

QUESTIONS

1. Is Williams overly ironic in calling the events of his story a "game"? Does the detachment suggested by the title, and the fourteen-year-old point of view from which the story is told, increase its emotional impact on you? Decrease it?

2. Is there any true communication in the story between any of the characters? Between Brick and his wife? Between Brick and his mistress? Between the mother and her daughter?

3. Discuss the imagery in the first long paragraph of the story. What is its intended effect? How does it create the tone of the whole story?

4. What is wrong with Brick? Does the story give any hint? Does it merely insist that his compulsive drinking be taken as without reason?

5. Are both the doctor's young widow and Brick Pollitt unusually lacking in a will to resist? Is this lack of aggressive defense of themselves a product of their sense of guilt? Fear? What?

6. Why is Dr. Grey's brain tumor not accurately described for what it is? Why call it "a fierce geranium"?

7. What is suggested about Brick and Isabel Grey's relationship when the mother calls her daughter "you fat little monster"? Is this a form of displaced anger?

8. What is the effect, late in the story, of describing Mrs. Grey's car, up for sale in a used car lot, as "standing with an air of haughty self-consciousness" among the other cars? What is created in the story by the use of this car, almost from the beginning? A sense of helpless elegance in its owner?

Flowering Judas

by KATHERINE ANNE PORTER

Katherine Anne Porter (1894-   ) is one of the most admired and most discussed of living American writers. She has not published a great deal, but her comparatively small fictional output is noted for its skillful portrayal of the intense inner drama and turmoil of its characters, and for its subtle penetration and revelation of their essential natures out of which they act, make decisions, sometimes create tragedy. Collections of her short stories include *Flowering Judas* (1930); *Pale Horse, Pale Rider* (1939) which republishes the novelette *Noon Wine; The Leaning Tower, and Other Stories* (1944). *Ship of Fools* is her latest novel.

"Flowering Judas" presents as its central character a young woman whose outward life is exemplary. Yet her odd isolation from the cause she is serving, from the men who wish to make love to her, is wholly real if an infinitely subtle one. The story is, in essence, her character: she is presented to us, by means of Miss Porter's sustained, ironic awareness, as wholly trapped within an ideal conception of herself.

Braggioni sits heaped upon the edge of a straight-backed chair much too small for him, and sings to Laura in a furry, mournful voice. Laura has begun to find reasons for avoiding her own house until the latest possible moment, for Braggioni is there almost every night. No matter how late she is, he will be sitting there with a surly, waiting expression, pulling at his kinky yellow hair, thumbing the strings of his guitar, snarling a tune under his breath. Lupe the Indian maid meets Laura at the door, and says with a flicker of a glance towards the upper room, "He waits."

Laura wishes to lie down, she is tired of her hairpins and the feel of her long tight sleeves, but she says to him, "Have you a new song for me this evening?" If he says yes, she asks him to sing it. If he says no, she remembers his favorite one, and asks him to sing it again. Lupe brings her a cup of chocolate and a plate of rice, and Laura eats at the small table under the lamp, first inviting Braggioni, whose answer is always the same: "I have eaten, and besides, chocolate thickens the voice."

Laura says, "Sing, then," and Braggioni heaves himself into song. He scratches the guitar familiarly as though it were a pet animal, and sings passionately off key, taking the high notes in a prolonged painful squeal. Laura, who haunts the markets listening to the ballad singers, and stops every day to hear the blind boy playing his reed-flute in Sixteenth of September Street, listens to Braggioni with pitiless courtesy, because she dares not smile at his miserable performance. Nobody dares to smile at him. Braggioni is cruel to everyone, with a kind of specialized insolence, but he is so vain of his talents, and so sensitive to slights, it would require a cruelty and vanity greater than his own to lay a finger on the vast cureless wound of his self-esteem. It would require courage, too, for it is dangerous to offend him, and nobody has this courage.

Braggioni loves himself with such tenderness and amplitude and eternal charity that his followers—for he is a leader of men, a skilled revolutionist, and his skin has been punctured in honorable warfare—warm themselves in the reflected glow, and say to each other: "He has a real nobility, a love of humanity raised above mere personal affections." The excess of this self-love has flowed out, inconveniently for her, over Laura, who, with so many others, owes her comfortable situation and her salary to him. When he is in a very good humor, he tells her, "I am tempted to forgive you for being a *gringa. Gringita!*" and Laura, burning, imagines herself leaning forward suddenly, and with a sound back-handed slap wiping the suety smile from his face. If he notices her eyes at these moments he gives no sign.

She knows what Braggioni would offer her, and she must resist tenaciously without appearing to resist, and if she could avoid it she would not admit even to herself the slow drift of his intention. During these long evenings which have spoiled a long month for her, she sits in her deep chair with an open book on her knees, resting her eyes on the consoling rigidity of the printed page when the sight and sound of Braggioni singing threaten to identify themselves with all her remembered afflictions and to add their weight to her uneasy premonitions of the future. The gluttonous bulk of Braggioni has become a symbol of her many disillusions, for a revolutionist should be lean, animated by heroic faith, a vessel of abstract virtues. This is nonsense, she knows it now and is ashamed of it. Revolution must have leaders, and leadership is a career for energetic men. She is, her comrades tell her, full of romantic error, for what she defines as cynicism in them is merely "a developed sense of reality." She is almost too willing to say, "I am wrong, I suppose I don't really understand the principles," and afterward she makes a secret truce with herself, determined not to surrender her will to such expedient logic. But she cannot help feeling that she has been betrayed irreparably by the disunion between her way of living and her feeling of what life should be, and at times she is almost contented to rest in this sense of grievance as a private store of consolation. Sometimes she wishes to run away, but she stays. Now she longs to fly out of this room, down the narrow stairs, and into the street where the houses lean together like conspirators under a single mottled lamp, and leave Braggioni singing to himself.

Instead she looks at Braggioni, frankly and clearly, like a good child who understands the rules of behavior. Her knees cling together under sound blue serge, and her round white collar is not purposely nun-like. She wears the uniform of an idea, and has renounced vanities. She was born Roman Catholic, and in spite of her fear of being seen by someone who might make a scandal of it, she slips now and again into some crumbling little church, kneels on the chilly stone, and says a Hail Mary on the gold rosary she bought in Tehuantepec. It is no good and she ends by examining the altar with its tinsel flowers and ragged brocades, and feels tender about the battered doll-shape of some male saint whose white, lace-trimmed drawers hang limply around his ankles below the hieratic dignity of his velvet robe. She has encased herself in a set of principles derived from her early training, leaving no detail of gesture or of personal taste untouched, and for this reason she will not wear lace made on machines. This is her private heresy, for in her special group the machine is sacred, and will be the salvation of the workers. She loves fine lace, and there is a tiny edge of fluted cobweb on this collar, which is one of twenty precisely alike, folded in blue tissue paper in the upper drawer of her clothes chest.

Braggioni catches her glance solidly as if he had been waiting for it, leans forward, balancing his paunch between his spread knees, and sings with tremendous emphasis, weighing his words.

He has, the song relates, no father and no mother, nor even a friend to console him; lonely as a wave of the sea he comes and goes, lonely as a wave. His mouth opens round and yearns sideways, his balloon cheeks grow oily with the labor of song. He bulges marvelously in his expensive garments. Over his lavender collar, crushed upon a purple necktie, held by a diamond hoop: over his ammunition belt of tooled leather worked in silver, buckled cruelly around his gasping middle: over the tops of his glossy shoes Braggioni swells with ominous ripeness, his mauve silk hose stretched taut, his ankles bound with the stout leather thongs of his shoes.

When he stretches his eyelids at Laura she notes again that his eyes are the true tawny yellow cat's eyes. He is rich, not in money, he tells her, but in power, and this power brings with it the blameless ownership of things, and the right to indulge his love of small luxuries. "I have a taste for the elegant refinements," he said once, flourishing a yellow silk handkerchief before her nose. "Smell that? It is Jockey Club, imported from New York." Nonetheless he is wounded by life. He will say so presently. "It is true everything turns to dust in the hand, to gall on the tongue." He sighs and his leather belt creaks like a saddle girth. "I am disappointed in everything as it comes. Everything." He shakes his head. "You, poor thing, you will be disappointed too. You are born for it. We are more alike than you realize in some things. Wait and see. Some day you will remember what I have told you, you will know that Braggioni was your friend."

Laura feels a slow chill, a purely physical sense of danger, a warning in her blood that violence, mutilation, a shocking death, wait for her with lessening patience. She has translated this fear into something homely, immediate, and sometimes hesitates before crossing the street. "My personal fate is nothing, except as the testimony of a mental attitude," she reminds herself, quoting from some forgotten philosophic primer, and is sensible enough to add, "Anyhow, I shall not be killed by an automobile if I can help it."

"It may be true I am as corrupt, in another way, as Braggioni," she thinks in spite of herself, "as callous, as incomplete," and if this is so, any kind of death seems preferable. Still she sits quietly, she does not run. Where could she go? Uninvited she has promised herself to this place; she can no longer imagine herself as living in another country, and there is no pleasure in remembering her life before she came here.

Precisely what is the nature of this devotion, its true motives, and what are its obligations? Laura cannot say. She spends part of her days in Xochimilco, near by, teaching Indian children to say in English, "The cat is on the mat." When she appears in the classroom they crowd about her with smiles on their wise, innocent, clay-colored faces, crying, "Good morning, my titcher!" in immaculate voices, and they make of her desk a fresh garden of flowers every day.

During her leisure she goes to union meetings and listens to busy important voices quarreling over tactics, methods, internal politics. She visits the prisoners of her own political faith in their cells, where they entertain themselves with counting cockroaches, repenting of their indiscretions, composing their memoirs, writing out manifestoes and plans for their comrades who are still walking about free, hands in pockets, sniffing fresh air. Laura brings them food and cigarettes and a little money, and she brings messages disguised in equivocal phrases from the men outside who dare not set foot in the prison for fear of disappearing into the cells kept empty for them. If the prisoners confuse night and day, and complain, "Dear little Laura, time doesn't pass in this infernal hole, and I won't know when it is time to sleep unless I have a reminder," she brings them their favorite narcotics, and says in a tone that does not wound them with pity, "Tonight will really be night for you," and though her Spanish amuses them, they find her comforting, useful. If they lose patience and all faith, and curse the slowness of their friends in coming to their rescue with money and influence, they trust her not to repeat everything, and if she inquires, "Where do you think we can find money, or influence?" they are certain to answer, "Well, there is Braggioni, why doesn't he do something?"

She smuggles letters from headquarters to men hiding from firing squads in back streets in mildewed houses, where they sit in tumbled beds and talk bitterly as if all Mexico were at their heels, when Laura knows positively they might appear at the band concert in the Alameda on Sunday morning, and no one would notice them. But Braggioni says, "Let them sweat a little. The next time they may be careful. It is very restful to have them out of the way for a while." She is not afraid to knock on any door in any street after midnight, and enter in the darkness, and say to one of these men who is really in danger: "They will be looking for you—seriously—tomorrow morning after six. Here is some money from Vicente. Go to Vera Cruz and wait."

She borrows money from the Roumanian agitator to give to his bitter enemy the Polish agitator. The favor of Braggioni is their disputed territory, and Braggioni holds the balance nicely, for he can use them both. The Polish agitator talks love to her over café tables, hoping to exploit what he believes is her secret sentimental preference for him, and he gives her misinformation which he begs her to repeat as the solemn truth to certain persons. The Roumanian is more adroit. He is generous with his money in all good causes, and lies to her with an air of ingenuous candor, as if he were her good friend and confidant. She never repeats anything they may say. Braggioni never asks questions. He has other ways to discover all that he wishes to know about them.

Nobody touches her, but all praise her gray eyes, and the soft, round under lip which promises gayety, yet is always grave, nearly always firmly closed: and they cannot understand why she is in Mexico. She walks back and forth on her errands, with puzzled eyebrows, carrying her little folder of drawings and music and school papers. No dancer dances more beautifully than Laura walks, and she inspires some amusing, unexpected ardors, which cause little gossip, because nothing comes of them. A young captain who had been a soldier in Zapata's army attempted, during a horeback ride near Cuernavaca, to express his desire for her with the noble simplicity befitting a rude folk-hero: but gently, because he was gentle. This gentleness was his defeat, for when he alighted, and removed her foot from the stirrup, and essayed to draw her down into his arms, her horse, ordinarily a tame one, shied fiercely, reared and plunged away. The young hero's horse careered blindly after his stable-mate, and the hero did not return to the hotel until rather late that evening. At breakfast he came to her table in full charro dress, gray buckskin jacket and trousers with strings of silver buttons down the leg, and he was in a humorous, careless mood. "May I sit with you?" and "You are a wonderful rider. I was terrified that you might be thrown and dragged. I should never have forgiven myself. But I cannot admire you enough for your riding!"

"I learned to ride in Arizona," said Laura.

"If you will ride with me again this morning, I promise you a horse that will not shy with you," he said. But Laura remembered that she must return to Mexico City at noon.

Next morning the children made a celebration and spent their playtime writing on the blackboard, "We lov ar titcher," and with tinted chalks they drew wreaths of flowers around the words.

The young hero wrote her a letter: "I am a very foolish, wasteful, impulsive man. I should have first said I love you, and then you would not have run away. But you shall see me again." Laura thought, "I must send him a box of colored crayons," but she was trying to forgive herself for having spurred her horse at the wrong moment.

A brown, shock-haired youth came and stood in her patio one night and sang like a lost soul for two hours, but Laura could think of nothing to do about it. The moonlight spread a wash of gauzy silver over the clear spaces of the garden, and the shadows were cobalt blue. The scarlet blossoms of the Judas tree were dull purple, and the names of the colors repeated themselves automatically in her mind, while she watched not the boy, but his shadow, fallen like a dark garment across the fountain rim, trailing in the water. Lupe came silently and whispered expert counsel in her ear: "If you will throw him one little flower, he will sing another song or two and go away." Laura threw the flower, and he sang a last song and went away with the flower tucked in the band of his hat. Lupe said, "He is one of the organizers of the Typographers Union, and before that he sold corridos in the Merced market, and before that, he came from Guanajuato, where I was born. I would not trust any man, but I trust least those from Guanajuato."

She did not tell Laura that he would be back again the next night, and the next, nor that he would follow her at a certain distance around the Merced market, through the Zócolo, up Francisco I. Madero Avenue, and so along the Paseo de la Reforma to Chapultepec Park, and into the Philosopher's Footpath, still with that flower withering in his hat, and an indivisible attention in his eyes.

Now Laura is accustomed to him, it means nothing except that he is nineteen years old and is observing a convention with all propriety, as though it were founded on a law of nature, which in the end it might well prove to be. He is beginning to write poems which he prints on a wooden press, and he leaves them stuck like hand-bills in her door. She is pleasantly disturbed by the abstract, unhurried watchfulness of his black eyes which will in time turn easily towards another object. She tells herself that throwing the flower was a mistake, for she is twenty-two years old and knows better; but she refuses to regret it, and persuades herself that her negation of all external events as they occur is a sign that she is gradually perfecting herself in the stoicism she

strives to cultivate against that disaster she fears, though she cannot name it.

She is not at home in the world. Every day she teaches children
who remain strangers to her, though she loves their tender round
hands and their charming opportunist savagery. She knocks at
unfamiliar doors not knowing whether a friend or a stranger
shall answer, and even if a known face emerges from the sour
gloom of that unknown interior, still it is the face of a stranger.
No matter what this stranger says to her, nor what her message
to him, the very cells of her flesh reject knowledge and kinship
in one monotonous word. No. No. No. She draws her strength
from this one holy talismanic word which does not suffer her
to be led into evil. Denying everything, she may walk anywhere
in safety, she looks at everything without amazement.

No, repeats this firm unchanging voice of her blood; and she
looks at Braggioni without amazement. He is a great man, he
wishes to impress this simple girl who covers her great breasts
with thick dark cloth, and who hides long, invaluably beautiful
legs under a heavy skirt. She is almost thin except for the incomprehensible fullness of her breasts, like a nursing mother's, and
Braggioni, who considers himself a judge of women, speculates
again on the puzzle of her notorious virginity, and takes the
liberty of speech which she permits without a sign of modesty,
indeed, without any sort of sign, which is disconcerting.

"You think you are so cold, *gringita!* Wait and see. You will
surprise yourself some day! May I be there to advise you!" He
stretches his eyelids at her, and his ill-humored cat's eyes waver
in a separate glance for the two points of light marking the opposite ends of a smoothly drawn path between the swollen curve
of her breasts. He is not put off by that blue serge, nor by her
resolutely fixed gaze. There is all the time in the world. His
cheeks are bellying with the wind of song. "O girl with the dark
eyes," he sings, and reconsiders. "But yours are not dark. I can
change all that. O girl with the green eyes, you have stolen my
heart away!" then his mind wanders to the song, and Laura feels
the weight of his attention being shifted elsewhere. Singing thus,
he seems harmless, he is quite harmless, there is nothing to do
but sit patiently and say "No," when the moment comes. She
draws a full breath, and her mind wanders also, but not far. She
dares not wander too far.

Not for nothing has Braggioni taken pains to be a good revolutionist and a professional lover of humanity. He will never die

of it. He has the malice, the cleverness, the wickedness, the sharpness of wit, the hardness of heart, stipulated for loving the world
profitably. He *will never die of it*. He will live to see himself
kicked out from his feeding trough by other hungry world-saviors.
Traditionally he must sing in spite of his life which drives him
to bloodshed, he tells Laura, for his father was a Tuscany peasant
who drifted to Yucatan and married a Maya woman: a woman of
race, an aristocrat. They gave him the love and knowledge of
music, thus: and under the rip of his thumbnail, the strings of the
instrument complain like exposed nerves.

Once he was called Delgadito by all the girls and married
women who ran after him; he was so scrawny all his bones showed
under his thin cotton clothing, and he could squeeze his emptiness
to the very backbone with his two hands. He was a poet and the
revolution was only a dream then; too many women loved him
and sapped away his youth, and he could never find enough to
eat anywhere, anywhere! Now he is a leader of men, crafty men
who whisper in his ear, hungry men who wait for hours outside
his office for a word with him, emaciated men with wild faces
who waylay him at the street gate with a timid, "Comrade, let
me tell you . . ." and they blow the foul breath from their empty
stomachs in his face.

He is always sympathetic. He gives them handfuls of small
coins from his own pocket, he promises them work, there will be
demonstrations, they must join the unions and attend the meetings, above all they must be on the watch for spies. They are
closer to him than his own brothers, without them he can do
nothing—until tomorrow, comrade!

Until tomorrow. "They are stupid, they are lazy, they are
treacherous, they would cut my throat for nothing," he says to
Laura. He has good food and abundant drink, he hires an automobile and drives in the Paseo on Sunday morning, and enjoys
plenty of sleep in a soft bed beside a wife who dares not disturb him; and he sits pampering his bones in easy billows of
fat, singing to Laura, who knows and thinks these things about
him. When he was fifteen, he tried to drown himself because he
loved a girl, his first love, and she laughed at him. "A thousand
women have paid for that," and his tight little mouth turns down
at the corners. Now he perfumes his hair with Jockey Club, and
confides to Laura: "One woman is really as good as another for
me, in the dark. I prefer them all."

His wife organizes unions among the girls in the cigarette factories, and walks in picket lines, and even speaks at meetings in the evening. But she cannot be brought to acknowledge the benefits of true liberty. "I tell her I must have my freedom, net. She does not understand my point of view." Laura has heard this many times. Braggioni scratches the guitar and meditates. "She is an instinctively virtuous woman, pure gold, no doubt of that. If she were not, I should lock her up, and she knows it."

His wife, who works so hard for the good of the factory girls, employs part of her leisure lying on the floor weeping because there are so many women in the world, and only one husband for her, and she never knows where nor when to look for him. He told her: "Unless you can learn to cry when I am not here, I must go away for good." That day he went away and took a room at the Hotel Madrid.

It is this month of separation for the sake of higher principles that has been spoiled not only for Mrs. Braggioni, whose sense of reality is beyond criticism, but for Laura, who feels herself bogged in a nightmare. Tonight Laura envies Mrs. Braggioni, who is alone, and free to weep as much as she pleases about a concrete wrong. Laura has just come from a visit to the prison, and she is waiting for tomorrow with a bitter anxiety as if tomorrow may not come, but time may be caught immovably in this hour, with herself transfixed, Braggioni singing on forever, and Eugenio's body not yet discovered by the guard.

Braggioni says: "Are you going to sleep?" Almost before she can shake her head, he begins telling her about the May-day disturbances coming on in Morelia, for the Catholics hold a festival in honor of the Blessed Virgin, and the Socialists celebrate their martyrs on that day. "There will be two independent processions, starting from either end of town, and they will march until they meet, and the rest depends . . ." He asks her to oil and load his pistols. Standing up, he unbuckles his ammunition belt, and spreads it laden across her knees. Laura sits with the shells slipping through the cleaning cloth dipped in oil, and he says again he cannot understand why she works so hard for the revolutionary idea unless she loves some man who is in it. "Are you not in love with someone?" "No." "Then it is your own fault. No woman need go begging. Why, what is the matter with you? The legless beggar woman in the Alameda has a perfectly faithful lover. Did you know that?"

Laura peers down the pistol barrel and says nothing, but a long, slow faintness rises and subsides in her; Braggioni curves his swollen fingers around the throat of the guitar and softly smothers the music out of it, and when she hears him again he seems to have forgotten her, and is speaking in the hypnotic voice he uses when talking in small rooms to a listening, close-gathered crowd. Some day this world, now seemingly so composed and eternal, to the edges of every sea shall be merely a tangle of gaping trenches, of crashing walls and broken bodies. Everything must be torn from its accustomed place where it has rotted for centuries, hurled skyward and distributed, cast down again clean as rain, without separate identity. Nothing shall survive that the stiffened hands of poverty have created for the rich and no one shall be left alive except the elect spirits destined to procreate a new world cleansed of cruelty and injustice, ruled by benevolent anarchy: "Pistols are good, I love them, cannon are even better, but in the end I pin my faith to good dynamite," he concludes, and strokes the pistol lying in her hands. "Once I dreamed of destroying this city, in case it offered resistance to General Ortíz, but it fell into his hands like an overripe pear."

He is made restless by his own words, rises and stands waiting. Laura holds up the belt to him: "Put that on, and go kill somebody in Morelia, and you will be happier," she says softly. The presence of death in the room makes her bold. "Today, I found Eugenio going into a stupor. He refused to allow me to call the prison doctor. He had taken all the tablets I brought him yesterday. He said he took them because he was bored."

"He is a fool, and his death is his own business," says Braggioni, fastening his belt carefully.

"I told him if he had waited only a little longer, you would have got him set free," says Laura. "He said he did not want to wait."

"He is a fool and we are well rid of him," says Braggioni, reaching for his hat.

He goes away. Laura knows his mood has changed, she will not see him any more for a while. He will send word when he needs her to go on errands into strange streets, to speak to the strange faces that will appear, like clay masks with the power of human speech, to mutter their thanks to Braggioni for his help. Now she is free, and she thinks, I must run while there is time. But she does not go.

Braggioni enters his own house where for a month his wife has spent many hours every night weeping and tangling her hair upon her pillow. She is weeping now, and she weeps more at the sight of him, the cause of all her sorrows. He looks about the room. Nothing is changed, the smells are good and familiar, he is well acquainted with the woman who comes toward him with no reproach except grief on her face. He says to her tenderly: "You are so good, please don't cry any more, you dear good creature." She says, "Are you tired, my angel? Sit here and I will wash your feet." She brings a bowl of water, and kneeling, unlaces his shoes, and when from her knees she raises her sad eyes under her blackened lids, he is sorry for everything, and bursts into tears. "Ah, yes, I am hungry, I am tired, let us eat something together," he says, between sobs. His wife leans her head on his arm and says, "Forgive me!" and this time he is refreshed by the solemn, endless rain of her tears.

Laura takes off her serge dress and puts on a white linen nightgown and goes to bed. She turns her head a little to one side, and lying stilly, reminds herself that it is time to sleep. Numbers tick in her brain like little clocks, soundless doors close of themselves around her. If you would sleep, you must not remember anything, the children will say tomorrow, good morning, my teacher, the poor prisoners who come every day bringing flowers to their jailor. 1-2-3-4-5—it is monstrous to confuse love with revolution, night with day, life with death—ah, Eugenio!

The tolling of the midnight bell is a signal, but what does it mean? Get up, Laura, and follow me: come out of your sleep, out of your bed, out of this strange house. What are you doing in this house? Without a word, without fear she rose and reached for Eugenio's hand, but he eluded her with a sharp, sly smile and drifted away. This is not all, you shall see—Murderer, he said, follow me, I will show you a new country, but it is far away and we must hurry. No, said Laura, not unless you take my hand, no; and she clung first to the stair rail, and then to the topmost branch of the Judas tree that bent down slowly and set her upon the earth, and then to the rocky ledge of a cliff, and then to the jagged wave of a sea that was not water but a desert of crumbling stone. Where are you taking me, she asked in wonder but without fear. To death, and it is a long way off, and we must hurry, said Eugenio. No, said Laura, not unless you take my hand. Then eat these flowers, poor prisoner, said Eugenio in a voice of pity, take and eat: and from the Judas tree he stripped the warm bleeding flowers, and held them to her lips. She saw that his hand was fleshless, a cluster of small white petrified branches, and his eye sockets were without light, but she ate the flowers greedily for they satisfied both hunger and thirst. Murderer; said Eugenio, and Cannibal! This is my body and my blood. Laura cried No! and at the sound of her own voice, she awoke trembling, and was afraid to sleep again.

EDITORS' ANALYSIS

"Flowering Judas," with its titular suggestion of betrayal, is told with an insistent richness of implication. It does not appear on the surface of the story, but comes from the direct appeal to one's mind made by the many suggestive phrases such as "the vast cureless wound of his self-esteem." It also comes from the effect on the reader of such suggestive symbolism in the story as the washing of Braggioni's feet and Laura's dream of the Judas Tree. One source of the story's great power over a reader comes from the fact that his own dulled awareness of human character is teased into new insights, fresh ways of thinking about people. Laura cannot go out in love to anyone or to any cause; yet on the surface of the life she sees herself as living, she gives the appearance of being just the opposite kind of person.

QUESTIONS

1. The Judas Tree is identified with Judas Iscariot, and with betrayal. Whom and what does Laura betray? Why can she suspect her own guilt only through a dream?

2. At what levels do you understand or identify with Laura? If she is no monster, then she is within the range of normal behavior. Does she represent an element or elements in all of us? Can they be named?

3. Why is the story told in the present tense? Does this tense eliminate the need to give us events in the life of Laura before the story begins? Does it have other effects on the tone of the story?

4. What element in Braggioni makes him worth his wife's tears? Does Laura lack this element completely?

5. Is Laura pitiable? Tragic? Something more subtle to you?

6. Why is Laura described as imagining "wiping the suety smile" from Braggioni's face with a back-handed slap? What does this line tell us about Laura.

7. What does the "solemn, endless rain" of Braggioni's wife's tears suggest about her character which separates her sharply from Laura?

8. Analyze Laura's dream, and its implications for the meaning of the story, as it is given in the final paragraph. Does this story device seem too obscure to you? Partially successful? Wholly successful?

7.

PREJUDICE

"The Imaginary Jew," by *John Berryman*

"Battle Royal," *by Ralph Ellison*

The Imaginary Jew

by JOHN BERRYMAN

John Berryman (1914-   ) is an American poet and literary critic of distinction who has written occasional fiction. He teaches at the University of Minnesota. His early poems were collected in *Five Young American Poets* (1940) and *Dispossessed* (1948). *Homage to Mistress Bradstreet* (1956) is his recent long poem in which he explores the inner life of this seventeenth-century American writer. His *Stephen Crane* (1950) is a brilliant critical and biographical study of the late 19th-century American novelist and short story writer.

Berryman's story "The Imaginary Jew," is not related to the main body of his poetry and criticism except perhaps by the acuteness of its feeling. The Jew is a Jew, he says, largely because he is accused of being one. Being thought different, he becomes different. He assumes the stance which society has created for him.

This story won the *Kenyon-Doubleday* award for the best short story of its year.

The second summer of the European war I spent in New York. I lived in a room just below street level on Lexington above Thirty-fourth, wrote a good deal, tried not to think about Europe, and listened to music on a small gramophone, the only thing of my own, except books, in the room. Haydn's London Symphony, his last, I heard probably fifty times in two months. One night when excited I dropped the pickup, creating a series of knocks at the beginning of the last movement where the oboe joins the strings which still, when I hear them, bring up for me my low dark long damp room and I feel the dew of heat and smell the rented upholstery. I was trying, as one says, to come back a little, uncertain and low after an exhausting year. Why I decided to do this in New York—the enemy in summer equally of soul and body, as I had known for years—I can't remember; perhaps I didn't, but we held on merely from week to week by the motive which presently appeared in the form of a young woman met the Christmas before and now the occupation of every evening not passed in solitary and restless gloom. My friends were away; I saw few other people. Now and then I went to the zoo in lower Central Park and watched with interest the extraordinary behavior of a female badger. For a certain time she quickly paced the round of her cage. Then she would approach the side wall from an angle in a determined, hardly perceptible, unhurried trot; suddenly, when an inch away, point her nose up it, follow her nose up over her back, turning a deft and easy somersault, from which she emerged on her feet moving swiftly and unconcernedly away, as if the action had been no affair of hers, indeed she had scarcely been present. There was another badger in the cage who never did this, and nothing else about her was remarkable; but this competent disinterested somersault she enacted once every five or ten minutes as long as I watched her—quitting the wall, by the way, always at an angle in fixed relation to the angle at which she arrived at it. It is no longer possible to experience the pleasure I knew each time she lifted her nose and I understood again that she would not fail me, or feel the mystery of her absolute disclaimer—she has been taken away or died.

The story I have to tell is no further a part of that special summer than a nightmare takes its character, for memory, from the phase of the moon one noticed on going to bed. It could have happened in another year and in another place. No doubt it did, has done, will do. Still, so weak is the talent of the mind for pure relation—immaculate apprehension of p alone—that everything helps us, as when we come to an unknown city: architecture, history, trade practices, folklore. Even more anxious our approach to a city—like my small story—which we have known and forgotten. Yet how little we can learn! Some of the history is the lonely summer. Part of the folklore, I suppose, is which I now unwillingly rehearse, the character which experience has given to my sense of the Jewish people.

Born in a part of the South where no Jews had come, or none had stayed, and educated thereafter in states where they are numerous, I somehow arrived at a metropolitan university without any clear idea of what in modern life a Jew was—without even a clear consciousness of having see one. I am unable now to explain this simplicity or blindness. I had not escaped, of course, a sense that humans somewhat different from ourselves, called "Jews," existed as in the middle distance and were best kept there, but this sense was of the vaguest. From what it was derived I do not know; I do not recall feeling the least curiosity about it, or about Jews; I had, simply, from the atmosphere of an advanced heterogeneous democratic society, ingathered a gently negative attitude toward Jews. This I took with me, untested, to college, where it received neither confirmation nor stimulus for two months. I rowed and danced and cut classes and was political; by mid-November I knew most of the five hundred men in my year. Then the man who rowed Number Three, in the eight of which I was bow, took me aside in the shower one afternoon and warned me not to be so chatty with Rosenblum.

I wondered why not. Rosenblum was stroke, a large handsome amiable fellow, for whose ability in the shell I felt great respect and no doubt envy. Because the fellows in the house wouldn't like it, my friend said. "What have they against him?" "It's only because he's Jewish," explained my friend, a second-generation Middle European.

I hooted at him, making the current noises of disbelief, and went back under the shower. It did not occur to me that he could be right. But next day when I was talking with Herz, the coxswain, whom I knew very well, I remembered the libel with some annoyance, and told Herz about it as a curiosity. Herz looked at me oddly, lowering his head, and said after a pause, "Why Al *is* Jewish, didn't you know that?" I was amazed. I said it was absurd, he couldn't be! "Why not?" said Herz, who must have been as astonished as I was. "Don't you know I'm Jewish?"

I did not know, of course, and ignorance has seldom cost me such humiliation. Herz did not guy me; he went off. But greater than my shame at not knowing something known, apparently, without effort to everyone else, were my emotions for what I then quickly discovered. Asking careful questions during the next week, I learned that about a third of the men I spent time with in college were Jewish; that they knew it, and the others knew it; that some of the others disliked them for it, and they knew this also; that certain houses existed *only* for Jews, who were excluded from the rest; and that what in short I took to be an idiotic state was deeply established, familiar, and acceptable to everyone. This discovery was the beginning of my instruction in social life proper—construing social life as that from which political life issues like a somatic dream.

My attitude toward my friends did not alter on this revelation. I merely discarded the notion that Jews were a proper object for any special attitude; my old sense vanished. This was in 1933. Later, as word of the German persecution filtered into this country, some sentimentality undoubtedly corrupted my no-attitude. I denied the presence of obvious defects in particular Jews, feeling that to admit them would be to side with the sadists and murderers. Accident allotting me close friends who were Jewish, their disadvantages enraged me. Gradually, and against my sense of impartial justice, I became the anomaly which only a partial society can produce, and for which it has no name known to the lexicons. In one area, not exclusively, "nigger-lover" is flung in a proximate way; but for a special sympathy and liking for Jews—which became my fate, so that I trembled when I heard one abused in talk—we have no term. In this condition I still was during the summer of which I speak. One further circumstance may be mentioned, as a product, I believe, of this curious training. I am spectacularly unable to identify Jews as Jews—by name, cast of feature, accent, or environment—and this has been true, not only of course before the college incident, but during my whole life since. Even names to anyone else patently Hebraic rarely suggest to me anything. And when once I learn that So-and-so is Jewish, I am likely to forget it. Now Jewishness—the religion or the race—may be a fact as striking and informative as someone's past heroism or his Christianity or his understanding of the subtlest human relations, and I feel sure that something operates to prevent my utilizing the plain signs by which such characters—in a Jewish man or woman—may be identified, and prevent my retaining the identification once it is made.

So to the city my summer and a night in August. I used to stop on Fourteenth Street for iced coffee, walking from the Village home (or to my room rather) after leaving my friend, and one night when I came out I wandered across to the island of trees and grass and concrete walks raised in the center of Union Square. Here men—a few women, old—sit in the evenings of summer, looking at papers or staring off or talking, and knots of them stay on, arguing, very late; these the unemployed or unemployable, the sleepless, the malcontent. There are no formal orators, as at Columbus Circle in the nineteen-thirties and at Hyde Park Corner. Each group is dominated by several articulate and strong-lunged persons who battle each other with prejudices and desires, swaying with intensity, and take on from time to time the interrupters: a forum at the bottom of the pot—Jefferson's fear, Whitman's hope, the dream of the younger Lenin. It was now about one o'clock, almost hot, and many men were still out. I stared for a little at the equestrian statue, obscure in the night on top of its pedestal, thinking that misty Rider would sweep away again all these men at his feet, whenever he liked—what symbol for power yet in a mechanical age rivals the mounted man?—and moved to the nearest group; or I plunged to it.

The dictator to the group was old, with dark cracked skin, fixed eyes in an excited face, leaning forward madly on his bench toward the half-dozen men in semicircle before him. "It's bread! It's bread!" he was saying. "It's bittersweet. All the bitter and all the sweetness. Of an overture. What else do you want? When you ask for steak and potatoes, do you want pastry with it? It's bread! It's bread! Help yourself! Help yourself!"

The listeners stood expressionless, except one who was smiling with contempt and interrupted now.

"Never a happy minute, never a happy minute!" the old man cried. "It's good to be dead! Some men should kill themselves."

"Don't you want to live?" said the smiling man.

"Of course I want to live. Everyone wants to live! If death comes suddenly, it's better. It's better!"

With pain I turned away. The next group were talking diffusely and angrily about the mayor, and I passed to a third, where a frantic olive-skinned young man with a fringe of silky beard was exclaiming:

"No restaurant in New York had the Last Supper! No. When people sit down to eat they should think of that!"

"Listen," said a white-shirted student on the rail, glancing around for approbation, "listen, if I open a restaurant and put *The Last Supper* up over the door, how much money do you think I'd lose? Ten thousand dollars?"

The fourth cluster was larger and appeared more coherent. A savage argument was in progress between a man of fifty with an oily red face, hatted, very determined in manner, and a muscular fellow half his age with heavy eyebows, coatless, plainly Irish. Fifteen or twenty men were packed around them, and others on a bench near the rail against which the Irishman was lounging were attending also. I listened for a few minutes. The question was whether the President was trying to get us into the war— or, rather, whether this was legitimate, since the Irishman claimed that Roosevelt was a goddamned warmonger whom all the real people in the country hated, and the older man claimed that we should have gone into the f—ing war when France fell a year before, as everybody in the country knew except a few immigrant rats. Redface talked ten times as much as the Irishman, but he was not able to establish any advantage that I could see. He ranted, and then Irish either repeated shortly and fiercely what he had said last, or shifted his ground. The audience were silent—favoring whom I don't know, but evidently much interested. One or two men pushed out of the group, others arrived behind me, and I was eddied forward toward the disputants. The young Irishman broke suddenly into a tirade by the man with the hat:

"You're full of s—. Roosevelt even tried to get us in with the communists in the Spanish war. If he could have done it we'd have been burning churches down like the rest of the Reds."

"No, that's not right," I heard my own voice, and pushed forward, feeling blood in my face, beginning to tremble. "No, Roosevelt, as a matter of fact, helped Franco by non-intervention, at the same time that Italians and German planes were fighting against the Government and arms couldn't get in from France."

"What's that? What are you, a Jew?" He turned to me contemptuously, and was back at the older man before I could speak. "The only reason we weren't over there four years ago is because you can only screw us so much. Then we quit. No New Deal bastard could make us go help the goddamned communists."

"That ain't the question, it's if we want to fight *now* or *later*. Them Nazis ain't gonna sit!" shouted the red-faced man. "They got Egypt practically, and then it's India if it ain't England first. It ain't a question of the communists, the communists are on Hitler's side. I tellya we can wait and wait and chew and spit and the first thing you know they'll be in England, and then who's gonna help us when they start after us? Maybe Brazil? Get wise to the world! Spain don't matter now one way or the other, they ain't gonna help and they can't hurt. It's Germany and Italy and Japan, and if it ain't too late now it's gonna be. Get wise to yourself. We shoulda gone in——"

"What with?" said the Irishman with disdain. "Pop, pop. Wooden machine guns?"

"We were as ready a year ago as we are now. Defense don't mean nothing, you gotta have to fight!"

"No, we're much better off now," I said, "than we were a year ago. When England went in, to keep its word to Poland, what good was it to Poland? The German Army——"

"Shut up, you Jew," said the Irishman.

"I'm not a Jew," I said to him. "What makes——"

"Listen, Pop," he said to the man in the hat, "it's O.K. to shoot your mouth off, but what the hell have you got to do with it? You aren't gonna do any fighting."

"Listen," I said.

"You sit on your big ass and talk about who's gonna fight who. Nobody's gonna fight anybody. If we feel hot, we ought to clean up some of the sons of bitches here before we go sticking our nuts anywhere to help England. We ought to clean up the sons of bitches in Wall Street and Washington before we take any ocean trips. You want to know something? You know why Germany's winning everything in this war? Because there ain't no Jews back home. There ain't no more Jews, first shouting war like this one here"—nodding at me—"and then skinning off to the synagogue with the profits. Wake up, Pop! You must have been around in the last war, you ought to know better."

I was too nervous to be angry or resentful. But I began to have a sense of oppression in breathing. I took the Irishman by the arm.

"Listen, told you I'm not a Jew."

"I don't give a damn what you are." He turned his half-dark eyes to me, wrenching his arm loose. "You talk like a Jew."

"What does that mean?" Some part of me wanted to laugh. "How does a Jew talk?"

"They talk like you, buddy."

"That's a fine argument! But if I'm not a Jew, my talk only——"

"You probably are a Jew. You look like a Jew."

"I *look* like a Jew? Listen"—I swung around eagerly to a man standing next to me—"do I look like a Jew? It doesn't matter whether I do or not—a Jew is as good as anybody and better than this son of a bitch." I was not exactly excited, I was trying to adapt my language as my need for the crowd, and sudden respect for its judgment possessed me. "But in fact I'm not Jewish and I don't look Jewish. Do I?"

The man looked at me quickly and said, half to me and half to the Irishman, "Hell, I don't know. Sure he does."

A wave of disappointment and outrage swept me almost to tears. I felt like a man betrayed by his brother. The lamps seemed brighter and vaguer, the night large. Glancing 'round, I saw sitting on a bench near me a tall, heavy, serious-looking man of thirty, well dressed, whom I had noticed earlier, and appealed to him, "Tell me, do I look Jewish?"

But he only stared up and waved his head vaguely. I saw with horror that something was wrong with him.

"You look like a Jew. You talk like a Jew. You *are* a Jew," I heard the Irishman say.

I heard murmuring among the men, but I could see nothing very clearly. It seemed very hot. I faced the Irishman again helplessly, holding my voice from rising.

"I'm *not* a Jew," I told him. "I might be, but I'm not. You have no bloody reason to think so, and you can't make me a Jew by simply repeating like an idiot that I am."

"Don't deny it, son," said the red-faced man, "stand up to him."

"God damn it"—suddenly I was furious, whirling like a fool (was I afraid of the Irishman? had he conquered me?) on the red-faced man—"I'm *not* denying it! Or rather I am, but only because I'm not a Jew! I despise renegades, I hate Jews who turn on their people, if I were a Jew I would say so, I would be proud to be. What is the vicious opinion of a man like this to me if I were a Jew? But I'm not. Why the hell should I admit I am if I'm not?"

"Jesus, the Jew is excited," said the Irishman.

"I have a right to be excited, you son of a bitch. Suppose I call you a Jew. Yes, you're a Jew. Does that mean anything?"

"Not a damn thing." He spat over the rail past a man's head. "Prove that you're not. I say you are."

"Now listen, you Jew. I'm a Catholic."

"So am I, or I was born one, I'm not one now. I was born a Catholic." I was a little calmer but goaded, obsessed with the need to straighten this out. I felt that everything for everyone there depended on my proving him wrong. If *once* this evil for which we have not even a name could be exposed to the rest of the men as empty—if I could *prove* I was not a Jew—it would fall to the ground, neither would anyone else be a Jew to be accused. Then it could be trampled on. Fascist America was at stake. I listened, intensely anxious for our fate.

"Yeah?" said the Irishman. "Say the Apostles' Creed."

Memory went swirling back. I could hear the little bell die as I hushed it and set it on the felt. Father Boniface looked at me tall from the top of the steps and smiled, greeting me in the darkness before dawn as I came to serve, the men pressed around me under the lamps, and I could remember nothing but *visibilium omnium, et invisibilium.*

"I don't remember it."

The Irishman laughed with his certainty.

The papers in my pocket; I thought them over hurriedly. In my wallet. What would they prove? Details of ritual, Church history: anyone could learn them. My piece of Irish blood. Shame, shame: shame for my ruthless people. I will not be his blood. I wish I were a Jew, I would change my blood, to be able to say *Yes* and defy him.

"I'm not a Jew." I felt a fool. "You only say so. You haven't any evidence in the world."

He leaned forward from the rail, close to me. "Are you cut?"

Shock, fear ran through me before I could make any meaning out of his words. Then they ran faster, and I felt confused.

From that point nothing is clear for me. I stayed a long time— it seemed impossible to leave, showing him victor to them— thinking of possible allies and new plans of proof, but without hope. I was tired to the marrow. The arguments rushed on, and I spoke often now but seldom was heeded except by an old fat woman, very short and dirty, who listened intently to everyone. Heavier and heavier appeared to me to press upon us in the fading night our general guilt.

In the days following, as my resentment died, I saw that I had not been a victim altogether unjustly. My persecutors were right: I was a Jew. The imaginary Jew I was was as real as the imaginary Jew hunted down, on other nights and days, in a real Jew. Every murderer strikes the mirror, the lash of the torturer falls on the mirror and cuts the real image, and the real and the imaginary blood flow down together.

EDITORS' ANALYSIS

This story exists, at a surface level, as the rather casual anecdote of a man frustrated because he is taken for a Jew. But the story has very deep roots, involving us with one of the basic contradictions of our time: ideally we stand for a classless, free existence, but actually we know that the angers and hatreds of one racial or one religious group for another smolder just below the surface of our life in America. Moreover the very ease in recognizing this problem of prejudice, in fiction, may create a too simple agreement between reader and writer merely to deplore the facts. In "The Imaginary Jew," it is Berryman's very casualness which acts to involve the reader with all the ramifications of prejudice. We realize, at the end, that we could all be Jews because we all, in some degree, are what people accuse us of being.

QUESTIONS

1. Discuss the details which create the autobiographical tone of the opening paragraph. How does it lead into the story proper? Do you think it a good beginning? Can you imagine a better one?

2. Do you think that the lack of a "sense of the Jewish people" which the teller of the story reveals suggests a peculiar blindness on his part? Is he oddly unaware of the everyday facts of existence in America? How does the story make him seem credible in his blindness?

3. Is the Irishman in the story what he is because he thinks of himself as part of a separate religious group rather than a generic American? Does the story stir your prejudice against him?

4. What is the nature of the "general guilt" felt by the teller of the story, as expressed in the next to the last paragraph?

5. Is the author's description of how a man becomes a Jew complete? Are there elements left out?

6. Note the clipped sentence structure in the second paragraph. Describe it and discuss its intent.

7. What is the intended effect of the mirror image in the final paragraph? Does it succeed for you?

8. What does Berryman mean when he says that the "lash of the torturer" falls on the mirror, but cuts "the real image"?

Battle Royal

by RALPH ELLISON

Ralph Ellison (1914-   ) is a leading novelist and spokesman
for the American Negro. He has lectured on American-Negro culture
at Columbia University, at Princeton, and elsewhere. His critical writing appears in *Saturday Review, Partisan Review,* and other magazines. *Invisible Man* (1952), his only full-length novel, is a study of a
Negro's attempt to find a livable existence in present-day America. As
its title suggests, the hero of the novel finds himself, at the book's end,
belonging to no culture, and so much the outsider that he thinks of
himself as an invisible man. This novel won Ellison the National Book
Award for 1952.

"Battle Royal," though a self-contained story and originally published separately, is actually the opening chapter of Ellison's novel. It
presents the usual excitement and the driving power of an American's
hoping and dreaming, but as they are stepped up in urgency when
felt by a young Negro. It presents a world strange to most readers,
where a young man can be goaded into indignities beyond nightmare
in order to try to capture a fragment of his dream.

It goes a long way back, some twenty years. All my life I
had been looking for something, and everywhere I turned someone tried to tell me what it was. I accepted their answers too,
though they were often in contradiction and even self-contradic-
tory. I was naïve. I was looking for myself and asking everyone
except myself questions which I, and only I, could answer. It took
me a long time and much painful boomeranging of my expec-
tations to achieve a realization everyone else appears to have
been born with: That I am nobody but myself. But first I had
to discover that I am an invisible man!

And yet I am no freak of nature, nor of history. I was in the cards, other things having been equal (or unequal) eighty-five years ago. I am not ashamed of my grandparents for having been slaves. I am only ashamed of myself for having at one time been ashamed. About eighty-five years ago they were told that they were free, united with others of our country in everything pertaining to the common good, and, in everything social, separate like the fingers of the hand. And they believed it. They exulted in it. They stayed in their place, worked hard, and brought up my father to do the same. But my grandfather is the one. He was an odd old guy, my grandfather, and I am told I take after him. It was he who caused the trouble. On his deathbed he called my father to him and said, "Son, after I'm gone I want you to keep up the good fight. I never told you, but our life is a war and I have been a traitor all my born days, a spy in the enemy's country ever since I give up my gun back in the Reconstruction. Live with your head in the lion's mouth. I want you to overcome 'em with yeses, undermine 'em with grins, agree 'em to death and destruction, let 'em swoller you till they vomit or bust wide open." They thought the old man had gone out of his mind. He had been the meekest of men. The younger children were rushed from the room, the shades drawn and the flame of the lamp turned so low that it sputtered on the wick like the old man's breathing. "Learn it to the younguns," he whispered fiercely; then he died.

But my folks were more alarmed over his last words than over his dying. It was as though he had not died at all, his words caused so much anxiety. I was warned emphatically to forget what he had said and, indeed, this is the first time it has been mentioned outside the family circle. It had a tremendous effect upon me, however. I could never be sure of what he meant. Grandfather had been a quiet old man who never made any trouble, yet on his deathbed he had called himself a traitor and a spy, and he had spoken of his meekness as a dangerous activity. It became a constant puzzle which lay unanswered in the back of my mind. And whenever things went well for me I remembered my grandfather and felt guilty and uncomfortable. It was as though I was carrying out his advice in spite of myself. And to make it worse, everyone loved me for it. I was praised by the most lily-white men of the town. I was considered an example of desirable conduct—just as my grandfather had been. And what puzzled me was that the old man had defined it as *treachery*. When I was praised for my conduct I felt a guilt that in some way I was doing something that was really against the wishes of the white folks, that if they had understood they would have desired me to act just the opposite, that I should have been sulky and mean, and that that really would have been what they wanted, even though they were fooled and thought they wanted me to act as I did. It made me afraid that some day they would look upon me as a traitor and I would be lost. Still I was more afraid to act any other way because they didn't like that at all. The old man's words were like a curse. On my graduation day I delivered an oration in which I showed that humility was the secret, indeed, the very essence of progress. (Not that I believed this—how could I, remembering my grandfather?—I only believed that it worked.) It was a great success. Everyone praised me and I was invited to give the speech at a gathering of the town's leading white citizens. It was a triumph for our whole community.

It was in the main ballroom of the leading hotel. When I got there I discovered that it was on the occasion of a smoker, and I was told that since I was to be there anyway I might as well take part in the battle royal to be fought by some of my schoolmates as part of the entertainment. The battle royal came first.

All of the town's big shots were there in their tuxedoes, wolfing down the buffet foods, drinking beer and whiskey and smoking black cigars. It was a large room with a high ceiling. Chairs were arranged in neat rows around three sides of a portable boxing ring. The fourth side was clear, revealing a gleaming space of polished floor. I had some misgivings over the battle royal, by the way. Not from a distaste for fighting, but because I didn't care too much for the other fellows who were to take part. They were tough guys who seemed to have no grandfather's curse worrying their minds. No one could mistake their toughness. And besides, I suspected that fighting a battle royal might detract from the dignity of my speech. In those pre-invisible days I visualized myself as a potential Booker T. Washington. But the other fellows didn't care too much for me either, and there were nine of them. I felt superior to them in my way, and I didn't like the manner in which we were all crowded together into the servants' elevator. Nor did they like my being there. In fact, as the warmly lighted floors flashed past the elevator we had words over the fact that I, by taking part in the fight, had knocked one of their friends out of a night's work.

We were led out of the elevator through a rococo hall into an anteroom and told to get into our fighting togs. Each of us was issued a pair of boxing gloves and ushered out into the big mirrored hall, which we entered looking cautiously about us and whispering, lest we might accidentally be heard above the noise of the room. It was foggy with cigar smoke. And already the whiskey was taking effect. I was shocked to see some of the most important men of the town quite tipsy. They were all there —bankers, lawyers, judges, doctors, fire chiefs, teachers, merchants. Even one of the more fashionable pastors. Something we could not see was going on up front. A clarinet was vibrating sensuously and the men were standing up and moving eagerly forward. We were a small tight group, clustered together, our bare upper bodies touching and shining with anticipatory sweat; while up front the big shots were becoming increasingly excited over something we still could not see. Suddenly I heard the school superintendent, who had told me to come, yell, "Bring up the shines, gentlemen! Bring up the little shines!"

We were rushed up to the front of the ballroom, where it smelled even more strongly of tobacco and whiskey. Then we were pushed into place. I almost wet my pants. A sea of faces, some hostile, some amused, ringed around us, and in the center, facing us, stood a magnificent blonde—stark naked. There was dead silence. I felt a blast of cold air chill me. I tried to back away, but they were behind me and around me. Some of the boys stood with lowered heads, trembling. I felt a wave of irrational guilt and fear. My teeth chattered, my skin turned to goose flesh, my knees knocked. Yet I was strongly attracted and looked in spite of myself. Had the price of looking been blindness, I would have looked. The hair was yellow like that of a circus kewpie doll, the face heavily powdered and rouged, as though to form an abstract mask, the eyes hollow and smeared a cool blue, the color of a baboon's butt. I felt a desire to spit upon her as my eyes brushed slowly over her body. Her breasts were firm and round as the domes of East Indian temples, and I stood so close as to see the fine skin texture and beads of pearly perspiration glistening like dew around the pink and erected buds of her nipples. I wanted at one and the same time to run from the room, to sink through the floor, or go to her and cover her from my eyes and the eyes of the others with my body; to feel the soft thighs, to caress her and destroy her, to love her and murder her, to hide from her, and yet to stroke where below the small American flag tattooed upon her belly her thighs formed a capital

V. I had a notion that of all in the room she saw only me with her impersonal eyes.

And then she began to dance, a slow sensuous movement; the smoke of a hundred cigars clinging to her like the thinnest of veils. She seemed like a fair bird-girl girdled in veils calling to me from the angry surface of some gray and threatening sea. I was transported. Then I became aware of the clarinet playing and the big shots yelling at us. Some threatened us if we looked and others if we did not. On my right I saw one boy faint. And now a man grabbed a silver pitcher from a table and stepped close as he dashed ice water upon him and stood him up and forced two of us to support him as his head hung and moans issued from his thick bluish lips. Another boy began to plead to go home. He was the largest of the group, wearing dark red fighting trunks much too small to conceal the erection which projected from him as though in answer to the insinuating low-registered moaning of the clarinet. He tried to hide himself with his boxing gloves.

And all the while the blonde continued dancing, smiling faintly at the big shots who watched her with fascination, and faintly smiling at our fear. I noticed a certain merchant who followed her hungrily, his lips loose and drooling. He was a large man who wore diamond studs in a shirtfront which swelled with the ample paunch underneath, and each time the blonde swayed her undulating hips he ran his hand through the thin hair of his bald head and, with his arms upheld, his posture clumsy like that of an intoxicated panda, wound his belly in a slow and obscene grind. This creature was completely hypnotized. The music had quickened. As the dancer flung herself about with a detached expression on her face, the men began reaching out to touch her. I could see their beefy fingers sink into the soft flesh. Some of the others tried to stop them and she began to move around the floor in graceful circles, as they gave chase, slipping and sliding over the polished floor. It was mad. Chairs went crashing, drinks were spilt, as they ran laughing and howling after her. They caught her just as she reached a door, raised her from the floor, and tossed her as college boys are tossed at a hazing, and above her red, fixed-smiling lips I saw the terror and disgust in her eyes, almost like my own terror and that which I saw in some of the other boys. As I watched, they tossed her twice and her soft breasts seemed to flatten against the air and her legs flung wildly as she spun. Some of the more sober ones helped her to escape. And I started off the floor, heading for the anteroom with the rest of the boys.

Some were still crying and in hysteria. But as we tried to leave we were stopped and ordered to get into the ring. There was nothing to do but what we were told. All ten of us climbed under the ropes and allowed ourselves to be blindfolded with broad bands of white cloth. One of the men seemed to feel a bit sympathetic and tried to cheer us up as we stood with our backs against the ropes. Some of us tried to grin. "See that boy over there?" one of the men said. "I want you to run across at the bell and give it to him right in the belly. If you don't get him, I'm going to get you. I don't like his looks." Each of us was told the same. The blindfolds were put on. Yet even then I had been going over my speech. In my mind each word was as bright as flame. I felt the cloth pressed into place, and frowned so that it would be loosened when I relaxed.

But now I felt a sudden fit of blind terror. I was unused to darkness. It was as though I had suddenly found myself in a dark room filled with poisonous cottonmouths. I could hear the bleary voices yelling insistently for the battle royal to begin.

"Get going in there!"

"Let me at the big nigger!"

I strained to pick up the school superintendent's voice, as though to squeeze some security out of that slightly more familiar sound.

"Let me at those black sonsabitches!" someone yelled.

"No, Jackson, no!" another voice yelled. "Here, somebody, help me hold Jack."

"I want to get at that ginger-colored nigger. Tear him limb from limb," the first voice yelled.

I stood against the ropes trembling. For in those days I was what they called ginger-colored, and he sounded as though he might crunch me between his teeth like a crisp ginger cookie.

Quite a struggle was going on. Chairs were being kicked about and I could hear voices grunting as with a terrific effort. I wanted to see, to see more desperately than ever before. But the blindfold was as tight as a thick skin-puckering scab and when I raised my gloved hands to push the layers of white aside a voice yelled, "Oh, no you don't, black bastard! Leave that alone!"

"Ring the bell before Jackson kills him a coon!" someone boomed in the sudden silence. And I heard the bell clang and the sound of the feet scuffling forward.

A glove smacked against my head. I pivoted, striking out stiffly as someone went past, and felt the jar ripple along the length of my arm to my shoulder. Then it seemed as though all nine of the boys had turned upon me at once. Blows pounded me from all sides while I struck out as best I could. So many blows landed upon me that I wondered if I were not the only blindfolded fighter in the ring, or if the man called Jackson hadn't succeeded in getting me after all.

Blindfolded, I could no longer control my motions. I had no dignity. I stumbled about like a baby or a drunken man. The smoke had become thicker and with each new blow it seemed to sear and further restrict my lungs. My saliva became like hot bitter glue. A glove connected with my head, filling my mouth with warm blood. It was everywhere. I could not tell if the moisture I felt upon my body was sweat or blood. A blow landed hard against the nape of my neck. I felt myself going over, my head hitting the floor. Streaks of blue light filled the black world behind the blindfold. I lay prone, pretending that I was knocked out, but felt myself seized by hands and yanked to my feet. "Get going, black boy! Mix it up!" My arms were like lead, my head smarting from blows. I managed to feel my way to the ropes and held on, trying to catch my breath. A glove landed in my mid-section and I went over again, feeling as though the smoke had become a knife jabbed into my guts. Pushed this way and that by the legs milling around me, I finally pulled erect and discovered that I could see the black, sweat-washed forms weaving in the smoky-blue atmosphere like drunken dancers weaving to the rapid drum-like thuds of blows.

Everyone fought hysterically. It was complete anarchy. Everybody fought everybody else. No group fought together for long. Two, three, four, fought one, then turned to fight each other, were themselves attacked. Blows landed below the belt and in the kidney, with the gloves open as well as closed, and with my eye partly opened now there was not so much terror. I moved carefully, avoiding blows, although not too many to attract attention, fighting from group to group. The boys groped about like blind, cautious crabs crouching to protect their mid-sections, their heads pulled in short against their shoulders, their arms stretched nervously before them, with their fists testing the smoke-filled air like the knobbed feelers of hypersensitive snails. In one corner I glimpsed a boy violently punching the air and heard him scream in pain as he smashed his hand against a ring post. For a second

I saw him bent over holding his hand, then going down as a blow caught his unprotected head. I played one group against the other, slipping in and throwing a punch then stepping out of range while pushing the others into the melee to take the blows blindly aimed at me. The smoke was agonizing and there were no rounds, no bells at three minute intervals to relieve our exhaustion. The room spun round me, a swirl of lights, smoke, sweating bodies surrounded by tense white faces. I bled from both nose and mouth, the blood spattering upon my chest.

The men kept yelling, "Slug him, black boy! Knock his guts out!"

"Uppercut him! Kill him! Kill that big boy!"

Taking a fake fall, I saw a boy going down heavily beside me as though we were felled by a single blow, saw a sneaker-clad foot shoot into his groin as the two who had knocked him down stumbled upon him. I rolled out of range, feeling a twinge of nausea.

The harder we fought the more threatening the men became. And yet, I had begun to worry about my speech again. How would it go? Would they recognize my ability? What would they give me?

I was fighting automatically when suddenly I noticed that one after another of the boys was leaving the ring. I was surprised, filled with panic, as though I had been left alone with an unknown danger. Then I understood. The boys had arranged it among themselves. It was the custom for the two men left in the ring to slug it out for the winner's prize. I discovered this too late. When the bell sounded two men in tuxedos leaped into the ring and removed the blindfold. I found myself facing Tatlock, the biggest of the gang. I felt sick at my stomach. Hardly had the bell stopped ringing in my ears than it clanged again and I saw him moving swiftly toward me. Thinking of nothing else to do I hit him smash on the nose. He kept coming, bringing the rank sharp violence of stale sweat. His face was a black blank of a face, only his eyes alive—with hate of me and aglow with a feverish terror from what had happened to us all. I became anxious. I wanted to deliver my speech and he came at me as though he meant to beat it out of me. I smashed him again and again, taking his blows as they came. Then on a sudden impulse I struck him lightly and as we clinched, I whispered, "Fake like I knocked you out, you can have the prize."

"I'll break your behind," he whispered hoarsely.

"For *them?*"

"For *me*, sonofabitch"

They were yelling for us to break it up and Tatlock spun me half around with a blow, and as a joggled camera sweeps in a reeling scene, I saw the howling red faces crouching tense beneath the cloud of blue-gray smoke. For a moment the world wavered, unraveled, flowed, then my head cleared and Tatlock bounced before me. That fluttering shadow before my eyes was his jabbing left hand. Then falling forward, my head against his damp shoulder, I whispered,

"I'll make it five dollars more."

"Go to hell!"

But his muscles relaxed a trifle beneath my pressure and I breathed, "Seven?"

"Give it to your ma," he said, ripping me beneath the heart.

And while I still held him I butted him and moved away. I felt myself bombarded with punches. I fought back with hopeless desperation. I wanted to deliver my speech more than anything else in the world, because I felt that only these men could judge truly my ability, and now this stupid clown was ruining my chances. I began fighting carefully now, moving in to punch him and out again with my greater speed. A lucky blow to his chin and I had him going too—until I heard a loud voice yell, "I got my money on the big boy."

Hearing this, I almost dropped my guard. I was confused: Should I try to win against the voice out there? Would not this go against my speech, and was not this a moment for humility, for nonresistance? A blow to my head as I danced about sent my right eye popping like a jack-in-the-box and settled my dilemma. The room went red as I fell. It was a dream fall, my body languid and fastidious as to where to land, until the floor became impatient and smashed up to meet me. A moment later I came to. An hypnotic voice said FIVE emphatically. And I lay there, hazily watching a dark red spot of my own blood shaping itself into a butterfly, glistening and soaking into the soiled gray world of the canvas.

When the voice drawled TEN I was lifted up and dragged to a chair. I sat dazed. My eye pained and swelled with each throb of my pounding heart and I wondered if now I would be allowed to speak. I was wringing wet, my mouth still bleeding. We were grouped along the wall now. The other boys ignored me as they congratulated Tatlock and speculated as to how much they would be paid. One boy whimpered over his smashed hand. Looking up front, I saw attendants in white jackets rolling the portable ring away and placing a small square rug in the vacant space surrounded by chairs. Perhaps, I thought, I will stand on the rug to deliver my speech.

Then the M.C. called to us, "Come on up here boys and get your money."

We ran forward to where the men laughed and talked in their chairs, waiting. Everyone seemed friendly now.

"There it is on the rug," the man said. I saw the rug covered with coins of all dimensions and a few crumpled bills. But what excited me, scattered here and there, were the gold pieces.

"Boys, it's all yours," the man said. "You get all you grab."

"That's right, Sambo," a blond man said, winking at me confidentially.

I trembled with excitement, forgetting my pain. I would get the gold and the bills, I thought. I would use both hands. I would throw my body against the boys nearest me to block them from the gold.

"Get down around the rug now," the man commanded, "and don't anyone touch it until I give the signal."

"This ought to be good," I heard.

As told, we got around the square rug on our knees. Slowly the man raised his freckled hand as we followed it upward with our eyes.

I heard, "These niggers look like they're about to pray!"

Then, "Ready," the man said. "Go!"

I lunged for a yellow coin lying on the blue design of the carpet, touching it and sending a surprised shriek to join those rising around me. I tried frantically to remove my hand but could not let go. A hot, violent force tore through my body, shaking me like a wet rat. The rug was electrified. The hair bristled up on my head as I shook myself free. My muscles jumped, my nerves jangled, writhed. But I saw that this was not stopping the other boys. Laughing in fear and embarrassment, some were holding back and scooping up the coins knocked off by the painful contortions of the others. The men roared above us as we struggled.

"Pick it up, goddamnit, pick it up!" someone called like a bass-voiced parrot. "Go on, get it!"

I crawled rapidly around the floor, picking up the coins, trying to avoid the coppers and to get greenbacks and the gold. Ignoring the shock by laughing, as I brushed the coins off quickly, I discovered that I could contain the electricity—a contradiction, but it works. Then the men began to push us onto the rug. Laughing embarrassedly, we struggled out of their hands and kept after the coins. We were all wet and slippery and hard to hold. Suddenly I saw a boy lifted into the air, glistening with sweat like a circus seal, and dropped, his wet back landing flush upon the charged rug, heard him yell and saw him literally dance upon his back, his elbows beating a frenzied tattoo upon the floor, his muscles twitching like the flesh of a horse stung by many flies. When he finally rolled off, his face was gray and no one stopped him when he ran from the floor amid booming laughter.

"Get the money," the M.C. called. "That's good hard American cash!"

And we snatched and grabbed, snatched and grabbed. I was careful not to come too close to the rug now, and when I felt the hot whiskey breath descend upon me like a cloud of foul air I reached out and grabbed the leg of a chair. It was occupied and I held on desperately.

"Leggo nigger! Leggo!"

The huge face wavered down to mine as he tried to push me free. But my body was slippery and he was too drunk. It was Mr. Colcord, who owned a chain of movie houses and "entertainment palaces." Each time he grabbed me I slipped out of his hands. It became a real struggle. I feared the rug more than I did the drunk, so I held on, surprising myself for a moment by trying to toppled *him* upon the rug. It was such an enormous idea that I found myself actually carrying it out. I tried not to be obvious, yet when I grabbed his leg, trying to tumble him out of the chair, he raised up roaring with laughter, and, looking at me with soberness dead in the eye, kicked me viciously in the chest. The chair leg flew out of my hand and I felt myself going and rolled. It was as though I had rolled through a bed of hot coals. It seemed a whole century would pass before I would roll free, a century in which I was seared through the deepest levels of my body to the fearful breath within me and the breath seared and heated to the point of explosion. It'll all be over in a flash, I thought as I rolled clear. It'll all be over in a flash.

But not yet, the men on the other side were waiting, red faces swollen as though from apoplexy as they bent forward in their chairs. Seeing their fingers coming toward me I rolled away as a fumbled football rolls off the receiver's fingertips, back into the coals. That time I luckily sent the rug sliding out of place and heard the coins ringing against the floor and the boys scuffling to pick them up and the M.C. calling, "All right, boys, that's all. Go get dressed and get your money."

I was limp as a dish rag. My back felt as though it had been beaten with wires.

When we had dressed the M.C. came in and gave us each five dollars, except Tatlock, who got ten for being last in the ring. Then he told us to leave. I was not to get a chance to deliver my speech, I thought. I was going out into the dim alley in despair when I was stopped and told to go back. I returned to the ballroom, where the men were pushing back their chairs and gathering in groups to talk.

The M.C. knocked on a table for quiet. "Gentlemen," he said, "we almost forgot an important part of the program. A most serious part, gentlemen. This boy was brought here to deliver a speech which he made at his graduation yesterday . . ."

"Bravo!"

"I'm told that he is the smartest boy we've got out there in Greenwood. I'm told that he knows more big words than a pocket-sized dictionary."

Much applause and laughter.

"So now, gentlemen, I want you to give him your attention."

There was still laughter as I faced them, my mouth dry, my eye throbbing. I began slowly, but evidently my throat was tense, because they began shouting, "Louder! Louder!"

"We of the younger generation extol the wisdom of that great leader and educator," I shouted, "who first spoke these flaming words of wisdom: 'A ship lost at sea for many days suddenly sighted a friendly vessel. From the mast of the unfortunate vessel was seen a signal: "Water, water; we die of thirst!" The answer from the friendly vessel came back: "Cast down your bucket where you are." The captain of the distressed vessel, at last heeding the injunction, cast down his bucket, and it came up full of fresh sparkling water from the mouth of the Amazon River.' And like him I say, and in his words, 'To those of my race who depend upon bettering their condition in a foreign land, or who underestimate the importance of cultivating friendly relations with the Southern white man, who is his next-door neighbor, I would say: "Cast down your bucket where you are"—cast it down in making friends in every manly way of the people of all races by whom we are surrounded . . .'"

I spoke automatically and with such fervor that I did not realize that the men were still talking and laughing until my dry mouth, filling up with blood from the cut, almost strangled me. I coughed, wanting to stop and go to one of the tall brass, sand-filled spittoons to relieve myself, but a few of the men, especially the superintendent, were listening and I was afraid. So I gulped it down, blood, saliva and all, and continued. (What powers of endurance I had during those days! What enthusiasm! What a belief in the rightness of things!) I spoke even louder in spite of the pain. But still they talked and still they laughed, as though deaf with cotton in dirty ears. So I spoke with greater emotional emphasis. I closed my ears and swallowed blood until I was nauseated. The speech seemed a hundred times as long as before, but I could not leave out a single word. All had to be said, each memorized nuance considered, rendered. Nor was that all. Whenever I uttered a word of three or more syllables a group of voices would yell for me to repeat it. I used the phrase "social responsibility" and they yelled:

"What's that word you say, boy?"

"Social responsibility," I said.

"What?"

"Social . . ."

"Louder."

". . . responsibility."

"More!"

"Respon—"

"Repeat!"

"—sibility."

The room filled with the uproar of laughter until, no doubt, distracted by having to gulp down my blood, I made a mistake and yelled a phrase I had often seen denounced in newspaper editorials, heard debated in private.

"Social . . ."

"What?" they yelled.

". . . equality—"

The laughter hung smokelike in the sudden stillness. I opened my eyes, puzzled. Sounds of displeasure filled the room. The M.C. rushed forward. They shouted hostile phrases at me. But I did not understand.

A small dry mustached man in the front row blared out, "Say that slowly, son!"

"What sir?"

"What you just said!"

"Social responsibility, sir," I said.

"You weren't being smart, were you, boy?" he said, not unkindly.

"No, sir!"

"You sure that about 'equality' was a mistake?"

"Oh, yes, sir," I said. "I was swallowing blood."

"Well, you had better speak more slowly so we can understand. We mean to do right by you, but you've got to know your place at all times. All right, now, go on with your speech."

I was afraid. I wanted to leave but I wanted also to speak and I was afraid they'd snatch me down.

"Thank you, sir," I said, beginning where I had left off, and having them ignore me as before.

Yet when I finished there was a thunderous applause. I was surprised to see the superintendent come forth with a package wrapped in white tissue paper, and, gesturing for quiet, address the men.

"Gentlemen, you see that I did not overpraise this boy. He makes a good speech and some day he'll lead his people in the proper paths. And I don't have to tell you that that is important in these days and times. This is a good, smart boy, and so to encourage him in the right direction, in the name of the Board of Education I wish to present him a prize in the form of this . . ."

He paused, removing the tissue paper and revealing a gleaming calfskin brief case.

". . . in the form of this first-class article from Shad Whitmore's shop."

"Boy," he said, addressing me, "take this prize and keep it well. Consider it a badge of office. Prize it. Keep developing as you are and some day it will be filled with important papers that will help shape the destiny of your people."

I was so moved that I could hardly express my thanks. A rope of bloody saliva forming a shape like an undiscovered continent drooled upon the leather and I wiped it quickly away. I felt an importance that I had never dreamed.

"Open it and see what's inside," I was told.

My fingers a-tremble, I complied, smelling the fresh leather and finding an official-looking document inside. It was a scholarship to the state college for Negroes. My eyes filled with tears and I ran awkwardly off the floor.

I was overjoyed; I did not even mind when I discovered that

the gold pieces I had scrambled for were brass pocket tokens advertising a certain make of automobile.

When I reached home everyone was excited. Next day the neighbors came to congratulate me. I even felt safe from grandfather, whose deathbed curse usually spoiled my triumphs. I stood beneath his photograph with my brief case in hand and smiled triumphantly into his stolid black peasant's face. It was a face that fascinated me. The eyes seemed to follow everywhere I went.

That night I dreamed I was at a circus with him and that he refused to laugh at the clowns no matter what they did. Then later he told me to open my brief case and read what was inside and I did, finding an official envelope stamped with the state seal; and inside the envelope I found another and another, endlessly, and I thought I would fall of weariness. "Them's years," he said. "Now open that one." And I did and in it I found an engraved document containing a short message in letters of gold. "Read it," my grandfather said. "Out loud."

"To Whom It May Concern," I intoned. "Keep This Nigger-Boy Running."

I awoke with the old man's laughter ringing in my ears.

(It was a dream I was to remember and dream again for many years after. But at that time I had no insight into its meaning. First I had to attend college.)

EDITORS' ANALYSIS

Ellison's "Battle Royal" sidesteps overt symbolism, presenting its raw and shocking portrait by a skillful and telling use of detail. All of us sense the inevitability of ambition in our lives and the hazards we invite when we seek to fulfill it. We can conceive of no other way of living. But the young Negro of "Battle Royal" has the special hazard of prejudice to intensify his everyday risks. And the story is not all horror for its own sake. It is horror which leads its central character to a great loss of faith. In one brief night, his "sensible" idealism concerning the role of the Negro is jettisoned. He becomes sickeningly and fully conscious of the actual price he will have to pay for the accident of his having been born an outsider.

QUESTIONS

1. What conclusions do you reach as to the value of humility in a Negro's attempting to get ahead? What other possibilities in attitude are suggested by the grandfather's dying repudiation of his own life?

2. Do you consider the leading white citizens of the town to be

accurately portrayed? What is the basis of your opinion? If they are accurately portrayed, what hope do you find for the American dream of equality?

3. Is there anything ritualistic in the reaction of the men at the smoker toward the young boy? Toward the dancer? Does Ellison suggest that they are behaving according to some unspoken notion of attitudes proper at such an occasion? Would they be somewhat different at other times and places?

4. Do you consider the boy's evaluation of his chances of success, at the end of the story, reasonable and proper? Overly cynical?

5. What is the basic pleasure the onlookers derive from the night's orgy? Pathological sexual teasing? Pathological and vicarious violence? What is lacking in their lives that makes them turn to such an evening?

6. What is meant by the phrase in the story "live with your head in the lion's mouth"? Does it apply exclusively to the young boy? To all of us?

7. What is the effect in the story of describing one of the more offensive onlookers as "an intoxicated panda"?

8·

DEATH

"The Interior Castle," *by Jean Stafford*

"Goose Pond," *by Thomas Williams*

The Interior Castle

by JEAN STAFFORD

Jean Stafford (1915-   ) is a novelist and a writer of short stories whose work, in style and in subject matter, is identified with the postwar tradition of serious fiction. Her work is published in such literary quarterlies as *Kenyon Review* and *Partisan Review,* and rather often in *The New Yorker.* Her first novel, *Boston Adventure* (1944) attracted wide attention, and her second, *The Mountain Lion* (1947), established her reputation as a writer concerned with atmosphere and tone (rather than with plot), and with nuances and subtleties of perception and feeling. Her third novel, *The Catherine Wheel* (1952), a further development of the special talents she had already displayed, was concerned with a woman who attempted to arrest the moment in time when she had given over her chance for a husband and a family. *Children Are Bored on Sunday* (1953) is a collection of ten of her short stories, six of which first appeared in *The New Yorker.*

"The Interior Castle" presents death in one of its most familiar ways, by automobile accident. A young woman whose cab driver has been killed, and who has barely survived the crash, holds on in frantic desperation, in a hospital, to a fantastic symbol of self, of personal identity, while her body is reduced to a receptacle of almost unendurable pain. This is Miss Stafford at her best, where communication of fictional "truth" between reader and writer is intense and complete.

Pansy Vanneman, injured in an automobile accident, often woke up before dawn when the night noises of the hospital still came, in hushed hurry, through her half-open door. By day, when the nurses talked audibly with the internes, laughed without inhibition, and took no pains to soften their footsteps on the resounding composition floors, the routine of the hospital seemed

---

as bland and commonplace as that of a bank or a factory. But in the dark hours, the whispering and the quickly stilled clatter of glasses and basins, the moans of patients whose morphine was wearing off, the soft squeak of a stretcher as it rolled past on its way from the emergency ward—these suggested agony and death. Thus, on the first morning, Pansy had faltered to consciousness long before daylight and found herself in a ward from every bed of which, it seemed to her, came the bewildered protest of someone about to die. A caged light burned on the floor beside the bed next to hers. Her neighbor was dying and a priest was administering Extreme Unction. He was stout and elderly and he suffered from asthma so that the struggle of his breathing, so close to her, was the basic pattern and all the other sounds were superimposed upon it. Two middle-aged men in overcoats knelt on the floor beside the high bed. In a foreign tongue, the half-gone woman babbled against the hissing and sighing of the Latin prayers. She played with her rosary as if it were a toy: she tried, and failed, to put it into her mouth.

Pansy felt horror, but she felt no pity. An hour or so later, when the white ceiling lights were turned on and everything— faces, counterpanes, and the hands that groped upon them—was transformed into a uniform gray sordor, the woman was wheeled away in her bed to die somewhere else, in privacy. Pansy did not quite take this in, although she stared for a long time at the new, empty bed that had replaced the other.

The next morning, when she again woke up before the light, this time in a private room, she recalled the woman with such sorrow that she might have been a friend. Simultaneously, she mourned the driver of the taxicab in which she had been injured, for he had died at about noon the day before. She had been told this as she lay on a stretcher in the corridor, waiting to be taken to the x-ray room; an interne, passing by, had paused and smiled down at her and had said, 'Your cab-driver is dead. You were lucky.'

Six weeks after the accident, she woke one morning just as daylight was showing on the windows as a murky smear. It was a minute or two before she realized why she was so reluctant to be awake, why her uneasiness amounted almost to alarm. Then she remembered that her nose was to be operated on today. She lay straight and motionless under the seersucker counterpane. Her blood-red eyes in her darned face stared through the window and saw a frozen river and leafless elm trees and a grizzled esplanade where dogs danced on the ends of leashes, their bundled-up owners stumbling after them, half blind with sleepiness and cold. Warm as the hospital room was, it did not prevent Pansy from knowing, as keenly as though she were one of the walkers, how very cold it was outside. Each twig of a nearby tree was stark. Cold red brick buildings nudged the low-lying sky which was pale and inert like a punctured sac.

In six weeks, the scene had varied little: there was promise in the skies neither of sun nor of snow; no red sunsets marked these days. The trees could neither die nor leaf out again. Pansy could not remember another season in her life so constant, when the very minutes themselves were suffused with the winter pallor as they dropped from the moon-faced clock in the corridor. Likewise, her room accomplished no alterations from day to day. On the glass-topped bureau stood two potted plants telegraphed by faraway well-wishers. They did not fade, and if a leaf turned brown and fell, it soon was replaced; so did the blossoms renew themselves. The roots, like the skies and like the bare trees, seemed zealously determined to maintain a status quo. The bedside table, covered every day with a clean white towel, though the one removed was always immaculate, was furnished sparsely with a water glass, a bent drinking tube, a sweating pitcher, and a stack of paper handkerchiefs. There were a few letters in the drawer, a hairbrush, a pencil, and some postal cards on which, from time to time, she wrote brief messages to relatives and friends: 'Dr. Nash says that my reflexes are shipshape *(sic)* and Dr. Rivers says the frontal fracture has all but healed and that the occipital is coming along nicely. Dr. Nicholas, the nose doctor, promises to operate as soon as Dr. Rivers gives him the go-ahead sign *(sic).*'

The bed itself was never rumpled. Once fretful and now convalescent, Miss Vannemann might have been expected to toss or to turn the pillows or to unmoor the counterpane; but hour after hour and day after day she lay at full length and would not even suffer the nurses to raise the head-piece of the adjustable bed. So perfect and stubborn was her body's immobility that it was as if the room and the landscape, mortified by the ice, were extensions of herself. Her resolute quiescence and her disinclination to talk, the one seeming somehow to proceed from the other, resembled, so the nurses said, a final coma. And they observed, in pitying indignation, that she might as *well* be dead for all the interest she took in life. Amongst themselves they scolded her for what they thought a moral weakness: an automobile accident, no matter how serious, was not reason enough for anyone to give

up the will to live or to be happy. She had not—to come down
bluntly to the facts—had the decency to be grateful that it was
the driver of the cab and not she who had died. (And how dread-
fully the man had died!) She was twenty-five years old and she
came from a distant city. These were really the only facts known
about her. Evidently she had not been here long, for she had no
visitors, a lack which was at first sadly moving to the nurses but
which became to them a source of unreasonable annoyance: had
anyone the right to live so one-dimensionally? It was impossible
to laugh at her, for she said nothing absurd; her demands could
not be complained of because they did not exist; she could not
be hated for a sharp tongue nor for a supercilious one; she could
not be admired for bravery or for wit or for interest in her fellow
creatures. She was believed to be a frightful snob.

Pansy, for her part, took a secret and mischievous pleasure in
the bewilderment of her attendants and the more they courted
her with offers of magazines, cross-word puzzles, and a radio
which she could rent from the hospital, the farther she retired
from them into herself and into the world which she had created
in her long hours here and which no one could even penetrate
nor imagine. Sometimes she did not even answer the nurses' questions; as they rubbed her back with alcohol and steadily dis-
coursed, she was as remote from them as if she were miles away.
She did not think that she lived on a higher plane than that of
the nurses and the doctors but that she lived on a different one
and that at this particular time—this time of exploration and
habituation—she had no extra strength to spend on making herself known to them. All she had been before and all the memories
she might have brought out to disturb the monotony of, say, the
morning bath, and all that the past meant to the future when she
would leave the hospital, were of no present consequence to
her. Not even in her thoughts did she employ more than a minimum of memory. And when she did remember, it was in flat
pictures, rigorously independent of one another: she saw her
thin, poetic mother who grew thinner and more poetic in her
canvas deck-chair at Saranac reading *Lalla Rookh*. She saw herself in an inappropriate pink hat drinking iced tea in a garden so
oppressive with the smell of phlox that the tea itself tasted of it.
She recalled an afternoon in autumn in Vermont when she had
heard three dogs' voices in the north woods and she could tell, by
the characteristic minor key struck three times at intervals, like
bells from several churches, that they had treed something; the

eastern sky was pink and the trees on the horizon looked like some eccentric vascular system meticulously drawn on colored paper.

What Pansy thought of all the time was her own brain. Not only the brain as the seat of consciousness, but the physical organ itself which she envisaged, romantically, now as a jewel, now as a flower, now as a light in a glass, now as an envelope of rosy vellum containing other envelopes, one within the other, diminishing infinitely. It was always pink and always fragile, always deeply interior and invaluable. She believed that she had reached the innermost chamber of knowledge and that perhaps her knowledge was the same as the saint's achievement of pure love. It was only convention, she thought, that made one say 'sacred heart' and not 'sacred brain.'

Often, but never articulately, the color pink troubled her and the picture of herself in the wrong hat hung steadfastly before her mind's eye. None of the other girls had worn hats and since autumn had come early that year, they were dressed in green and rusty brown and dark yellow. Poor Pansy wore a white eyelet frock with a lacing of black ribbon around the square neck. When she came through the arch, overhung with bittersweet, and saw that they had not yet heard her, she almost turned back, but Mr. Oliver was there and she was in love with him. She was in love with him though he was ten years older than she and had never shown any interest in her beyond asking her once, quite fatuously but in an intimate voice, if the yodeling of the little boy who peddled clams did not make her wish to visit Switzerland. Actually, there was more to this question than met the eye, for some days later Pansy learned that Mr. Oliver, who was immensely rich, kept an apartment in Geneva. In the garden that day, he spoke to her only once. He said, 'My dear, you look exactly like something out of Katherine Mansfield,' and immediately turned and within her hearing asked Beatrice Sherburne to dine with him that night at the Country Club. Afterward, Pansy went down to the sea and threw the beautiful hat onto the full tide and saw it vanish in the wake of a trawler. Thereafter, when she heard the clam boy coming down the road, she locked the door and when the knocking had stopped and her mother called down from her chaise longue, 'Who was it, dearie?' she replied, 'A salesman.'

It was only the fact that the hat had been pink that worried her. The rest of the memory was trivial, for she knew that she could never again love anything as ecstatically as she loved the spirit of Pansy Vanneman, enclosed within her head.

But her study was not without distraction, and she fought two adversaries: pain and Dr. Nicholas. Against Dr. Nicholas, she defended herself valorously and in fear; but pain, the pain, that is, that was independent of his instruments, she sometimes forced upon herself adventurously like a child scaring himself in a graveyard.

Dr. Nicholas greatly admired her crushed and splintered nose which he daily probed and peered at, exclaiming that he had never seen anything like it. His shapely hands ached for their knives; he was impatient with the skull-fracture man's cautious delay. He spoke of 'our' nose and said 'we' would be a new person when we could breathe again. His own nose, the trademark of his profession, was magnificent. Not even his own brilliant surgery could have improved upon it nor could a first-rate sculptor have duplicated its direct downward line which permitted only the least curvature inward toward the end; nor the delicately rounded lateral declivities; nor the thin-walled, perfectly matched nostrils. Miss Vanneman did not doubt his humaneness nor his talent—he was a celebrated man—but she questioned whether he had imagination. Immediately beyond the prongs of his speculum lay her treasure whose price he, no more than the nurses, could estimate. She believed he could not destroy it, but she feared that he might maim it: might leave a scratch on one of the brilliant facets of the jewel, bruise a petal of the flower, smudge the glass where the light burned, blot the envelopes, and that then she would die or would go mad. While she did not question that in either eventuality her brain would after a time redeem its original impeccability, she did not quite yet wish to enter upon either kind of eternity, for she was not certain that she could carry with her her knowledge as well as its receptacle.

Blunderer that he was, Dr. Nicholas was an honorable enemy, not like the demon, pain, which skulked in a thousand guises within her head, and which often she recklessly willed to attack her and then drove back in terror. After the rout, sweat streamed from her face and soaked the neck of the coarse hospital shirt. To be sure, it came usually of its own accord, running like a wild fire through all the convolutions to fill with flame the small sockets and ravines and then, at last, to withdraw, leaving behind a throbbing and an echo. On these occasions, she was as helpless as a tree in a wind. But at the other times when, by closing her eyes and rolling up the eyeballs in such a way that she fancied she looked directly on the place where her brain was, the pain woke sluggishly and came toward her at a snail's pace. Then, bit by bit, it gained speed. Sometimes it faltered back, subsided altogether, and then it rushed like a tidal wave driven by a hurricane, lashing and roaring until she lifted her hands from the counterpane, crushed her broken teeth into her swollen lip, stared in panic at the soothing walls with her ruby eyes, stretched out her legs until she felt their bones must snap. Each cove, each narrow inlet, every living bay was flooded and the frail brain, a little hat-shaped boat, was washed from its mooring and set adrift. The skull was as vast as the world and the brain was as small as a seashell.

Then came calm weather and the safe journey home. She kept vigil for a while, though, and did not close her eyes, but gazing pacifically at the trees, conceived of the pain as the guardian of her treasure who would not let her see it; that was why she was handled so savagely whenever she turned her eyes inward. Once this watch was interrupted: by chance she looked into the corridor and saw a shaggy mop slink past the door, followed by a senile porter. A pair of ancient eyes, as rheumy as an old dog's, stared uncritically in at her and the toothless mouth formed a brutish word. She was so surprised that she immediately closed her eyes to shut out the shape of the word and the pain dug up the unmapped regions of her head with mattocks, ludicrously huge. It was the familiar pain, but this time, even as she endured it, she observed with detachment that its effect upon her was less than that of its contents, the by-products, for example, of temporal confusion and the bizarre misapplication of the style of one sensation to another. At the moment, for example, although her brain reiterated to her that *it* was being assailed, she was stroking her right wrist with her left hand as though to assuage the ache, long since dispelled, of the sprain in the joint. Some minutes after she had opened her eyes and left off soothing her wrist, she lay rigid experiencing the sequel to the pain, an ideal terror. For, as before on several occasions, she was overwhelmed with the knowledge that the pain had been consummated in the vessel of her mind and for the moment the vessel was unbeautiful: she thought, quailing, of those plastic folds as palpable as the fingers of locked hands containing in their very cells, their fissures, their repulsive hemispheres, the mind, the soul, the inscrutable intelligence.

The porter, then, like the pink hat and like her mother and the hounds' voices, loitered with her.

Dr. Nicholas came at nine o'clock to prepare her for the operation. With him came an entourage of white-frocked acolytes, and one of them wheeled in a wagon on which lay knives and scissors and pincers, cans of swabs and gauze. In the midst of these was a bowl of liquid whose rich purple color made it seem strange like the brew of an alchemist.

'All set?' he asked her, smiling. 'A little nervous, what? I don't blame you. I've often said I'd rather lose an arm than have a submucuous resection.' Pansy thought for a moment he was going to touch his nose. His approach to her was roundabout. He moved through the yellow light shed by the globe in the ceiling which gave his forehead a liquid gloss; he paused by the bureau and touched a blossom of the cyclamen; he looked out the window and said, to no one and to all, 'I couldn't start my car this morning. Came in a cab.' Then he came forward. As he came, he removed a speculum from the pocket of his short-sleeved coat and like a cat, inquiring of the nature of a surface with its paws, he put out his hand toward her and drew it back, gently murmuring, 'You must not be afraid, my dear. There is no danger, you know. Do you think for a minute I would operate if there were?'

Dr. Nicholas, young, brilliant, and handsome, was an aristocrat, a husband, a father, a clubman, a Christian, a kind counselor, and a trustee of his school alumni association. Like many of the medical profession, even those whose speciality was centered on the organ of the basest sense, he interested himself in the psychology of his patients: in several instances, for example, he had found that severe attacks of sinusitis were coincident with emotional crises. Miss Vanneman more than ordinarily captured his fancy since her skull had been fractured and her behavior throughout had been so extraordinary that he felt he was observing at first hand some of the results of shock, that incommensurable element, which frequently were too subtle to see. There was, for example, the matter of her complete passivity during a lumbar puncture, reports of which were written down in her history and were enlarged upon for him by Dr. Rivers' interne who had been in charge. Except for a tremor in her throat and a deepening of pallor, there were no signs at all that she was aware of what was happening to her. She made no sound, did not close her eyes nor clench her fists. She had had several punctures; her only reaction had been to the very first one, the morning after she had been brought in. When the interne explained to her that he was going to drain off cerebro-spinal fluid which was pressing against her brain, she exclaimed, 'My God!' but it was not an exclamation of fear. The young man had been unable to name what it was he had heard in her voice; he could only say that it had not been fear as he had observed it in other patients.

He wondered about her. There was no way of guessing whether she had always had a nature of so tolerant and undemanding a complexion. It gave him a melancholy pleasure to think that before her accident she had been high-spirited and loquacious; he was moved to think that perhaps she had been a beauty and that when she had first seen her face in the looking glass she had lost all joy in herself. It was very difficult to tell what the face had been, for it was so bruised and swollen, so hacked-up and lopsided. The black stitches the length of the nose, across the saddle, across the cheekbone, showed that there would be unsightly scars. He had ventured once to give her the name of a plastic surgeon but she had only replied with a vague, refusing smile. He had hoisted a manly shoulder and said, 'You're the doctor.'

Much as he pondered, coming to no conclusions, about what went on inside that pitiable skull, he was, of course, far more interested in the nose, deranged so badly that it would require his topmost skill to restore its functions to it. He would be obliged not only to make a submucuous resection, a simple run-of-the-mill operation, but to remove the vomer, always a delicate task but further complicated in this case by the proximity of the bone to the frontal fracture line which conceivably was not entirely closed. If it were not and he operated too soon and if a cold germ then found its way into the opening, the patient would be carried off by meningitis in the twinkling of an eye. He wondered if she knew in what potential danger she lay; he desired to assure her that he had brought his craft to its nearest perfection and that she had nothing to fear of him, but feeling that she was perhaps both ignorant and unimaginative and that such consolation would create a fear rather than dispel one, he held his tongue and came nearer to the bed.

Watching him, Pansy could already feel the prongs of his pliers opening her nostrils for the insertion of his fine probers. The pain he caused her with his instruments was of a different kind from that she felt unaided: it was a naked, clean, and vivid pain which made her faint and ill and made her wish to die. Once she had fainted as he ruthlessly explored and after she was brought around, he continued until he had finished his investigation. The memory of this outrage had afterwards several times made her cry.

This morning she looked at him and listened to him with hatred. Fixing her eyes upon the middle of his high, protuberant brow, she imagined the clutter behind it and she despised its obtuse imperfection, the reason's oblique comprehension of itself. In his bland unawareness, this nobody, this nose-bigot, was about to play with fire and she wished him ill.

He said, 'I can't blame you. No, I expect you're not looking forward to our little party. But I expect you'll be glad to be able to breathe again.'

He stationed his lieutenants. The interne stood opposite him on the left side of the bed. The surgical nurse wheeled the wagon within easy reach of his hands and stood beside it. Another nurse stood at the foot of the bed. A third drew the shades at the windows and attached the blinding light which shone down on the patient hotly, and then she left the room, softly closing the door. Pansy stared at the silver ribbon tied in a great bow round the green crepe paper of one of the flower pots. It made her realize for the first time that one of the days she had lain here had been Christmas, but she had no time to consider this strange and thrilling fact, for Dr. Nicholas was genially explaining his anaesthetic. He would soak packs of gauze in the purple fluid, a cocaine solution, and he would place them then in her nostrils, leaving them there for an hour. He warned her that the packing would be disagreeable (he did not say 'painful') but that it would be well worth a few minutes of discomfort not to be in the least sick after the operation. He asked her if she were ready and when she nodded her head, he adjusted the mirror on his forehead and began.

At the first touch of his speculum, Pansy's fingers mechanically bent to the palms of her hands and she stiffened. He said, 'A pack, Miss Kennedy,' and Pansy closed her eyes. There was a rush of plunging pain as he drove the sodden gobbet of gauze high up into her nose and something bitter burned in her throat so that she retched. The doctor paused a moment and the surgical nurse wiped her mouth. He returned to her with another pack, pushing it with his bodkin doggedly until it lodged against the first. Stop! Stop! cried all her nerves, wailing along the surface of her skin. The coats that covered them were torn off and they shuddered like naked people screaming. Stop! Stop! But Dr.

Nicholas did not hear. Time and again he came back with a fresh pack and did not pause at all until one nostril was finished. She opened her eyes and saw him wipe the sweat off his forehead and saw the dark interne bending over her, fascinated. Miss Kennedy bathed her temples in ice water and Dr. Nicholas said, 'There. It won't be much longer. I'll tell them to send you some coffee, though I'm afraid you won't be able to taste it. Ever drink coffee with chicory in it? I have no use for it.'

She snatched at his irrelevancy and, though she had never tasted chicory, she said severely, 'I love it.'

Dr. Nicholas chuckled. 'De gustibus. Ready? A pack, Miss Kennedy.'

The second nostril was harder to pack since the other side was now distended and the passage was anyhow much narrower, as narrow, he had once remarked, as that in the nose of an infant. In such pain as passed all language and even the farthest fetched analogies, she turned her eyes inward thinking that under the obscuring cloak of the surgeon's pain, she could see her brain without the knowledge of its keeper. But Dr. Nicholas and his aides would give her no peace. They surrounded her with their murmuring and their foot-shuffling and the rustling of their starched uniforms, and her eyelids continually flew back in embarrassment and mistrust. She was claimed entirely by this present, meaningless pain and suddenly and sharply, she forgot what she had meant to do. She was aware of nothing but her ascent to the summit of something; what it was she did not know, whether it was a tower or a peak or Jacob's ladder. Now she was an abstract word, now she was a theorem of geometry, now she was a kite flying, a top spinning, a prism flashing, a kaleidoscope turning.

But none of the others in the room could see inside and when the surgeon was finished, the nurse at the foot of the bed said, 'Now you must take a look in the mirror. It's simply too comical.' And they all laughed intimately like old, fast friends. She smiled politely and looked at her reflection: over the gruesomely fattened snout, her scarlet eyes stared in fixed reproach upon the upturned lips, gray with bruises. But even in its smile of betrayal, the mouth itself was puzzled: it reminded her that something had been left behind, but she could not recall what it was. She was hollowed out and was as dry as a white bone.

They strapped her ankles to the operating table and put leather nooses round her wrists. Over her head was a mirror with a thousand facets in which she saw a thousand travesties of her face. At her right side was the table, shrouded in white, where lay the glittering blades of the many knives, thrusting out fitful rays of light. All the cloth was frosty; everything was white or silver and as cold as snow. Dr. Nicholas, a tall snowman with silver eyes and silver finger-nails, came into the room soundlessly for he walked on layers and layers of snow which deadened his footsteps; behind him came the interne, a smaller snowman, less impressively proportioned. At the foot of the table, a snow figure put her frozen hands upon Pansy's helpless feet. The doctor plucked the packs from the cold, numb nose. His laugh was like a cry on a bitter, still night: 'I will show you now,' he called across the expanse of snow, 'that you can feel nothing.' The pincers bit at nothing, snapped at the air and cracked a nerveless icicle. Pansy called back and heard her own voice echo: 'I feel nothing.'

Here the walls were gray, not tan. Suddenly the face of the nurse at the foot of the table broke apart and Pansy first thought it was in grief. But it was a smile and she said, 'Did you enjoy your coffee?' Down the gray corridors of the maze, the words rippled, ran like mice, birds, broken beads: Did you enjoy your coffee? your coffee? your coffee? Similarly once in another room that also had gray walls, the same voice had said, 'Shall I give her some whiskey?' She was overcome with gratitude that this young woman (how pretty she was with her white hair and her white face and her china-blue eyes!) had been with her that first night and was with her now.

In the great stillness of the winter, the operation began. The knives carved snow. Pansy was happy. She had been given a hypodermic just before they came to fetch her and she would have gone to sleep had she not enjoyed so much this trickery of Dr. Nicholas' whom now she tenderly loved.

There was a clock in the operating room and from time to time she looked at it. An hour passed. The snowman's face was melting; drops of water hung from his fine nose, but his silver eyes were as bright as ever. Her love was returned, she knew: he loved her nose exactly as she loved his knives. She looked at her face in the domed mirror and saw how the blood had streaked her lily-white cheeks and had stained her shroud. She returned to the private song: Did you enjoy your coffee? your coffee?

At the half-hour, a murmur, sanguine and slumbrous, came to her and only when she had repeated the words twice did they engrave their meaning upon her. Dr. Nicholas said, 'Stand back now, nurse. I'm at this girl's brain and I don't want my elbow jogged.' Instantly Pansy was alive. Her strapped ankles arched angrily; her wrists strained against their bracelets. She jerked her head and she felt the pain flare; she had made the knife slip.

'Be still!' cried the surgeon. 'Be quiet, please!'

He had made her remember what it was she had lost when he had rammed his gauze into her nose: she bustled like a housewife to shut the door. She thought, I must hurry before the robbers come. It would be like the time Mother left the cellar door open and the robber came and took, of all things, the terrarium.

Dr. Nicholas was whispering to her. He said, in the voice of a lover, 'If you can stand it five minutes more, I can perform the second operation now and you won't have to go through this again. What do you say?'

She did not reply. It took her several seconds to remember why it was her mother had set such store by the terrarium and then it came to her that the bishop's widow had brought her an herb from Palestine to put in it.

The interne said, 'You don't want to have your nose packed again, do you?'

The surgical nurse said, 'She's a good patient, isn't she, sir?'

'Never had a better,' replied Dr. Nicholas. 'But don't call me "sir." You must be a Canadian to call me "sir."'

The nurse at the foot of the bed said, 'I'll order some more coffee for you.'

'How about it, Miss Vanneman?' said the doctor. 'Shall I go ahead?'

She debated. Once she had finally fled the hospital and fled Dr. Nicholas, nothing could compel her to come back. Still, she knew that the time would come when she could no longer live in seclusion, she must go into the world again and must be equipped to live in it; she banally acknowledged that she must be able to breathe. And finally, though the world to which she would return remained unreal, she gave the surgeon her permission.

He had now to penetrate regions that were not anaesthetized and this he told her frankly, but he said that there was no danger at all. He apologized for the slip of the tongue he had made: in point of fact, he had not been near her brain, it was only a figure of speech. He began. The knives ground and carved and curried and scoured the wounds they made; the scissors clipped hard gristle and the scalpels chipped off bone. It was as if a tangle of tiny nerves were being cut dexterously, one by one; the pain writhed spirally and came to her who was a pink bird and sat on the top of a cone. The pain was a pyramid made of a diamond; it was an intense light; it was the hottest fire, the coldest chill, the highest peak, the fastest force, the furthest reach, the newest time. It possessed nothing of her but its one infinitesimal scene: beyond the screen as thin as gossamer, the brain trembled for its life, hearing the knives hunting like wolves outside, sniffing and snapping. Mercy! Mercy! cried the scalped nerves.

At last, miraculously, she turned her eyes inward tranquilly. Dr. Nicholas had said, 'The worst is over. I am going to work on the floor of your nose,' and at his signal she closed her eyes and this time and this time alone, she saw her brain lying in a shell-pink satin case. It was a pink pearl, no bigger than a needle's eye, but it was so beautiful and so pure that its smallness made no difference. Anyhow, as she watched, it grew. It grew larger and larger until it was an enormous bubble that contained the surgeon and the whole room within its rosy luster. In a long ago summer, she had often been absorbed by the spectacle of flocks of yellow birds that visited a cedar tree and she remembered that everything that summer had been some shade of yellow. One year of childhood, her mother had frequently taken her to have tea with an aged schoolmistress upon whose mantelpiece there was a herd of ivory elephants; that had been the white year. There was a green spring when early in April she had seen a grass snake on a boulder, but the very summer that followed was violet, for vetch took her mother's garden. She saw a swatch of blue tulle lying in a raffia basket on the front porch of Uncle Marion's brown house. Never before had the world been pink, whatever else it had been. Or had it been, one other time? She could not be sure and she did not care. Of one thing she was certain: never had the world enclosed her before and never had the quiet been so smooth.

For only a moment the busybodies left her to her ecstasy and then, impatient and gossiping, they forced their way inside, slashed at her resisting trance with questions and congratulations, with statements of fact and jokes. 'Later,' she said to them dumbly. 'Later on, perhaps. I am busy now.' But their voices would not go away. They touched her, too, washing her face with cloths so cold they stung, stroking her wrists with firm, anti-septic fingers. The surgeon, squeezing her arm with avuncular pride, said, 'Good girl,' as if she were a bright dog that had retrieved a bone. Her silent mind abused him: 'You are a thief,' it said, 'you are a heartless vagabond and you should be put to death.' But he was leaving, adjusting his coat with an air of vainglory, and the interne, abject with admiration, followed him from the operating room smiling like a silly boy.

Shortly after they took her back to her room, the weather changed, not for the better. Momentarily the sun emerged from its concealing murk, but in a few minutes the snow came with a wind that promised a blizzard. There was great pain, but since it could not serve her, she rejected it and she lay as if in a hammock in a pause of bitterness. She closed her eyes, shutting herself up within her treasureless head.

EDITORS' ANALYSIS

The immediate impact of Miss Stafford's story comes from the clarity of the details of hospital life, and the clarity of the young woman's febrile reactions to them. At this level, the story stirs into being the reader's own private fears of pain and mutilation. But at a more subtle level, the story takes on a more general meaning. It suggests, through the girl's protective attitude toward her precious brain, that a person needs desperately to remain inviolable in some remote part of his being, lest he lose a sense of self. The story also makes clear that to the very young, the possibility of death is intolerable, and must be rejected savagely and at whatever cost.

QUESTIONS

1. Does the densely detailed style add to, or subtract from, the central passion for survival of the Pansy Vanneman of the story? How can this style be characterized? In what ways is the writer's manner linked to her subject?

2. Is Pansy Vanneman's mask of passivity an unusual disguise for sharp, deadly fear? Is it a sort of animal paralysis?

3. What motivates Pansy's shift from horror, in paragraph two, to pity, in paragraph three, as she remembers the driver of her taxicab, who has died?

4. Does the title suggest a central meaning to this story? What is the "interior castle"?

5. Do you find the last line of the story puzzling? Why is the girl finally so bitter?

6. What is the association between Pansy Vanneman's throwing away her pink hat, and her picture of her brain "always pink and always fragile"?

7. Why does Pansy Vanneman think of Dr. Nicholas, as he begins the operation, as a man "she tenderly loved"?

8. Why does the girl of the story think her surgeon "should be put to death" after the operation? Is this part of her illness? Something more radically true to her genuine feelings?

Goose Pond

by THOMAS WILLIAMS

Thomas Williams (1926-   ) is a young writer at the beginning of his career, and at present teaches literature at the University of
New Hampshire. He has published two novels, *Ceremony of Love*
(1954), and *Town Burning* (1960). "Goose Pond," his first short
story to be published, was written while Mr. Williams was a member
of a writing seminar at the State University of Iowa. It was published
in *Esquire,* and received honorable mention from Martha Foley, in
her annual collection, *Best Stories 1958.*

In "Goose Pond," a man on the far edge of middle age, who has
watched his wife slowly diminish and die, abandons his recent history
and retreats in loneliness to a remote mountain lake which he hopes
will restore him to the clear outlines of his youthful experience. He
accepts death quite simply as personal extinction. Mr. Williams' central character is a modern, secular man, living and dying in a secular
world.

Robert Hurley's wife died in September, and by the
middle of October he had more or less settled everything. His
son and daughter were both married and lived far away from
New York; his son in Los Angeles, his daughter in Toledo. They
came East for the funeral and each wanted him to come and
visit. "I'm not about to retire. I won't be an old man in a guest
room," he told them, knowing the great difference between the
man he looked at fifty-eight and the man he felt himself to be.
It had taken Mary six months to die, and during the last few of
those months he began quietly to assume many of her symptoms.
The doctors noticed it and understood, but his children, accustomed to a father who had always been to them a common-sense,
rather unimaginative figure, were shocked by his loss of weight,
by a listlessness as unlike him, as unsettling to them as if the
earth's rotation had begun to slow down.

But he would do no visiting, even though his business did not need him. "I know what visiting is," he wrote to his son. "I don't do it very well. Please don't call so much. You know how to write letters." "Daddy," his daughter said, long distance. "The children are crazy to have their grandfather come and see them."

And he thought, there is one place I would like to go, and there are no children I know there: "I'm going to New Hampshire, to Leah."

"All by yourself? What for?" She began to get excited, almost hysterical. He could see her biting her lower lip—a habit of her mother's. Afterwards she would be calling Charles in Los Angeles.

"I was born there. Your mother and I lived there before you were born. Do I need any other reason? It's October. Anyway, I'll be back in a couple of weeks."

"But, Daddy, we felt that you shouldn't be alone. . . ."

"I haven't been alone for thirty years," he said. "I want to try it again. Now go back to whatever you were doing. I can hear a baby crying in your house. Go take care of it. I'm going to stay with the Pedersens. Do you remember the old people in the big house on the mountain? If they still take boarders, that's where I'll be." *If they're still alive,* he thought. He wanted to walk in the woods again, but he had other reasons. The sight of his grandchildren, the hundred times a day when their small disasters caused screaming, tears; he couldn't stand it. They were always about to hurt themselves, they nearly fell so many times. They had so many deadly years to make. Automobiles, knives, leukemia, fire. . . . On the afternoon of the funeral he had watched his granddaughter, Ann, and suddenly he saw her having his wife's senseless pain, saw her crying not because of a bumped knee, but at more serious wounds. And the Pedersens? They were so old, they had somehow escaped, and as he remembered them they lived dried-up and careful, in a kind of limbo. He would go to the Pedersens, on Cascom Mountain.

Nana fussed with the Edison lamp, turning the white flame up in the mantle, moving the broad base across the crack made by the table leaf; then with the side of her hand she wiped the shiny surface of the table where it had been. The light shone past the tinted shade, up the glass chimney and sharpened her old face, made her glasses glint for a second until she moved away, tall and always busy, her small eyes always alert. She rarely sat down, and even then seemed poised, ready for busy duty. The old man settled himself cautiously, as he did now, one piece at a time. Nana had his zither out of its case, the light just right, made sure he had his hearing aid, his pick, an ash tray near. In spite of his age, he smoked cigarettes.

Back in the shadows, between a lacy, drooping vine and the narrow window, Nana's older sister, blue dress and high black shoes, composed and fragile face, sat in a rocker and never spoke. Nana herself was seventy-nine. For forty years she had bossed the seven-mile trek down to Leah in the late fall, back up the mountain again to this high old house in the spring. It was Nana who dealt with the world, who shut the windows when it rained, herded great-grandchildren when the family came in the summer, locked the house for the winter. In a few weeks they would be going down to their small apartment in Leah, to take their chances on another winter.

The old man tuned his zither, humming in a dry, crackly falsetto and turning his wrench as he picked the short strings. Tuned against the windy old voice, the crisp notes of the zither were startling, clear and metallic. There seemed to be no connection between the voice and the sounds of the strings, as if the old man heard other notes, the sounds of memory to check his instrument against.

"German *concert* zither," Nana said proudly, still hovering over the lamp. She rearranged his cigarettes, the coffee cup. She spoke from behind him, "He don't hear so good," nodding vigorously. "But he got the hearing aid." She pointed into his ear, where the pink button shone like a flower against brown freckles. "He don't wear it all the time, like he should." She moved quickly away on some sudden errand, and the old man looked up and winked at Hurley.

"Sometimes it makes too much noise," he said, smiling benevolently at his wife. She began to move the table. "It's all right. It's all right!" he said. In his fifty years in America he had mastered the sounds of English, but the rhythms of his speech were Scandinavian. "I'm going to play first a Norwegian song."

Nana poised herself upon a chair, folded her hands firmly, set herself for a moment and then began energetically to smooth her apron down her long thighs. The old lady against the wall stopped rocking. It always startled Hurley when, out of her silent effacement, she responded.

The old man bent over his zither, his shiny face as ruddy as a baby's. His mottled, angular fingers worked over the strings; he swayed back and forth to keep time and snorted, gave little gasps and grunts he evidently did not hear himself, in time with the music. Beneath, occasionally overcoming the sibilant, involuntary breaths, the music was poignantly clear, ordered, cascading, vivid as little knives in the shadowy room. At the end they all applauded, and the old man bowed, very pleased.

That night Hurley climbed the staircase that angled around the central chimney, an oil lamp to light his way, and entered his cold room in moonlight almost as bright as the lamp, but colder, whiter against the lamp's yellow. Two little windows looked down across the old man's garden—"Mostly for the deer,'" the old man had said of it—then over the one still-mown pasture left to the farm, down the long hills silvery in moonlight to Lake Cascom in the valley, white among black surrounding spruce. Behind, on the other side of the house, he could feel the dark presence of Cascom Mountain.

He wondered if it would be a night for sleep. He was tired enough. In the last few days he had taken many of the familiar trails, especially following those that he remembered led through hardwood. Although the leaves had turned and mostly fallen, here or there one tree flamed late among the bare ones, catching light and casting it in all directions as if it were an orange or soft red sun. He stopped often in the woods, surprised by each molten maple branch, even the smallest bright veins of each leaf golden and precious against a gnarled black trunk or the green twilight of a spruce grove. He walked carefully, resting often, sampling the few cold, sweet apples from the abandoned mountain trees, eating Nana's sandwiches a little at a time. He wanted the day to last as long as possible. At night he thought of his wife.

The high, sloping bed was wide and lonesome as a field of snow. During his wife's illness he could not sleep in their own bed, but slept every night on a studio couch where he could reach the sides, holding himself down, remember exactly where he was and why she was not beside him. If he woke in the night and for a second forgot, he had to learn over again from the beginning that Mary was going to die. It was always the first time over again, when they had left the doctor (the poor doctor, according to Mary) at the cancer hospital and walked together to Grant's Tomb. Mary finally said, "You know? They should pay a man a thousand dollars a minute for having to say those words."

Then the inevitable sequence of hours came through his mind, one after the other, until the afternoon when she was not so brave any more and shook her head back and forth as if to throw off the plastic tube that went into her nose and down, jiggling the clamps and the bottle on its hanger. Tears rolled from the outside corners of her drowned eyes and she cried pettishly, "Help me, help me."

She had taken pain better than most, was better at taking it by far than her husband or her children. When she had the compound fracture of her wrist she had been the calm one, the strong one. And he thought, *My God, how much pain she must have if she is caused to do this—if it is Mary who is caused to do this. . . .*

As they cut nerves, cutting off pain in little bits and pieces, it was as if they cut off her life, too, by shreds—the pain, the possibility of it forever gone; the life forever gone. But new pain took the place of the old. She lived for six months and died almost weightless, ageless, the little lines and wrinkles of her familiar body smoothed as if by a filling pulp. Her arms turned to thin tubes, her forehead waxed as taut, as translucent as a yellow apple. Her eyes, before the final cutting, watched him, blameful as a beaten child's. She whined for help: "What is happening to me?" And being a man only, he could stand, and stand, and stand, helpless at the foot of her crank-operated bed, the simple handle drawing his eyes, mocking, it seemed to him, telling him to crank, to grasp the handle in his strong hands and crank, sweat at it, crank faster and harder, crank until she is well again.

He turned and his hand touched the firm, virginal pillow next to his. The linen smelled country new, of washdays and clotheslines.

At midnight he heard what he first supposed to be a hundred dogs barking in the distance, and as the barking changed on the wind he suddenly knew, in exactly the same way he had known in his childhood that it was the Canada geese flying over, low here because of the height of the land, streaming over in the darkness. *Lorlorn, lorlorn, lorlorn,* the geese called to each other as they passed. He ran to the window—remembering an old excitement, feet numb on the cold boards—but the geese did not cross the moon. He remembered them well enough that way: the long wavering files of geese, necks thrust out straight, dark wings arching tirelessly on their long journey over the guns, through all the deadly traps set for them—the weather, the ice, the hunting animals and the traitor decoys. Each one its own warm life deep in the cold sky, and they called to each other, kept close and on course together, facing with disciplined bravery that impossible journey.

He came awake in the indeterminate time when night was

breaking and the small windows were luminous squares upon the wall. He lay on his back and watched the light grow, the corners arrange themselves and the moldings darken, wondering at a curved shape above the closet door. As the morning increased (he heard pans banging down in the kitchen, Nana's sharp morning voice) he finally saw that the curved shape was a bow hung on pegs. This room evidently had been a young boy's during the summer: a huge fungus platter hung between the windows and in the back of the closet he had found a fly rod enmeshed in kinky leader. Nana had missed a trout hook crusted with dried worm, stuck high on a curtain.

Before he went downstairs he remembered the bow, took it down and, wondering at the easy memories of his youth, strung it. He instinctively placed the lower end against the inside of his right foot, his left hand slid easily up the wood with the string lightly guided by his finger tips. The string vibrated tautly, and he remembered, too, how a bow seemed lighter after being strung, the tense pressure communicating energy to the arm. He estimated the pull at sixty pounds—quite a powerful bow.

"Oh, you found the bow'n arrow!" Nana said when he came into the kitchen with it. "You going to shoot? Say, how did you cock it?"

He placed the bow against his foot, pulled with his right hand and pushed with the heel of his left hand, his fingers working the string out of the notch.

"Nobody could fix it. The children going crazy they couldn't shoot, nobody could cock it," Nana said admiringly.

"Do you have any arrows?"

The old man had decided to listen. "In the umbrella stand is some arrows," he said, and Nana rushed out after them. After breakfast she insisted they all go out and watch him shoot, and he was surprised at his own excitement when he fitted the nock of one of the warped target arrows to the string. He drew and loosed the arrow across the thirty yards between the driveway and the barn. *Whap* as the arrow hit the silvery, unpainted wood of the barn and stuck, quivering. A cloud of swallows streamed out of a sashless window, and shreds of dusty hay fell from between the boards. The old people were impressed.

As he drew his second arrow the bow split apart above the grip. Arrow, string, half the bow fell loosely over his arms.

"Ooooh!" the old people sighed. "The wood was too old," the old man said. "It all dries up and it got no give to it."

"I'll get you another one," Hurley said. They shushed him up, said it wasn't any good, that nobody could cock it anyway. But later when he drove his Drive-Ur-Self Chevrolet down into Leah for groceries and the mail, he stopped in at Follansbees' hardware store.

Old Follansbee remembered him from the times he and Mary had come up to ski, possibly not from the earlier time when Follansbee was a young man working in his father's store and Hurley was a boy.

"Do for you?" Old Follansbee's bald head (once covered with black, bushy hair, parted in the middle) gleamed softly, approximately the same color and texture as his maple roll-top desk.

"I'd like to buy a bow—and some arrows," Harley added in order to specify what kind of bow he meant. In Leah he had always been constrained to come immediately to the point. The old man led him to the sporting-goods corner where rifles and shotguns, fish poles and outboard motors, knives, rubber boots, decoys, pistols lay in cases on counters, hung on racks. He remembered this part of the store and the objects he had fallen in love with as a boy. No girl had meant as much to him at fifteen as had the beautifully angular lines of a Winchester model 62, .22 pump. He even remembered the model number, but from this distance he wondered how a number could have meant so much.

He tried out a few of the pretty, too-modern bows until he found one that seemed to have the same pull as the one he had broken.

"That one's glass," Old Follansbee said. "My boy says it don't want to break."

"Glass? It's made of glass?"

"Correct. Strange, ain't it? What they can do these days? You'll want some arrows, did you say?"

He bought two arrows. When he'd pulled the one out of the barn it came apart in his hands, split all the way up the shaft. He decided to replace it with two, even though he knew the New Hampshire way was to resent such prodigality. He bought a leather arm guard and finger tabs; then he saw the hunting arrows. The slim, three-bladed heads suggested Indians and his youth. The target arrows, beside them, seemed to have no character, no honest function. He bought two hunting arrows and, under old Follansbee's suspicious conventional eye, a bow-hunting license, feeling like a child who had spent his Sunday-school money on a toy.

At the Post Office he found a joint communiqué from his worried children. "We have decided that it would be best. . . ." the words went. He sent two identical telegrams: *Having wonderful time. Tend your business. Love, Dad.* They all believed in the therapy of youth—in this case, grandchildren. He couldn't think of a way to tell them that he loved them all too much.

Nana and the old man walked with him as far as the ledges at the top of the wild orchard, careful in their white tennis shoes. Nana stood splayfooted on the granite, queen of the hill, and surveyed the valley, the advancing forest with a disapproving eye. "I see Holloways is letting their north pasture go back," she said, shaking her head. She had seen whole hills go back to darkness, many fine houses fall into their cellar holes. She turned toward Hurley accusingly, he being from the outside and thus responsible for such things. "You got to pay money to have them take the hay!"

"Tell me it's cheaper to buy it off the truck," the old man said. "But I told them it don't grow on trucks." He stood beside his tall wife, in his baggy pants and old mackinaw. His new tennis shoes were startlingly white. "I call this 'the hill of agony,'" he said, winking at Hurley.

"You see where the deer come down to eat our garden?" Nana said, pointing to the deer trails through the apple trees. "We tell the game warden to shoot. Nothing. They hang bangers in the trees. All night, 'Bang! Bang!' Nobody can sleep."

"Neither could the deer. They stayed up all night and et my lettuce," the old man said. He laughed and whacked his thigh.

"You shoot me a nice young deer," Nana said. "I make mince-meat, roasts, nice sausage for your breakfast.

He had tried to tell them that he didn't want to shoot anything with the bow, just carry it. Could he tell them that it gave a peculiar strength to his arm, that it seemed to be a kind of dynamo? When he was a boy in these same woods he and his friends had not been spectators, but actors. Their bows, fish poles, skis, rifles had set them apart from the mere hikers, the summer people.

"I won't be back tonight unless the weather changes," he said. The sun was warm on the dry leaves, but the air was crisply cool in the shadows. He said good-by to the old people, took off his pack and waited on the ledges to see them safely back to the house below, then unrolled his sleeping bag and rolled it tighter. The night before he had noticed on his geodetic map a small, five-acre pond high in the cleft between Cascom and Gilman mountains. It was called Goose Pond, and he seemed to remember having been there once, long ago, perhaps trout fishing. He remembered being very tired, yet not wanting to leave; he remembered the cat tails and alders and a long beaver dam, the pond deep in a little basin. He was sure he could follow the brook that issued from the pond—if he could pick the right one from all the little brooks that came down between Gilman and Cascom.

His pack tightened so that it rode high on his back, he carried his bow and the two hunting arrows in one hand. He soon relearned that arrows pass easily through the brush only if they go points first.

Stopping often to rest he climbed past the maples into ground juniper and pine, hearing often the soft explosions of partridge, sometimes seeing them as they burst up and whistled through the trees. He passed giant beeches crossing their noisy leaves, then walked silently through softwood until he came to a granite knob surrounded by stunted, wind-grieved hemlock. To the northwest he could see the Presidential Range, but Leah, the lake and the Pedersens' farm were all out of sight. He ate a hard-boiled egg and one of the bittersweet wild apples he had collected on the way. The wind was delightfully cool against his face, but he knew his sweat would soon chill. At two o'clock the sun was fairly low in the hard blue sky—whole valleys were in shadow below.

He took out his map. He had crossed three little brooks, and the one he could hear a short way ahead must be Goose Pond's overflow. By the sound it was a fair-sized brook. When he climbed down through the hemlock and saw it he was sure. White water angled right and left, dropping over boulders into narrow sluices and deep, clear pools. He knelt down and lowered his head into the icy water. His forehead turned numb, as if it were made of rubber. A water beetle darted to the bottom. A baby trout flashed green and pink beside a stone. It was as if he were looking through a giant lens into an alien world, where life was cold and cruel, and even the light had a quality of darkness about it. Odd little sticks on the bottom were the camouflaged larvae of insects, waiting furtively to hatch or to be eaten. Fish hid in the shadows under stones, their avid little mouths ready to snap. He shuddered and raised his head—a momentary flash of panic, as if some carnivorous animal with a gaping mouth might come darting up to tear his face.

Following the brook, jumping from stone to stone, sometimes having to leave it for the woods in order to get around tangles of blowdown or waterfalls, he came suddenly into the deep silence of the spruce, where the channel was deep. In the moist, cathedral silence of the tall pillars of spruce he realized how deafening the white water had been. The wind stirred the tops of the trees and made the slim trunks move slowly, but could not penetrate the dim, yet luminous greenness of the place.

And he saw the deer. He saw the face of the deer beside a narrow tree, and for a moment there was nothing but the face: a smoky-brown eye deep as a tunnel, it seemed, long delicate lashes, a black whisker or two along the white-shaded muzzle. The black nose quivered at each breath, the nostrils rounded. Then he began to follow the light brown line, motionless and so nearly invisible along the back, down along the edge of the white breast. One large ear turned slowly toward him. It was a doe, watching him carefully, perfect in the moment of fine innocence and wonder—a quality he suddenly remembered—the expressionless readiness of the deer. But other instincts had been working on him. He hadn't moved, had breathed slowly, put his weight equally on both legs. The light sharpened as if it had been twilight and the sun had suddenly flashed. Every detail—the convolutions of the bark on the trees, tiny twigs, the fine sheen of light on each hair of the doe, each curved, precious eyelash—became vivid and distinct. Depth grew, color brightened; his hunter's eyes became painfully efficient, as if each needle-like detail pierced him. The world became polarized on the axis of their eyes. He was alone with the doe in a green world that seemed to cry for rich red, and he did not have time to think: it was enough that he sensed the doe's quick decision to leave him. An onyx hoof snapped, her white flag rose and the doe floated in a slow arc, broadside to him, clear of the trees for an endless second. He watched down the long arrow, three blades moved ahead of the doe and at the precise moment all tension stopped; his arms, fingers, eyes and the bow were all one instrument. The arrow sliced through the deer.

Her white flag dropped. Gracefully, in long, splendid leaps, hoofs stabbing the hollow-sounding carpet of needles, the doe flickered beyond the trees. One moment of crashing brush, then silence. A thick excitement rose like fluid into his face, his arms seemed to grow to twice their normal size, become twice as strong. And still his body was governed by the old, learned patterns. He walked silently forward and retrieved his bloody arrow, snapped the feathers alive again. The trail was a vivid line of jewels, brighter than the checkerberries against their shiny green leaves, unmistakable. He rolled the bright blood between his fingers as he slowly moved forward. He must let the doe stop and lie down, let her shock-born strength dissipate in calm bleeding. Watching each step, figuring out whole series of steps, of brush bendings in advance, he picked the silent route around snags and under the blowdown.

In an hour he had gone a hundred yards, still tight and careful, up out of the spruce and onto a small rise covered with birch and poplar saplings. The leaves were loud underfoot and, as he carefully placed one foot, the doe rose in front of him and crashed downhill, obviously weak, staggering against the whippy birch. A fine mist of blood sprayed at each explosion of breath from the holes in her ribs. He ran after her, leaping over brush, running along fallen limbs, sliding under low branches that flicked his cheeks like claws. His bow caught on a branch and jerked him upright. After one impatient pull he left it. He drew his knife. The brown shape ahead had disappeared, and he dove through the brush after it, witch hobble grabbing at his legs.

The doe lay against a stump, one leg twitching. He knelt down and put one hard arm around her neck and, not caring for the dangerous hoofs, the spark of life, raised the firm, warm neck against his chest and, sighing, stabbed carefully into the sticking place. Blood was hot on the knife and on his hand.

He rolled over into the leaves, long breaths bending him, making his back arch. His shirt vibrated over his heart, his body turned heavy and pressed with unbelievable weight into the earth. He let his arms melt into the ground, and a cool, lucid sadness came over his flesh.

He made himself get up. In order to stand he had to fight gravity, to use all his strength—a quick fear for his heart. His joints ached and had begun to stiffen. He must keep moving. Shadows were long and he had much to do before dark. He followed the blood trail back and found his bow and one arrow. He limped going back down the hill; at a certain angle his knees tended to jackknife, as if gears were slipping.

He stood over the clean body of the doe, the white belly snowy against brown leaves. One hind leg he hooked behind a sapling, and he held the other with his knee as he made the first long incision through the hair and skin, careful not to break the peritoneum.He ran the incision from the breast to the tail, then worked the skin back with his fingers before making the second cut through the warm membrane, the sticky blue case for the stomach and entrails. He cut, and the steamy innards rolled unbroken and still working out onto the ground. A few neat berries of turd rattled on the leaves. He cut the anus and organs of reproduction clear of the flesh, then found the kidneys and liver and reached arm-deep into the humid chest cavity, the hot smell of blood close in his nostrils, and removed the yellow lungs in handfuls. Then he pulled out the dark red heart. Kidneys, liver and heart he wrapped carefully in his sandwich wrappings, then rose and painfully stretched. Goose Pond lay just below; he could see a flicker of water through the skein of branches, and there he would make camp.

With his belt looped around the neck and front hoofs, he slid the doe down toward the pond. It was dusk by the time he found a dry platform of soft needles beneath a hemlock, next to the water. The doe had become stiff enough so that he could hang it in a young birch, head wedged in a fork. He spread his sleeping bag, tried it for roots and stones, and found none. The last high touch of sun on the hill above him had gone; he had even prepared ground for a fire when he realized that he had no energy left, no appetite to eat the liver of the doe.

Darkness had settled in along the ground,, but the sky was still bright; one line of cirrus clouds straight overhead still caught orange sunlight. Across the silver water the alder swamp was jet black, and the steep hill rose behind, craggy with spruce. A beaver's nose broke water and even, slow circles spread across the pond. The dark woods filled with cold, and one of his legs began to jerk uncontrollably. He took off his boots and slid into his sleeping bag.

The doe was monstrous, angular against the sky, her neck stretched awkwardly, head canted to one side. The black hole in her belly gaped empty. He drew his sleeping bag up around his face.

If he were twenty again he would be happy. To have shot a deer with a bow—he'd be a hero, a woodsman, famous in Leah. How it would have impressed Mary! She would have said little about it—she went to great lengths never to flatter him; her compliments had been more tangible, seldom in words. He must think of something else. The world was too empty. The cold woods, the darkening water were empty. He was too cold, too tired to manipulate his thoughts. And the progression of hours began again. Mary's eyes watched him, deep in sick hollows. How could her flesh turn so brown? Why could he do nothing to stop the pain? She watched him, in torment, her frail body riven, cut beyond endurance. The disease had killed her bravery with pain and left her gruesomely alive, without dignity, whimpering like a spoiled brat, asking for help she should have known did not exist. And he stood by and watched, doing nothing. Nothing. He was not a man to do nothing. *Mary, did I do nothing to help you?*

He heard, far away, the lonely cry of the Canada geese. He was alone, hidden in the blind night, high on the stony mass of Cascom Mountain.

And then they came in, circling, calling to each other above the doubtful ground. Perhaps they had seen the reflected circle of fading sky, or remembered; generations remembering that geese had rested safely in the high pond and found food there. The scouts came whistling on their great wings, searching and listening. They sent their messages back to the flock waiting above, then planed down, braking, smeared the water with wind and came to rest in a flash of spray. The flock circled down after, careless now it was safe, honking gaily, giving the feeding call prematurely, echoing the messages of the leaders and landing masters. "Come in, come down and rest," they seemed to call, until everyone had landed safely. Then the voices grew softer, less excited, and only an occasional word drifted across the water.

Robert Hurley lay in the warm hollow of his sleeping bag, where the hours had stopped. He thought for a moment of the doe's death, and of his knife. The geese spoke softly to each other on the water—a small splash, a flutter of wings and the resting, contented voices in the deep basin of the pond. As sleep washed over him he seemed to be among them; their sentinels guarded him. When they had rested well they would rise and continue the dangerous journey down the world.

EDITORS' ANALYSIS

The impact of this story is based upon quiet subtleties of attitude and feeling. The actions and the sensibilities of the central character are rarely conscious ones. But they bring into focus the reader's submerged, animal awareness of the brief, painful, and wholly seasonal nature of individual lives. The story relies strongly on symbols for their continual impact: the deer, for example, as an implied alternative to disease and death. In addition, "Goose Pond" catches, in essence, an alternative response to death from that found in Miss Stafford's story —the reluctant toleration of it by the not-so-young.

QUESTIONS

1. There is a serenity in Mr. Williams' story not found in "The Interior Castle," by Jean Stafford. Account for this difference by comparing the kind of incident used, in each story, to create its atmosphere or tone.

2. Is Robert Hurley's flight, in "Goose Pond," from his children and his grandchildren normal in our society? Why does he make it? Is he, closed in with his personal loss, in some way an outsider?

3. Explain his excitement in pursuing and killing the deer. How is it related to the subsequent quiet moment as he lies in his sleeping bag, by Goose Pond?

4. In what symbolic ways, if any, is the deer linked to Hurley's wife? What is the satisfaction of the hunt and the subsequent preparation of the deer's body?

5. How does the flight of the Canadian geese add to the tone or mood of the story?

6. Does "Goose Pond" show the reader things about death that would be difficult to convey in any other way than by fiction? If so, can you say, in a general way, what they are?

9.

RELIGION

"King Solomon," *by Isaac Rosenfeld*

"The Morning Watch," *by James Agee*

King Solomon

by ISAAC ROSENFELD

Isaac Rosenfeld (1918-1956) was considered one of the most significant young writers of his generation. He had been literary editor of the *New Leader,* and at the time of his death was a member of the Humanities Faculty of the University of Chicago. His stories and literary criticism were published largely in the literary quarterlies and in the *New Republic.* He was the author of one novel, *Passage from Home* (1946), a study of the mind of a fourteen-year-old boy during a year that he lived away from his parents. This novel, as an example of his special qualities as a writer, shows Rosenfeld to have been more analytical in his fiction than dramatic, more concerned with the motives of his characters than with plot.

"King Solomon" is close to pure allegory. It creates a generic spiritual-secular leader out of the aging Old Testament Solomon in order to question and to explore the sources of such a person's power over others. Rosenfeld invites the reader to consider the mystery of human personality and human mortality. The effectiveness of his story lies in the fact that the mystery has been skillfully presented, but not explained away.

1. WITH HIS WOMEN

Every year, a certain number of girls. They come to him, lie down beside him, place their hands on his breast and offer to become his slaves.

This goes on all the time. "I will be your slave," say the girls, and no more need be said. But Solomon's men, his counselors, can't bear it—what is this power of his? Some maintain it is no power at all, he is merely the King. Oh yes, admit the rest, his being the King has something to do with it—but there have been other kings, so it can't be that. Nor is it anything else. Consider how unprepossessing he is, what a poor impression he makes— why, most of the counselors are taller, handsomer, and leaner

King Solomon. Reprinted from *Harper's Magazine,* July 1956. Copyright 1956 by *Harper's Magazine.* Reprinted with permission of Vasiliki Rosenfeld.

than he. To be sure, he has an excellent voice. But his voice comes through best on the telephone, and he has an unlisted number which no one would give out. Certainly not, say the men. Still the girls keep coming, and they lie down beside him with their hands on his breast.

It is not enough to say the counselors are jealous. After all, there is something strange here, the like of it has not been seen. But who shall explain the King?

Solomon himself makes no comment, he does not speak of his personal affairs. He may drop a hint or two, but these hints are contradictory and vague, and he drops them only for his own amusement; perhaps he, too, doesn't know. Every few years he publishes a collection of his sayings, most of which he has never said, but the sayings have little to do with the case, and their melancholy tone is held to be an affectation. The wisest counselors pay no attention to his words. If anything is to be learned, the wise men say, it had better be sought among his girls.

But the girls also say nothing. The rejected go away in tears—in which case one cannot expect them to speak coherently or with regard for truth; or they are determined yet to win his love—and again they will tell lies. As for the women he accepts, they are useless. Almost at once they become so much like Solomon, adopting his mannerisms of gesture and speech and sharing his views of things, that they say only what he would say—and Solomon does not speak his heart.

So it has become the custom in the court to study Solomon's women in their work; perhaps the manner in which they serve him will make it clear. The counselors watch over the harem, each chooses a woman to follow about the palace, over the grounds and through the town. One woman . . . there she goes! . . . sets out early in the morning with a basket, trailed by a counselor. She makes her way to the largest and most crowded kosher market, where she will stand in line for hours, haggling and hefting, crying highway robbery! And what delicacies does she buy? Surely pickles and spices, the rarest and the best. . . . Not necessarily, it may even be noodles. So who is the wiser? And as for the obvious conclusion—that Solomon sets store by economy—this has long since been drawn. He even lunches on left-overs.

Others clean his shoes, open and sort the mail, tend the garden and the vineyards, keep his instruments polished and in tune. A few go to the well for water—a curious assignment, as the palace has had hot and cold running water for years. Perhaps he sends them to the well on purpose, to confuse the counselors. But if this occupation serves only to deceive, why not all the rest? This may well be the case. King Solomon has a staff of regular servants, quite capable of looking after his needs.

Therefore nothing has been learned. The counselors are always confronted by the same questions at nightfall, when their need to know the King is greatest. Much of the time, he sits quietly with a girl or two, pasting stamps in an album, while they massage his scalp. On festive nights, the counselors note the revelry and participate, when invited, in the dancing and carousing. Not that this enchants them; many counselors complain that the King has no taste in entertainment, that he relies, for instance, too heavily on tambourines, which he has his dancing girls flutter in their hands till the jingling gives one a headache; that much the same or better amusements can be had in the cabarets about the town which—so much for Solomon's originality—have been the source of many a spectacle of the King's court—and they even have newspaper clippings to prove the point. Nevertheless, they succumb to the King's merrymaking, and even if it makes them puke with disdain, still they lose the essential detachment. And then at the hour when the King retires to his chamber with his chosen love, all is lost, the counselors are defeated and go disgruntled to their own quarters, to lie awake or dream enviously through the night.

All the same a pertinacious lot. What stratagems, disguising themselves as eunuchs or hiding in vases or behind the furniture to learn what goes on at night! Here, too, they have been disappointed. Though Solomon burns soft lights beside his couch, no one has witnessed anything—or at least has ever reported what he saw. At the last moment the hidden counselors have shut their eyes or turned away; no one has dared look at the King's nakedness, dared to witness his love. Still, sounds have been heard floating in deep summer air over the garden and the lily pond, mingling with the voices of frogs—but the intrusion has been its own punishment, maddening those who have overheard the King and driving them wild with lust or despair. Sooner or later, the counselors have been compelled to stopper their ears. Now when these sounds issue from the King's apartments, the counselors take up instruments and play, softly but in concert, to hide his sounds within their own.

None has seen the King's nakedness; yet all have seen him in shirt sleeves or suspenders, paunchy, loose-jowled, in need of a trim. Often in the heat of the day he appears bareheaded, and all have looked upon his baldness; sometimes he comes forth in his bare feet, and the men have observed bunions and corns. When he appears in this fashion with, say, a cigar in his mouth and circles under his eyes; his armpits showing yellowish and hairy over the arm holes of his undershirt; his wrinkles deep and his skin slack; a wallet protruding from one hip pocket and a kerchief from the other—at such moments, whether he be concerned with issues of government or merely the condition of the plumbing, he does show himself in human nakedness after all, he is much like any man, he even resembles a policeman on his day off or a small-time gambler. And sometimes, unexpectedly, he summons the cabinet to a game of pinochle—then all are aware he has again transcended them.

Of late, King Solomon has turned his attention to the young. He has organized bicycle races for children, entertained them with magicians, taken them on picnics and excursions to the zoo. He loves to sit on a shady bench with a youngster on either knee, a boy and a girl, about four or five in age. They pull at his beard, tug at his ears, and finger his spectacles till he can no longer see through the smudges. Sometimes, the children are his own, more often not. It makes no difference, the King has many sons and daughters. He tells stories, not nearly so amusing as they should be, old stories which the children grew tired of in the nursery, or poor inventions, rather pointless on the whole. And he seldom finishes a story but begins to nod in the telling, his words thicken and stumble; eventually he falls asleep. Solomon is a disappointment to the young, seldom will children come twice to his garden. Yet for them he is truly a king: robed and gowned, golden-sandaled, wearing a crown, his hair trimmed, his beard washed lustrous, combed, and waved, and the hairs plucked out of his nostrils.

And in this splendor, in which he seldom appears, not even for the reception of ambassadors, he loves to bounce a rubber ball and play catch with the children. He is unskilled at these games, they call him butter-fingers. A man turning sixty, an aging king.

But how clear is the expression of his eyes as he plays with the children—if only one knew what it meant! Perhaps he longs to reveal himself but doe not know how; or does not know that the people await this revelation; or is unable to see beyond the children, who are bored with him. Perhaps he has nothing to reveal, and all his wisdom lies scattered from his hand: he is merely this, that, and the other, a few buildings raised, roads leveled, a number of words spoken, unthinking, on an idle afternoon. Occasionally, when he recognizes the expectation of the people, he tries to remember an appropriate saying from one of the collections he has published. Most of the time, he is unaware of all this.

The children are fretful in the garden, they wait to be delivered. They have been brought by mothers, nurses, older sisters, who stand outside the gate, looking through the palings. The mothers and nurses whisper together, their feet and eyes and hands are restless, they look at his shining beard. Later in the afternoon, when the children have been led home, perhaps one of the older girls, one of the sisters, will enter the same garden, approach the spot where the King lies resting, lie down beside him, fold her hands upon his breast, and offer to become his slave.

2. THE QUEEN OF SHEBA

From all over they have come, and they keep coming, though the King is now an old man. It may be owing to his age that he has grown lenient, admitting women to concubinage whom, the counselors swear, he would have sent packing in the old days. He has reached the years when anything young looks good to him. This may not be true, there may be other reasons; but the counselors have a point in saying that the standards have fallen, and they tell the story of the Queen of Sheba.

A letter came, it was the first application to be received by mail. From a foreign country, the woman signed herself The Queen. She flattered Solomon's wisdom, word of which had reached her from afar; her own ears longed to hear his discourse, her own eyes, to behold his person. An unorthodox application, written in a powerful, forward-rushing though feminine hand on strangely scented paper: the King said it reminded him of jungles. He inspected the postmark, clipped off the stamp, and pasted it on a page by itself in his album. His expression was hidden in his beard.

The woman meant it. Boxes began to arrive, plastered with travel stickers. They came on sand-choked, sneezing camels, in long trains, attended by drivers, natives of the Land of Sheba. The next day, more boxes, and again on the third. Gifts of all description, of money and goods, spangles and bangles for the entire court. It made an excellent impression, but Solomon, who distributed the gifts, did not seem pleased. . . . Here the counselors pretend to know the King's mind. First of all, they say, he was annoyed at having to put up so many camels, whole droves of them—his stables were crowded, and there was a shortage of feed for his own animals. Then the camel drivers, rough and barbarous men, were inflamed by the sight of Solomon's women, and the King had to double the guard and pay overtime; this killed him. But their greatest presumption lies in saying that Solomon thought, "*Adonai Elohenu!* Is she coming to stay?" No one knows what the King thought.

He may well have been glad that the Queen was coming. No queen had ever before asked to be his slave—and she was a queen for sure, and of a rich country, think of the gifts she had sent. Solomon put his economists to work and they submitted a report: the financial structure was sound, and the country led in the production of myrrh, pepper and oil. Now to be sure, the Queen's letter made no direct application; apart from the flattery, it merely said, *coming for a visit*, as an equal might say. But the interpretation was clear. An equal would not come uninvited, only one who meant to offer herself would do so—unless the Queen was rude; but the gifts she had sent took care of that. Yet as a queen, writing from her own palace, she could not have expressed the intention, it would have been treason to her own people. Nevertheless, she had every intention: otherwise, why would she have gone to the trouble? The fact is, there was rejoicing in the palace, Solomon himself led the dancing, and he declared a holiday when the Queen of Sheba arrived.

She came in a howdah, on a camel, preceded by troops of archers and trumpeters. Solomon helped her down, and washed and anointed her feet in the courtyard. This didn't come off so well. Sheba used coloring matter on her toenails and the soles of her feet, and the coloring ran; Solomon was out of practice, he tickled her feet a few times and made her laugh. The ceremony was supposed to be a solemn one, the people took it very seriously, and they were offended by her toenails—feet were supposed to be presented dusty: as for the giggling, it was unpardonable, and the priests took offense. A poor set of omens.

Besides, Sheba was not quite so young as the autographed picture, which she had sent in advance to Solomon, would have led one to expect. Her skin was nearly black, and her black hair, which she had apparently made some effort to straighten, had gone frizzled and kinky again in the heat of the desert crossing. She wore anklets of delicate chain, gold bracelets all over her arms, and jewels in both obvious and unexpected places, so that the eye was never done seeing them; their light was kept in constant agitation by the massive rhythm of her breathing, which involved her entire body. A sense of tremendous power and authenticity emanated from her breasts. Some thought she was beautiful, others, not.

No one knows what the King thought; but he may well have felt what everyone else did who came to witness her arrival—drawn, and at the same time, stunned.

But the King is glad in his heart as he leads Sheba to the table, where he has put on a great spread for her. He is attended by his court and surrounded by his women—and how lordly are his movements as he eats meat and rinses his mouth with wine! At the same time he is uneasy in the Queen's presence—after all, this is no maiden lurking in the garden to trip up to him and fold her hands upon his breast. The meal goes well enough: Sheba asks for seconds, and seems impressed with the napkins and silverware. But suddenly, right in the middle of dessert, she turns to him and demands, in front of everyone and that all may hear, that he show her his famous wisdom. This comes as something of a shock. The implication is two-fold: that so far he has spoken commonplaces; and secondly, that he is to suffer no illusions, it was really for the sake of his wisdom that she made the difficult trip. The people turn their eyes on the King, who handles the awkward moment with skill; he clears his throat on schedule, and raises his hand in the usual gesture, admonishing silence. But nothing comes.

In the official account of the visit, which Solomon had written to order, he was supposed to have

> . . . told her all questions: There was not anything . . . which he told her not. And when the Queen of Sheba had seen all Solomon's wisdom, and the house that he had built, and the meat of his table and the sitting of his servants . . .

etc.,

> there was no more spirit in her. And she said to the King, It was a true report that I heard in mine own land, of thy acts and thy wisdom. Howbeit, I believed not the words, until I came and mine eyes had seen it; and behold, the half was not told me: Thy wisdom and prosperity exceedeth the fame which I heard. Happy are thy men . . . which stand continually before thee and that hear thy wisdom.

After which there was supposed to have been a further exchange of compliments and gifts.

Now this is not only a bit thick, it gets round the question of Solomon's wisdom. What *did* the King say, when put to it by the Queen? That there were so many feet in a mile? That all circles were round? That the number of stars visible on a clear night from a point well out of town was neither more nor less than a certain number? Did he advise her what to take for colds, give her a recipe for salad dressing, or speak of building temples and ships? Just what does a man say under the circumstances?

Certainly, he hadn't the nerve, the gall, to repeat the abominable invention to her face of the two women who disputed motherhood of a child. She would have seen through it right away. And surely he knew this was not the time to quote his sayings; besides, he always had trouble remembering them. Then what did he say?

His economists had worked up a report on the Land of Sheba. He may have sent for a copy; more likely, he knew the essential facts cold, and spoke what came to mind: industry, agriculture, natural resources. Of the financial structure, the public debt, the condition of business. Of the production of pepper, myrrh, and oil, especially oil. Grant him his wisdom.

Certainly, the Queen was impressed, but one need not suppose that the spirit was knocked out of her or that she said, "It was a true report that I heard in mine own land . . ." etc. Chances are, she paid no attention to his words (except to note the drift) but watched him as he spoke, taking in the cut of his beard, the fit of his clothes, and wondering, betimes, what sort of man he was. She saw his initial uncertainty give way and his confidence grow as he reached the meaty part of his delivery. And all along, she observed how he drew on the admiring glances of his girls, soaked up their adoration, as they lay open-mouthed on couches and rugs at his feet, all criticism suspended, incapacitated by love. Love ringed him round, love sustained him, he was the splendid heart of their hearts. She must have forgotten the heat and sand images of the desert crossing, she, too, lapped from all sides and borne gently afloat. . . .

So much, one may imagine. But the Queen spent a number of days or weeks, perhaps even a month or two in the King's company, and of what happened during the time of her stay, let alone the subsequent events of the first night, the official chronicles say nothing. A merciful omission, according to the counselors, who report that it went badly from the start. When the King had finished his discourse, they say the Queen felt called upon to answer. But words failed her, or she felt no need of words: she was the Queen. What she did was to lean forward and, in utter disregard of the company, take his head into her hands, gaze at him for a long time with a smile on her thick lips, and at last bestow on him a kiss, which landed somewhere in his beard.

Then she jumped onto the table, commanded music, and danced among the cups and bowls, the dishes and the crumpled napkins. The counselors were shocked, the girls smirked painfully, the servants held their breath. Nor was Sheba so slender as the autographed picture may have led one to believe. When she set her feet down, the table shook, and the carafes of wine and sweetened water swayed and threatened to topple. Solomon himself hastily cleared a way for her, pushing the dishes to one side; his hands were trembling. But she proceeded with the dance, the chain anklets tinkled, her fingers snapped, the many jewels she wore flashed wealthily. Her toes left marks on the tablecloth, as though animals had run there. And run she did, back and forth over the length of the table, bending over the counselors to tweak this one's nose and that one's ear. But always she glanced back to see if she had the King's eye.

She had it, darker than usual. To her, this meant that he was admiring her, gravely, as befits King and Queen, and her feet quickened. How stern she was! Already she felt the King's love, harder than any courtier's and so much more severe. She increased the tempo, the musicians scrambling to keep up with her, and whirled. Round and round she sped, drawing nearer the end of the table where the King sat. It was a dance in the style of her country, unknown in these parts, and she did it with the abandon of a tribesgirl, though one must assume she was conscious, in her abandonment, that it was she, the Queen, none other than Sheba, who abandoned herself to King Solomon. That was the whole point of it, the mastery of the thing. Pride did not leave her face, it entered her ecstasy and raised it in degree. Already cries, guttural, impersonal, were barking in her throat; then with a final whoop she spun round and threw herself, arms outstretched and intertwined, like one bound captive, to fall before him on the table where his meal had been.

It was a terrible mistake. The women and the counselors knew the King so much better than she, and their hearts went out in pity. The Queen had offered herself in the only way she knew —majesty, power, and reign implied—throwing herself prone with a condescending crash for the King to rise and take her. What presumption! He did not move. He sat infinitely removed, almost sorrowing over this great embarrassment. The music had stopped, there was an unbearable silence in the banquet hall. The King rumbled something deep in his beard; perhaps he was merely clearing his throat, preparatory to saying a few words (if only his wisdom did not fail him!). Some of the servants took it to mean more wine, others, more meat, still others, fingerbowls. They ran in all directions. Sheba lowered herself into her seat at the King's side. Her dark face burned. . . . Somehow the time went by, and the evening was over. Solomon led Sheba off to his chamber, as courtesy demanded. Even as she went with him, it was apparent that she still went in hope; even at the last moment. The older women wept.

Day by day, the strain mounted. Sheba was sometimes with the King, they played chess or listened to the radio, they bent their heads over maps, discussed politics, and played croquet. But there were no festivities and she did not dance again. She bore herself with dignity, but she had grown pale, and her smile, when she forgot herself, was cringing and meek. Sometimes, when she was alone, she was seen to run her finger over the table tops and the woodwork, looking for dust. She could not bear the sight of her waiting women—lest the revival of her hope, as they did her toilet, become apparent to them—and would chase them out of the room; only to call them back, and help her prepare for an audience with the King. Finally, she quarreled with some of the girls of the harem. And when this happened, Sheba knew that the day had come and she began to pack.

A pinochle game was in progress when the Queen of Sheba, unannounced and without knocking, came into the room to say she wanted a word with the King. He dismissed his counselors, but one of them swears he managed to hide behind the draperies, where he witnessed the scene.

The King was in his undershirt, smoking a cigar. He apologized for his dishevelment and offered to repair it. The affairs of state, he explained, were so trying lately, he found he worked better in dishabille. Had he been working? asked the Queen with a smile. She thought this was some sort of game, and she fingered the cards with pictures of kings and queens. Solomon, knowing that women do not play pinochle, told her the cabinet had been in extraordinary session, trying fortunes with the picture cards. The

times were good, but one must look to the future, and he offered
to show her how it was done.

"No, I don't want to keep you," said the Queen of Sheba, "I
beg only a few words."

"Speak," said Solomon.

"Solomon, Solomon," said the Queen, "I am going away. No,
don't answer me. You will say something polite and regretful,
but my decision can only be a relief to you." She paused, taking
on courage. "You must not allow this to be a disappointment to
you, you must let me take the whole expense of our emotion upon
myself. I did a foolish thing. I am a proud woman, being a Queen,
and my pride carried me too far. I thought I would take pride in
transcending pride, in offering myself to the King. But still that
was pride, you did wisely to refuse me. Yes, you are wise, Solomon, let no one question your wisdom. Yours is the wisdom of
love, which is the highest. But your love is love only of yourself;
yet you share it with others by letting them love you—and this
is next to the highest. Either way you look at it, Solomon is wise
enough. Understand me—" She took a step forward, a dance step,
as though she were again on the table top, but her eyes spoke a
different meaning.

"I am not pleading with you that you love me or allow me to
love you. For you are the King, your taking is your giving. But
allow me to say, your power rests on despair. Yours is the power
of drawing love, the like of which has not been seen. But you
despair of loving with your own heart. I have come to tell the
King he must not despair. Surely, Solomon who has built temples
and made the desert flourish is a powerful king, and he has the
power to do what the simplest slave girl or washerwoman of his
harem can do—to love with his own heart. And if he does not
have this power, it will come to him, he need only accept the
love which it is his nature to call forth in everyone, especially in
us poor women. This is his glory. Rejoice in it, O King, for you
are the King!"

The counselor who hid behind the drapes said he regretted his
action, to see how his King stood burdened before the Queen. His
own heart filled with loving shame. Solomon looked lost, deprived
of his power, as though the years in the palace and the garden
had never been. He made an effort to stand dignified in his undershirt, he bore his head as though he were wearing the crown, but
it was pitiful to see him.

"The Queen is wise," said he. Then he broke down, and the

counselor did not hear his next words. He did hear him say that the Queen was magnificent, that she had the courage of lions and tigers . . . but by now his head was lowered. Suddenly, he clasped the Queen to his breast in an embrace of farewell, and the Queen smiled and stroked his curly beard. They did not immediately take leave of each other, but went on to speak of other matters. Before the Queen of Sheba left the country, King Solomon had leased her oil lands for ninety-nine years.

But on the day of her departure, he stood bareheaded in the crowded courtyard to watch her set out, with her trumpeters and archers mounted on supercilious camels. He extended his hand to help her up, and she, with her free hand, chucked him under the chin. Then she leaned out of the howdah to cry, "Long live the King!" King Solomon stood with bowed head to receive the ovation. Now more than ever they yearned for him.

When Sheba moved off, at the head of the procession, Solomon led the people onto the roof, to watch the camels file across the sand. He stood till evening fell, and the rump of the last plodding animal had twitched out of sight beyond the sand hills. Then he averted his face and wept silently lest the people see their King's tears.

3. WITH HIS FATHERS

So the counselors have a point when they say the standards have fallen. Once the Queen of Sheba herself was unable to make it; and now, look. But no wonder, her like will not come again, and besides, Solomon is old. He has been running the country forty years, and has begun to speak of retiring; but the people know he will never retire, and so they whisper, it is time for the King to die.

How does this strike him? To look at him—his beard is white, his spotted hands shake, he walks bent, his eyes are rheumy and dim—to look at him one would suppose he dwells on the thought of death. But he is no better known now than he was in his prime. The only certainty is that the King is old.

But what follows from this, how does it reveal him? Or this? —that he had an attack of pleurisy not long ago, and since then his side has been taped. And what does it mean to say that he now has more women that ever cluttering up the palace, one thousand in all, including seven hundred wives? (It is merely that the standards have fallen?) It was necessary to tear down the harem (while the women, to everyone's displeasure, were quartered in the town) and raise a new building, so large it has taken up ground formerly allotted to the garden. They are a great source of trouble to him, these women, and the counselors complain—that's where all the money is going, to support the harem. Harem? Why, it's a whole population, the country will be ruined! And the priests complain, every week they send fresh ultimatums, objecting to the fact that so many of Solomon's girls are heathen; they have even accused him of idolatry and threatened him with loss of the Kingdom and the wrath of God. And the people grumble, it's a shame, when they find his women loitering in beauty shops or quarreling right out in the open, as they have begun to do, in the very streets. But Solomon ignores the discontent and goes on collecting women as he once collected stamps.

Why? Or what does this mean?—that he seldom takes the trouble to interview applicants, but establishes a policy for several months, during which time the rule is, no vacancies. Then he will change the rule and take on newcomers by the dozen, most of whom he does not even see, the work being done by the counselors. And how complicated the work has become, compared with the old days, when all that was necessary was for a girl to lie beside the King with her hands upon his breast. Now there are forms to fill out and letters of recommendation to obtain, several interviews and a medical examination to go through, and even then the girls must wait until their references have been checked. The filing cabinets have mounted to the ceiling. What sense does it make?

And above all in view of the following? The counselors vouch for it, they swear they have seen the proof. That King Solomon now takes to bed, not with a virgin, as his father, David, did in his old age, or even with a dancing girl, but with a hot water bottle. If this report is true, then doesn't something follow? For this is the extreme, between life and death, where all thoughts meet; an extreme, not a mean; and a wrong guess is impossible, everything is true, as at the topmost point, where all direction is down. It follows that he warms his hands on the water bottle, presses it to his cheek, passes it down along his belly.

Now when he thinks of his pride, he of all men must wonder: what was the glory of the King? Who bestowed the power, and what did it consist in? When he had it, he did not consider, and now it is gone. Passing the rubber bottle down to his feet and digging with his toes for warmth, he sees he did everything possible in his life, and left no possibility untouched, of manhood, statesmanship, love. What else can a man do? There is no answer. Except to say, he was in God's grace then? And now no longer? Or is he still in a state of grace, witness the water bottle at his feet? And perhaps he is only being tried, and may look forward to even greater rewards? Such are the advantages of being a believer. If he were one, he would know—at least believe that he knew. But a man who knows only that once love was with him, which now is no more—what does he know, what shall he believe, old, exhausted, shivering alone in bed at night with a hot water bottle, when all's quiet in the palace? And if all's not quiet, that's no longer his concern.

No, if there were any rewards, he'd settle for a good night's sleep. But sleep does not come. He hears strange noises in the apartment, scratching. . . . Mice? He must remember to speak to the caretakers. . . . At last he drowses off, to sleep a while. And if he does not sleep? Or later, when he wakes, and it is still the same night? . . . Does he think of the Queen of Sheba and wonder, whom is she visiting now? Does he remember how she danced upon the table? Or the song he wrote soon after her departure, with her words still fresh in his mind, when he resolved to pour out his love for her, but from the very first line poured out, instead, her love for him? *Let him kiss me with the kisses of his mouth, for thy love is better than wine.* It has been years since he heard from her. . . .

Meanwhile, the bottle has grown cold. Shall he ring for another? He shifts the bottle, kneads it between his knees. *And be thou like a young hart upon the mountains of spices.* Look forward, look back, to darkness, at the light, both ways blind. He raises the bottle to his breast; it does not warm him. He gropes for the cord, and while his hand reaches, he thinks, as he has thought so many times, there is a time and a season for everything, a time to be born and a time to die. Is it time now? They will lay him out, washed, anointed, shrouded. They will fold his arms across his chest, with the palms turned in, completing the figure. Now his own hands will lie pressed to his breast, and he will sleep with his fathers.

EDITORS' ANALYSIS

Concern with religion is a major activity in contemporary America, but stories dealing with religion are rare. Perhaps writers feel more comfortable portraying the secularity than the divinity in people. Perhaps religious experience, by its nature, is not easily translatable into words we associate with the business of day-to-day living. Rosenfeld's "King Solomon" presents an official of a particular religion, but the story is religious only by indirection. It concerns the nature of the love which his people feel for Solomon as their leader, which ranges from sexual passion to a kind of awe. Solomon himself is both God's anointed and a rather bemused and aging human being. Rosenfeld insists upon making his Solomon more than just the biblical figure. By using anachronistic details, his Solomon becomes a type of person who might exercise religious and secular power in any age. The story is ironic, if one wishes it to be. But one can also read it as a presentation of the inexplicable nature of worship and awe.

QUESTIONS

1. Does Rosenfeld's inclusion of anachronistic details such as the telephones, stamp collections, etc., in a story of biblical characters, give you a sense of the generic nature of their behavior? Does it act as a too disturbing element in the story?

2. Is the Queen of Sheba's analysis of Solomon as one who draws love, but who cannot give it, meant to be one of the meanings of the story? Are we to assume that this is a necessary condition of greatness in a religious leader?

3. Is King Solomon, in all his wisdom, merely the projection of a people's wish that there be greatness in their time? Is this part of the intended meaning of the story?

4. Do you ask the questions concerning the source of a Roosevelt's, an Eisenhower's power that Rosenfeld asks about King Solomon? Do you merely accept the awe of the office as synonymous with awe for the man?

5. Solomon's counselors pay no attention to what the leader says. If anything is to be learned about him, they feel "it had better be sought among his girls." What is the intent of this comment?

6. Why does Solomon weep as the Queen of Sheba leaves him? At her loss? At a lack in himself?

7. What is so embarrassing in the Queen of Sheba's dancing on the table? That she failed to lure the King? It is described as "a terrible mistake." Why?

8. Comment on the implications as to the meaning of religious or secular power suggested by the final paragraph of the story.

The Morning Watch

by JAMES AGEE

James Agee (1909-1955) was a professional journalist, writing feature articles for *Fortune* and motion picture criticism for *Time* and the *Nation*. In addition he wrote the commentary and dialogue for the unusual documentary film, *The Quiet One*, and was the author of a number of television scripts. He had a special talent as a purely creative writer, however, which ran somewhat counter to his professional work. Yale University published a collection of his early poetry, *Permit Me Voyage* (1934), in its Yale Series of Younger Poets. His book *Let Us Now Praise Famous Men* (1941 and 1960) was a detailed and passionate evocation of life in the South during the worst of the depression. He published occasional short stories in the literary quarterlies, but *A Death in the Family*, issued posthumously in 1957, was his only full-length novel. Like *Let Us Now Praise Famous Men*, it was an evocative and a poetic account of actual things: his "novel" was essentially an episode of Agee's own personal grief as a small boy.

"The Morning Watch" is also close to autobiography. It is an exploration of the most private feelings of a young boy in a Catholic school as he goes through the required religious ceremonies celebrating the arrival of the Good Friday of Holy Week, and then takes off for a swim in a pond in the woods near the school. The short novel is Agee at his best: it is a long, prose meditation, in which every event is examined in minute detail, with every shadow of the boy's thought revealed with tender clarity.

> *My soul fleeth unto the Lord*
> *before the morning watch: I say,*
> *before the morning watch.*
> —PSALM CXXX

In hidden vainglory he had vowed that he would stay awake straight through the night, for he had wondered, and not

---

The Morning Watch. Published in *Partisan Review*, March-April 1951, and republished in book form by Houghton Mifflin Company. This reprinting of James Agee's *The Morning Watch*, 1951, is by permission of and arrangement with Houghton Mifflin Company, the authorized publishers.

without scorn, how they, grown men, could give way to sleep on this night of all nights in their life, leaving Him without one friend in His worst hour; but some while before midnight, still unaware that he was so much as drowsy, he had fallen asleep; and now this listening sleep was broken and instantly Richard lay sharp awake, aware of his failure and of the night.

Too late: already it was time: now it was the deepest hour of the deepest night. Already while he slept, with wrathful torches and with swords and staves they had broken among the branches of the Garden; Judas, gliding, had stretched against that clear Face his serpent's smile; Peter in loyal rage had struck off the dazed servant's ear and He in quiet had healed him: and without struggle had yielded Himself into their hands. Could ye not watch with me one hour? No, Lord, his humbled soul replied: not even one: and three times, silently, gazing straight upward into the darkness, he struck his breast, while tears of contrition, of humility and of a hunger to be worthy, solaced his eyes, and awakened his heart. O yes it was an hour more deep by far than the Agony and Bloody Sweat: no longer alone, unsure; resolved, and taken. That was already fully begun which could come only to one ending. By now He stood peaceful before Pilate, the one calm and silence amid all that tumult of malice and scorn and guile and hatred and beating of unhabitual light through all the sleepless night of spring; while in the dark porchway, even at this moment, the servant girl persistently enquired of Peter and he in fury and in terror denied his Lord: now the bitter terrible weeping and now, saluting this mortal morning, the cock's triumphal and reproaching cry. A deep, deep hour. Soon now the sentence and the torment, the scourging, the mocking robe, the wreathed, wretched Crown: King of the Jews.

O God, he silently prayed, in solemn and festal exaltation: make me to know Thy suffering this day. O make me to know Thy dear Son's suffering this day.

Within Thy Wounds hide me.

Suffer me not to be separated from Thee.

From the Malicious Enemy defend me.

By a habit of their own, meanwhile, his hands searched and tested along the undersheet, and now they told him that this time he had wet the bed so little that by morning nobody would know. He let out a long thankful breath and looked down along his bed.

All he could see at first throughout the long room was a kind of gelatin glimmer at the alcoved windows, and the aisled ends of the iron cots at right angles to his own: but when the foot which had awakened him lifted from the yielding board and it creaked again he saw in his mind's eye, large and close, the coarse-ribbed shambling stocking, flecked with lint, and knew that Father Whitman must be very tired; for to judge by the hissing sound, his feet scarcely left the floor. He wondered whether Father Whitman was sleeping at all, tonight.

Father Whitman touched a foot and whispered: "Quarter of four."

"Okay Fathuh," Hobe Gillum said in his clear hard voice.

"Quiet," Father Whitman said sharply.

"Okay Fathuh," Hobe whispered.

Now that the priest came near as silently as he could between the ends of the cots, Richard could see the tall ghostly moving of his white habit.

Father Whitman stopped at Jimmy Toole's cot, touched his foot, and whispered: "Quarter of four." Jimmy mumbled something in a light sad rapid voice and stuck his head under his pillow.

Father Whitman stepped between the cots and touched his shoulder. "Quarter of four," he whispered more loudly.

"Cut it out," Jimmy whined in his sleep.

Richard heard Hobe's knees hit the floor.

Father Whitman shook Jimmy's shoulder. "Quarter of——"

"*Quit* it you *God damn*—" Jimmy snarled, wrenching aside the pillow; then, with servile Irish charm: "Aw sure Father, I didn't know it was *you* Father."

At the far end of the dormitory there was a wild stifled snicker.

"Time to get up," Father Whitman whispered.

The snickering became happier and happier. Father Whitman spoke more loudly into the darkness: "Now cut that out fast or you'll be sorry you ever started it."

The snickering persisted as if uncontrollably, but now it was blunted in a pillow. Father Whitman ignored it. "Better get straight out of bed," he told Jimmy. "You'll go back to sleep."

Hobe was buttoning his shirt.

Without a word Jimmy rolled out of bed onto his knees and buried his head in his arms.

Now that Father Whitman came toward him, Richard shut his eyes. When he knew he was about to be touched he opened his eyes and whispered, "All right Father." He saw the stopped hand and, much nearer and larger than he had expected, the beaten, enduring horse face; he became aware of his deceitfulness and was ashamed of it.

"All right," Father Whitman said. Bet he says quarter of four, Richard thought. "Quarter of four," Father Whitman said.

"Yes Father."

"Put your shoes on downstairs," he whispered, and turned away. "Put your shoes on downstairs," he told Hobe, "and don't let Jimmy go to sleep again."

"Okay Fathuh," Hobe said, gallusing himself into his overalls.

"And don't you dawdle when you're done," Father Whitman told him. "You kids see to it you come right back here to bed."

"Yes suh Fathuh."

"Don't think I won't be watching for you."

"No suh Fathuh."

Richard knelt by his cot and sank his face in his hands. O God, he prayed, I thank Thee that I did not wet the bed this night—enough to get caught, he added carefully, remembering Thou God seest me; for Jesus' sake Amen.

He said swiftly to himself the prayer Father Weiler had taught them as enough when, for any good reason, you did not have time enough for more: I praise my God this day I give myself to God this day I ask God to help me this day Amen.

Gripping his hair and pressing the heels of his hands tightly against his closed eyes he tried as hard as he could to realize what was happening as he had in the moment of waking. But now he could realize only what a special night this was, what grave and holy hours these were. There seemed to be a strange stillness and power in the air as there always was on very special occasions and never at ordinary times; it made him feel dry, light of weight, very watchful, expectant and still, and it almost made his scalp tingle. It was something like the feeling of his birthday, and of Christmas, and of Easter, and it was still more like the feeling he now seldom and faintly recalled, during the morning just after he learned of his father's death, and during the day he was buried. But it was not really like any of these, or anything else, except itself. These were the hours of Our Lord's deepest Passion. For almost forty days now this feeling had grown and deepened, not without interruption, for he had not managed perfectly to keep either his public or his secret Lenten Rules; yet he had been sufficiently earnest and faithful, and sufficiently grieved in his failures, that the growth had been deeper and more cumulative and more rewarding than he had ever known before; and now he was coming into the heart of it, the holiest and most solemn of its shrines, with heart and soul prepared and eager. Already it was no longer Maundy Thursday, the birthday of the Eucharist; that sorrowfully jubilant magnificence was turned under the world; already the world was brought a few hours forward into the most gravely majestic of all days, Good Friday; already the wheel was so turned that high upon darkened heaven white Easter dazzled, suspended, the crown of the year, like the already trembling start of an avalanche. Easter was very soon now, so soon, with his throat brimming with its hymns and his soul ardent for release and celebration, that it was difficult to be patient; yet his faith and absorption were such that at the same time he came into this day as sorrowing and careful as if Christ had never been crucified before, and could never rise from the dead. Yet now that he desired to retrieve his waking awareness he could not, but only knelt, sad, trying to taste the peculiar quality of the night and to distinguish it from other auras of momentousness, until, realizing how he had misled himself, he gripped his hair and pressed his eyeballs the more tightly, repeating in his heart: Jesus our Lord is crucified. Jesus our Lord is crucified. He saw the Head.

Thrown with fury, a shoe struck the wall next Jimmy's bed: the noise broke upon Richard with sickening fright. Then Hobe's voice:

"All right some mothuhf——kin sonofabitch is agoana git the livin s——t beat outn him if I find out who throwed that!"

"Shet yer God damn mouf," said a coldly intense, deeper voice at the far end of the dormitory.

"Yeah fer Chrise sakes *shut up,*" said another voice, as several neutral voices said "Shut up."

In the rigid silence Richard and Jimmy dressed quickly while Hobe waited. Carrying their shoes they stole barefoot on tiptoe from the room and along the hall and past the iron cot which had been set up by the stairhead for this one night for Father Whitman. They could just make out how he lay there in the dark in his long white habit, giving off a current of silent and ominous power because they could not be sure as they passed whether he was asleep or aware of them; the clacking of his tin clock filled the pine stairwell with its flagrant loudness. They tried hard not to creak the stairs. The pit of Richard's stomach still felt as it did when, without being too mad or too desperate to care, he knew it was impossible not to fight. By trying hard he was able to restore whole to his mind the thorn-crowned image of his Lord, but now it was not as he had seen it in prayer beside his cot but was very little different from a pious painting he knew: the eyes rolled up in a way that seemed affected, and in his cold sickness the image meant little to him. It was not until they came onto the back porch that the open night put them once more at their ease.

"Sonofabitchin mothuhf——kin bastud," Hobe said. "At shoe bettah be gone by mawnin or *some* bastudly c——ksuckuh's agoana be sorry."

"Aw shut up Hobie," Jimmy said. "This ain't no time to talk like that."

"Hell do *I* keer," Hobe said. "*I* hain't been to Confession yet."

But he started on down the steps without saying anything more. "What happened?" Richard asked.

"Jis trine wake up Jimmy," Hobe said. "God All Mighty Christ, can't even wake nobody up in this friggin School—"

Richard followed them down the steps. He was glad he had learned hardly even to think of saying anything. If Jimmy told Hobie to shut up and quit cussing Hobie would take it off of him, they were buddies; but by now he knew enough to keep *his* mouth shut. He felt uneasy, though, because he was glad he had not sworn. That was like being thankful you were not as other men and that was one of the worst sins of all; the Pharisee.

He had forgotten all about the shoes he carried and now that unexpectedly, for the first time this year, he felt the ground against the bare soles of his feet it was as if, fumbling among clothes in a dark closet, he had put his hand on living flesh. Even though the ground in the schoolyard was skimmed with dusty gravel, its aliveness soared through him like a sob and lifted his eyes in wonder upon the night. There was no moon and what few stars were out, were made faint by a kind of smiling universal milky silence, not fog, or even the lightest kind of mist, but as if the whole air and sky were one mild supernal breath. Downhill in the Chapel a line of small windows meekly smoldered, dark orange; he followed his companions and saw that they too were carrying their shoes. When they came to the lawn beyond their building they left the gravel; the ground, with its scarce new grass, felt like a fish. There was a thick oak near the center of the lawn and Hobe and Jimmy, as they passed, stung it several times expertly with gravel. It had not occurred to Richard to pick up gravel and now he was glad, for he was sure he would have missed as often as hit.

II

The night smelled like new milk; the air which exhaled upon them when they opened the side door of the chapel was as numb and remote as the air of a cave. Without knowing it they hesitated, subdued by the stagnant darkness and its smell of waxed pine and spent incense. Across the unlighted nave the open door of the Lady Chapel brimmed with shaken light; but just at their left, through the door to the vestry, came a friendlier and more mundane light, a delicious smell, and the tired grinding of the voice they most admired in the world. When he became aware of their hesitation beside this partly closed door, George Fitzgerald spoke to them with a formality as unaccustomed and gentle as if a dead body lay in the room behind him and they came in, silent and shy. By the loud hurrying little clock it was still only four minutes to four. They squatted on their bare heels against the wall and looked on, their six eyes emphatic in the sleepless night.

The inward wall of this long corridor was hung solid with cassocks, and they were all lengths from a size almost big enough for the giant sad boy they all called Undertaker, to the all but baby size of Dillon Prince. At first Richard wondered where all the cottas were; in the laundry for Easter, he realized. The room was so weakly lighted by candlestubs that at the far end it was hardly possible to distinguish the red cassocks from the black. Just within the surer light, his jaw and his shoulders sloping more heavily even than usual with fatigue and with his low posture, Willard Rivenburg sat on a folding-chair which gave out dangerous splintering noises whenever he stirred. It was he who was talking, aimlessly, quietly, almost in his sleep; and Richard could see that George and Lee Allen answered him only so often as courtesy required, never turning their attention from their work. Not only where they Prefects; it was also believed by some of the older people that they alone among the boys now at the School, might have a Vocation. They were in their last year now and it was generally understood that they were both praying hard for this to be made clear to them before they graduated. It was their privilege, tonight, to trim and change the candles and to remove and replace the withering flowers, and now white-girdled, incongruous in red cassocks, they stood wearily beside a soup plate, replying gravely in short words while, their eyes bright with the lateness of the hour and fixed in the profound attentiveness of great scientists, they revolved candlestubs between thumb and forefinger, just above a flame, and watched the meltings add themselves to the already considerable cone of wax and tallow which they had developed on the plate. The shining melt spilled roundly, rambling and congealing; wherever it ridged, they smoothed it delicately with their fingertips. From the apex of this rounded cone sprang three long fiery wicks.

Because they were to be up all night these two had been forgiven the fast and had supplied themselves against possible hunger. But neither had yet eaten or drunk, nor did either privately intend to unless, as seemed unlikely, he became too faint or too sleepy to attend properly to his share of the work. Their coffee frothed so noisily over its can of Sterno rather because this enhanced their feeling of privilege and maturity; Willard was drinking some while he talked although, Richard reflected, it was long after midnight, when the fast began. He had also practically finished off a box of Fig Newtons.

The coffee was so strong that it empurpled the wall of the cup, and its smell was almost as enviably masculine as that of white lightning. The three younger boys kept respectfully quiet and looked on, eagerly and sleepily. They watched now the lapped purple rings in the slanted cup, now the shining of the living wax and its satin look where it had slowed and had been smoothed, now the strong loose smoky flame and the hypnotized faces which leaned above it, and now the reckless primitive profile and the slash-lined blue-black cheek of the great athlete Willard Rivenburg, whom they had never seen in quite such quiet intimacy. Nobody knew for sure just how old Willard was, but he looked as many men can only at thirty or so, and then only if they have been through a war, or years of the hardest kind of work. Richard tried to imagine why he was here tonight. He was fairly sure it was not for any kind of religious reason: Willard had been confirmed, and made his Confession and his Communion, but it was obviously just as a matter of course; when he took his turn serving Mass or swinging the Censer or carrying the Crucifix he was never exactly irreverent yet he always looked as if secretly he might be chewing tobacco; it looked as odd and out of place, somehow, as watching a horse dressed up in cassock and cotta and doing these things. He never even crossed himself at a hard time in a game, the way some of the others did. No, he wouldn't be here because he felt pious. It might be because everybody and everything on the place was thinking about just these things that were happening, and moving around them; a kind of shadow and stillness came over everything during Holy Week and it might be that Willard felt this and was made uneasy by it. But mainly it must be just that he was much too grown-up to be able to stand all the silly rules, and tame hours, and good behavior, that were expected of living in a school; he must be even gladder than the little boys were to grab at any chance to break out of that routine, especially anything that would give him an excuse for staying up so long after hours. And yet, Richard reflected, Willard needed and took an awful lot of sleep, dropping off in dull classrooms or wherever he had to sit still, except for eating, as easily as a colored man or a dog. But maybe all that sleep was why he was able to be awake now, though as a matter of fact he wasn't really more than half awake, not nearly as wide awake as Richard felt. But then probably he had been up all night, and probably it wasn't for the first time in his life either.

In some way which it did not occur to him to think about or try to understand, Richard felt a warm rich comforting kind of pride in him and sense of glory as he watched him, as much, in a far quieter and even happier way, as when he watched his almost magical ability in sports; and he began to feel a sense of honor and privilege in having this surprising chance to be so near him and to watch him so closely, to really see him. For normally, when Willard was not playing or practicing or sleeping or eating, he was kidding with somebody, in a loudly reckless, crazy way which was a pleasure to see because everything Willard did was a pleasure to see, but was impossible to see through; but now he wasn't kidding at all, only talking quietly and steadily like a grown man, among others whom he treated as grown men. He was finishing up about his grandfather who had come over from Switzerland to settle way back on the Mountain and who had never bothered to learn much English, and he was saying the few words and phrases of German he himself knew, and Richard was deeply impressed in realizing that Willard, who always seemed to him to know about as little as anyone could, except as an athlete and captain of genius and a powerful and experienced man, actually knew words in a foreign language. He himself was accustomed to feel a good deal of complacency because with Father Fish's help he had learned several hundred words of French, but now he felt ashamed of himself, and resolved to learn German, which seemed to him a much more virile language.

He was watching with shy and particular interest the hump between Willard's heavy shoulders, which he had often wondered about but never yet had the chance to examine so privately. It was almost as if Willard were slightly hunchbacked, the low way he always carried his head and sloped his shoulders and the way this hump bulged out just below the base of his neck; yet if he were deformed, he could not have such ability and strength. It must be a very greatly developed muscle, Richard realized, yet it was a funny place to have a muscle; he felt there now on his own body and there wasn't even the beginning of a muscle there; just bone. Could it be bone? But that would be a deformity; and on Willard, more than any other thing, it was what made him unique among others, and marked his all but superhuman powers. Whenever he had done anything physically creditable Richard carried his head low, let his mouth hang open, and tried to hump his back, scarcely knowing of it any more; and so, though it was not generally realized, did many other boys in this school.

"Hey you," Lee said, and startled, they looked: one minute past four. Richard felt a spasm of shame: could ye not watch with me one hour? Besides, they were keeping somebody over his time. "*Jesus!*" Hobe Gillum said, and they stood up quickly. Both of the boys in cassocks ducked in shocked acknowledgement of the Name and Willard's dark face brightened with his satanic parody of falsetto laughter. Lee Allen said with unusually kind gravity: "I sure would hate to have to report anyone for cussin right in Chapel, and on Good Friday too." Hobe's eyes turned Indian, with pride toward Willard, in defiance toward Lee. "Aw forget about it Lee," George Fitzgerald said, "he just wasn't thinking." "I don't want to report you or nobody else," Lee said. "You just watch your mouth, Hobie." "He didn't mean anything," Richard said; and even before everyone looked at him and said nothing, he was miserable. "Better put your shoes on you kids," George said, and with relief Richard sank his hot face over his shoelaces. They felt contempt for him, he was sure, and he felt contempt for himself. Willard thought better of Hobe for cussing than of him for standing up for him, and so did he. Lee jumped on Hobie because Willard's cackling about it bothered him and he couldn't jump on Willard. If it hadn't been Good Friday and Richard had spoken up like that, he knew that somebody would have said, coldly, "Well look who's talking." Keep your mouth shut, he kept whispering within himself intensely. Just keep your fool mouth shut. And as they left the room he tried to exorcise the feelings of injustice, self-pity and pain by crossing himself quickly and surreptitiously. Fine time to go worrying about *yourself,* he sneered at himself.

The nave replied to their timid noises with the threatening

resonance of a drumhead. Not even the sanctuary lamps were lighted, but the night at the windows made just discernible the effigies and the paintings and the crucifix, no longer purple veiled but choked in black, and the naked ravagement of the High Altar. The tabernacle gawped like a dead jaw. By this ruthless flaying and deracination only the skeleton of the Church remained; it seemed at once the more sacred in dishonor, and as brutally secular as a boxcar. To cross its axis without the habitual genuflection felt as uneasy as to swim across a sudden unimaginable depth, and as Richard turned and bowed before the central devastation he realized: nothing there. Nothing at all; and with the breath of the Outer Darkness upon his soul remembered the words: And the Veil of the Temple was rent in twain.

But here in peace and victory before the adoration of all creatures past and breathing and uncreated, shrined and enthroned, starred round with unabating light and with the stars of all the fields of spring as well, exiled there yet abides throughout this night the soul and substance of the everliving God Who shall, within these few hours now, be restored to His High Altar and there devoured, leaving His whole Church desecrate and unconsoled until the hour of His glorious Resurrection from the Dead. Tied in its white veil, stifled, a huge masked Head, a thinly clouded Sun, the monstrance stood from the top of the tabernacle and broke at its center a dense tissue of flowers and light: candles it seemed by thousands, spear-high and merely tall, and short, and guttering, each an abiding upright fiery piercing and, crisp and wearying, withering, dying, the frugal harvest of the dawn of the year: from faint orchards the last apple blossoms, still tenderly raveling their slow-borne blizzard; branches of mild-starred dogwood and of the hairy wild azalea, pink and white, from the mulled gray woods, and little fistfuls of those breathless violets which break the floor of winter, even the rare may-apple, the twinleaf, whose bloom stays just a day; and, of the first shivering domestic flowers, cold jonquils, crowds of them, greenish with chill or butter yellow or flaming gold, and clear narcissus, reaching, bowing, staring, fainting in vases and jars of metal and glass and clay and in drinking glasses and mason jars and in small and large tin cans, all these each in their kind and sufferance bore witness before God while they might. Few of these early flowers have strong fragrance, or any, yet the heat and brightness and the fragrance brought forth by the burning wax and tallow and by the heat in the closed room, all one wall of dizzying dazzle, were

such that it was at first almost as difficult to breathe the freighted
air as to breathe water, and this air was enriched the more by the
devotions of those who knelt subsumed within the trembling
light; and at the instant of stepping into this hot and fragrant
gold, going upon one knee and gazing upon the blind rondure of
the monstrance and the thousand-pointed blossoming of fire and
flower, his heart was lifted up and turned vague and shy as the
words broke within him, upon each other, God: Death; so that
the two were one. Death: Dead, the word prevailed; and before
him, still beyond all other stillness, he saw as freshly as six years
before his father's prostrate head and, through the efforts to hide
it, the mortal blue dent in the impatient chin. He remembered
within this instant how for the first time he had been convinced,
and how eternally convincing it had been, when he saw how
through that first full minute of looking his father had neither
stirred nor spoken, and how the powerful right hand had lain half
open against the exact center of his body; the cloth of his coat
was not moved by any breathing and it was as if the hand were
only a magically expert imitation of a hand, a hand of wax and,
now looking again at the head, lips and a face of wax, a dent of
wax, a head of wax immense upon this whole rich waxen air.
Dead, the word came again, and shutting his eyes he prayed
swiftly for his father the prayer of all his childhood, God bless
daddy and keep him close to Thee and may light perpetual shine
upon him, Amen; and casually, obviously, as a trout into shadow,
the image and memory vanished. It is Our Lord's death today, he
said to himself, but at this moment he could see neither face, that
of his father, or that of his Lord; only the words returned, God:
Death.

No praying-benches were available at first, and they knelt
where they entered, the waxed floor brutal against their bones. In
the Name of the Father and of the Son and of the Holy Ghost,
Richard whispered rapidly to himself, moving his lips and closing
his eyes again. He crossed himself with care. There was a sound
of arising and departure and through his eyelashes he saw Knox
Peyton complete his genuflection and step ungainly between him
and Jimmy, trying to subdue the reproach and annoyance in his
face. They stayed where they knelt, all on their good manners
before the one empty bench, and Richard heard the whispered
"go on" several times before he realized that it was directed at
him. Two worshipers glanced unhappily behind him, shut their
eyes, and tucked their chins down, trying hard to pray. "I be

damned if I will," Richard thought, and caught himself; he shut his eyes tightly and in despairing shame tucked his own chin down. "Go *on*," he heard. He decided that he ought to make a penance of it. Trying to look and to feel neither humble nor proud he crossed himself, got up, genuflected, tiptoed to the empty bench, genuflected, knelt, and crossed himself. Mr. Bradford closed his eyes, frowned, and deeply bowed his head. Home stretch, Richard said to himself, and quickly begged forgiveness for an irreverence which had not been premeditated but spontaneous. But wasn't it even worse to be so unaware of where you were that such a thought could occur spontaneously? Mr. Bradford completed his devotions and tiptoed toward the door, his eyes downcast. His effort to stay within himself was too successful; Richard heard him bump against one of the two boys, and his whispered accusing apology, and their feckless and ill-subdued reply. Deaconess Spenser, at the desk opposite his own, compressed her lips, crossed herself, got up, genuflected, and stepped behind him; he could hear the harsh whispered reprimand whistling through her false teeth. He looked carefully at his clasped hands, but he heard movement as the door was cleared and along the side of his eye Jimmy advanced and swiftly established himself at the newly empty bench and the Deaconess, her wattles a violent red and her mouth pulled in tight, returned to her own bench, genuflected, knelt, crossed herself, and sank her forehead into her hands. Behind him somebody else stood up and he heard the knee touch the floor and, knowing he ought not to, glanced back; it was Hog Eye Kelsey, one of the littler boys from his own dormitory; already Hobe was standing to replace him. Not Hog Eye, he told himself; he can't help it: Jeff.

Pay attention, he told himself. Mind your own business.

He looked at the veiled monstrance; the brightest threads of the veil sparkled like mica, gold-white on silver-white, and in one place a rigid shaft of metal radiance almost pierced the fabric. One azalea bloom strayed against it as if it were straining to be near it. Tiny threads sprang out of the flare of the blossom, the way small straight lines are drawn in a funny-paper to show music coming out of a horn. An apple-blossom fell. Looking at the tired sleepless flames of the candles, Richard felt as if he could almost hear them burning.

Soul of Christ sanctify me, he prayed silently; Body of Christ save me; but he was just saying it mechanically, and too fast. Slowly now, thinking carefully of each word, he began again.

Soul of Christ sanctify me: make me holy: absolve me from all spot of sin:

Body of Christ save me: save me: Thy Body which has already begun to suffer and die:

He braced his mind.

Blood of Christ inebriate me:

Carefully as he tried, he could not avoid it. Inebriate meant just plain drunken, or meant a drunken person, especially habitual drunkard, and as it was used here, it meant to make drunk, to intoxicate. And inebriety meant drunkenness and the habit of drunkenness. He had been fond of the word for a long time before he knew, or realized that he did not know, its meaning—which must of course be simply what the Blood of Christ might most naturally be expected to do: but what would that be, that sounded as nice as inebriate? During the past winter it had occurred to him to look it up in a dictionary. Since then the correct and disconcerting meanings had been indelible, and that part of the prayer had become thin ice. He could only get past it without irreverent or skeptical thoughts by saying it so fast or so shallowly that it was impossible to bear its meaning in mind, and that was no way to pray. He had asked Father Fish about it and Father Fish had shown him that it was possible to be amused by the word without feeling irreverent. He had said that some of these ancient prayers were rather extravagant in their way of putting things, and that there was no need to take them with absolute literalness. Although he had no way of being sure, Richard had a feeling that Father Fish had been as amused at him, as at the word; once again he wondered why, and stopped himself from wondering why because this was no time to. Don't take it literally, he told himself firmly; but the literal words remained and were even more firm: make drunk. Intoxicate. Good ole whiskey, he suddenly heard in his mind, and he remembered how, drinking sodapop in Knoxville, boys slightly more worldly than he would twist the bottle deep into the mouth and cock it up vertically to drink, and taking it down, breathless, would pat their stomachs or rub them in circles and gasp, "Ahhh, good ole whiskey!" But this wasn't even on whiskey. On blood. Jesus' blood, too. His uncle had once sneered, "There is a pudding filled with blood," scornfully exploding the first syllable of "pudding," and Richard had been both shocked and amused, and he was shocked to find that he remembered it with amusement now. Forgive us our trespasses, he whispered, shutting his eyes tight. It was only a hymn, and so it was not as bad to make fun of as some things were. But the blood was "drawn from Emmanuel's veins," so that did make it pretty awful. And his uncle had said it with a kind of hatred which included much more than the hymn: all of religion, and everybody who was religious, even his own sister, Richard's mother, and his Aunt Patty, and him, Richard, and his own sister. Forgive us our trespasses as we forgive those who trespass against us, he prayed, and pushed the matter out of his mind. He does like us all the same, he reflected, same as grandpa does. They just don't like the Church.

Passion of Ch——

Water from the side of Christ wash me; and he felt that his thoughts badly needed washing:

Passion of Christ strengthen me:

Within Thy Wounds hide me, he thought swiftly and with great uneasiness, hugging the ground and the leaf coverage as if beneath the skimming of a bird of prey: but try as he could, the image plunged and took him. An older boy, the only one Richard knew who also liked to read, had with great sophistication and delight explained to him what was meant, in Shakespeare's *Venus and Adonis,* by the words *he saw more wounds than one,* and this had instantly become identical in his mind with a rawly intimate glimpse he had had, three or four years before, of Minnielee Henley when they were climbing a tree; and now with these words *within Thy Wounds hide me* the image fought in his mind with the image of those small but deadly wounds in the body of Jesus, in which surely nobody could hide, not even the one the spear made in His side. But not there either, he insisted to himself; not even if He wasn't a man. Yet there in his mind's eye, made all the worse by all the most insipid and effeminate, simpering faces of Jesus that he had ever seen in pictures, was the hideous image of a huge torn bleeding gulf at the supine crotch, into which an ant-swarm of the pious, millions of them, all pleading and rolling up their eyes, laden souls, by thousands meekly stealing, struggled to crowd themselves, and lose themselves, and dissolve.

It was the Devil, that was all. Just the Devil Himself, tempting him.

O good Jesu hear me, he prayed with deep self-loathing, almost aloud: realized with gratitude that for once he had been able to say these words, which for months now had seemed to him fulsome and insincere, with complete desire and sincerity. You just have to mean it, he thought, for it to mean anything.

Suffer me not to be separated from Thee (a mortal sin is a sin that cuts us off from God):

From the Malicious Enemy defend me:

Of these closing lines he never felt doubt and now he repeated, with reverent emphasis and relish:

From the Malicious Enemy defend me:

In the hour of my death call me and bid me come to Thee:

That with Thy

No there was something really wrong about

He prayed, with fear and determination: That with Thy Saints I may praise Thee, forever and ever, Amen.

All the same it was wrong for people to ask to be saints, as flat as all that. Or even just to be *with* the saints, if that was what it meant. To just barely manage through God's infinite mercy to escape burning eternally in the everlasting fires of Hell ought to be just about as much as any good Catholic could pray for; and now Richard remembered still another prayer at which, when he was serving at Mass, he had for quite a while now been accustomed to keep silence or at most to make approximate sounds of the words, with his fingers crossed: where, in the General Confession, reviewing his iniquities, the penitent cries, "The remembrance of them is grievous unto us, the burden of them is intolerable." As a rule he was able to say "the remembrance of them is grievous unto us" with adequate sincerity; but it was seldom that he could feel, at the particular moment he felt required to feel, that "the burden of them is intolerable." It wasn't anywhere near intolerable, no matter how much it ought to be. At first he had been able to say it in the realization that it was intolerable to his soul, whether or not he in his mind and feelings was capable of feeling it just then, and that prayers are said by and for the soul, not the mind or the feelings; but in this he came to feel that he was mistaken: for it was, he noticed, only when he believed and felt deeply with his mind or his emotions that he was able to be aware that his soul, as such, existed. But that isn't true, he now thought with alarm. No matter what I think or feel, the soul is always there and always alive unless it has been killed by impenitence for mortal sin. The hardening of the heart toward God. I'm only trying to suit myself, he told himself; not my soul, and not God.

But how can you say things when you only ought to mean them and don't really mean them at all?

Have mercy upon us O God have mercy upon us, he found

himself praying. These were the words of the Confession which followed "the burden of them is intolerable," and always, as now, he was able to mean them when he spoke them.

But not "that with Thy Saints I may praise Thee."

Now it occurred to Richard that perhaps this prayer had been written by a saint or by someone near sainthood, who was able to mean every extreme thing that was said; and he knew that anyone who could fully mean those things, and who could mean them every time they were said, was to be humbly respected. But in that case it was a prayer which was good only for saints and near saints to say, not for ordinary people, no matter how good they hoped to be. Nobody's got any business even hoping he can be a saint, he told himself.

God no! he exclaimed to himself, for now suddenly it became vivid and shameful in his memory that he himself had for a while cherished, more secretly even than his lust, exactly this inordinate ambition. Good golly! he whispered within his soul, feeling the back of his neck and then his cheeks go hot; and with a cold and marveling, compassionate contempt for the child he had so recently been, he lost himself in reflective remembrance, unaware that it was for the first time in his life.

It was hardly more than a year ago, when he was only eleven, that the image and meaning of Jesus and the power and meaning of the Sacraments of the teachings of the Church, all embodied and set forth in formalities of language and of motion whose sober beauties were unique, and in music which at that time moved and satisfied him as no other music could, had first and, it had seemed, irreducibly, established upon all his heart and mind their quality, their comfort, their nobility, their sad and soaring weight; and, entering upon his desolation of loneliness, had made of suffering a springing garden, an Eden in which to walk, enjoying the cool of the evening. It had become a secret kind of good to be punished, especially if the punishment was exorbitant or unjust; better to be ignored by others, than accepted; better still to be humiliated, than ignored. He remembered how on mornings when he had waked up and found his bed dry, he had felt as much regret as relief. He had begun to take care to read in conspicuous places, where he would be most liable to interruption and contempt. He had pretended not to know lessons he had in fact prepared, in order that even such teachers as thought well of him, or thought "at least he's smart," or "he studies, anyway," might think ill of him. He had continued his solitary wanderings in the woods until it occurred to him that these excursions, for all their solitude and melancholy, were more pleasant than unpleasant; from then on he had put himself into the middle of crowds, especially on the drearier afternoons when even the hardiest boys stayed indoors and the restive, vindictive, bored, mob feelings were at their most sullen and light-triggered. The leaden melodies of the Lenten hymns had appealed to him as never before; lines in certain hymns seemed, during that time, to have been written especially for him. *Jesus, I my Cross have taken,* he would sing, already anticipating the lonely solace of tears concealed in public: *all to leave and follow Thee; destitute, despis'd, forsaken,* were words especially dear to him; *Thou from hence my All shalt be.* As he sang that he felt: no body else wants me; and did his best to believe it, even of his mother. He remembered now that this kind of singing had satisfied him most at Stations of the Cross, on cold rainy nights. *Perish ev'ry fond ambition,* he would sing magnanimously; (no I *won't* become a naturalist; I'll never explore the source of the Amazon; I'll never even own a monkey, or be junior tennis champion); *all I've thought or hoped or known;* then tears and their subdual rewarded him: *Yet how rich is my condition* (never to live at home again, never to be loved or even liked), *God and Heaven are still my own;* and he saw crowned God and Heaven shining and felt, in a humble kind of way, that he literally owned them.

Now remembering it he shook his head almost as if in disbelief, but he knew it had been so. Everything. He had done just about everything he could think of. He had gone seldom to Father Fish's cottage, for friendliness was certain there, and often cookies and cocoa too, and he had found that these luxuries meant most to him, in his desire to suffer for religious advantage, only when they were indulged so rarely that even while they were being enjoyed they enhanced the bleakness of the rest of living. He even schemed to intensify his homesickness to the utmost possible, asking permission of the Master of the Day the more often, that it be the more curtly or impatiently or, at best, contemptuously refused; watching his mother's cottage, the one place he was almost never allowed to go, sometimes by the hour; sometimes in ambush under dripping trees, relishing the fact that only he knew of the miserableness of that watch; sometimes openly, hanging against the fence, relishing the fact that she knew, and others could see, and that even though she knew, she would try to ignore him and stay out of his sight, and that when at last she could ignore him no longer, she would hurt him by trying to be stern with him as she told him to go away, and would sharpen his unhappiness into agony by her idea of a sensible explanation why this senseless cruelty had to be a law.

"Because dear, mother thinks it's best for you not to be too near her, all the more because you miss her so much." "Because your father isn't with us." "Because mother thinks you need to be among other boys Richard. In charge of men." And worst of all: "I know how hard it is now but I know that when you're older you'll understand why I did it, and thank me for it." *Thank her!* his heart sneered now, in bitter paroxysm. And for a moment so brief that the realization did not stay with him, he felt hatred and contempt for his mother, for her belief in submissiveness and for her telling him, on certain infuriating occasions, that it is only through submitting bravely and cheerfully to unhappiness that we can learn God's Will, and how most truly to be good. God's Will, he thought now: I bet it isn't just for people to be unhappy! Who want to be *good!* I do, he answered himself. But not like that. I sure was crazy then, he thought, pleased that he was now able to recognize the fact. Just a crazy fool. The whole crazy thing had begun to fade away soon after Easter, with the good weather, and had vanished so completely during the free summer in Knoxville that he had forgotten the whole of it until just now: but all through that dreary winter and increasingly throughout that drizzling season of penitence, he realized now with incredulous and amused self-scorn, he had ever more miserly cherished and elaborated his wretchedness in every one of its sorry ramifications, as indispensable to the secret, the solution, he had through God's Grace discovered; and had managed easily to forgive himself those parts of his Lenten Rule which he meekly enjoyed in public, by inventing still other, harder rules which were private.

His mother had tried uneasily to suggest to him that there might be a kind of vanity mixed up in his extreme piety—"not that you *mean* it, of course, dear"—against which he must be on his guard; but remembering the role of dismayed parents and scornful villagers in the early lives of many of the saints, he had answered her gently and patiently, with forbearance, that was the word, as befitted communication between creatures of two worlds so unbridgeably different. He had been tempted on more than one occasion to say to her, "Woman, what have I to do with thee? Mine hour is not yet come"; but he had suspected that this might be thought impudent or absurd or even blasphemous. Nor had he ever said aloud, when others jeered or tormented, "Father, forgive them, for they know not what they do"; but had often fortified himself with the silent words, "And He held His peace."

It had only gradually been borne upon him that he himself might aspire to actual sainthood; he had quickly realized that if that was to be his goal it was necessary, starting young, he might already be too late, to perform in private for God's eyes alone and in public that others might see, and be edified, and remember, and revere him, a long and consistent series of remarkable spiritual feats. Let your lights so shine before men that they may see your good works and glorify your Father, Which is in Heaven. But meditating what these might be, he had realized that there in truth he did run the danger of sinning through Pride, as those people do who look hungry when they fast; whereas his own ambitions were prompted (or so it seemed) by true religious feeling and by nothing else. These ambitions had crystallized during the late weeks of Lent, into a desire to do for Jesus as much as Jesus was doing for him and for all souls. He had experimented with extra fasting, but it was not possible to carry this far, since it was virtually impossible to be excused from meals without the sin of lying, and almost as difficult, he found, to sit at the table without eating, or eating little enough to give the fast any dignity or meaning. So he had chosen self-mortification instead. He had gone into the woods and eaten worms, but this had disgusted him, and he had been even worse disgusted when, on one occasion, he had come near tasting his own excrement. It had suddenly struck him as very doubtful indeed that Jesus would ever have done any such thing, and he had thrown the twig deep into the bushes and had carefully buried the filth. Efforts to scourge himself had been moderately painful but not sufficiently effective to outweigh the sense of bashfulness, even of ridiculousness, which he felt over the clumsiness of the attempt, in relation to the severity of the intention. So he had been reduced, mainly, to keeping very bitter vigil over his thoughts and his language and over his sensuous actions upon himself, and to finding out times and places in which it would be possible to kneel, for much longer than it was comfortable to kneel, without danger of getting caught at it. (He had been as frightened, once, by such an interruption, as if he had been surprised in a sexual act.)

It was during one of these protracted and uncomfortable sojourns on his knees that his mind, uneasily strained between its own wanderings and efforts at disciplined meditation, had become absorbed in grateful and overwhelmed imagination of Christ Crucified, and had without warning brought to its surface the possibility of his own crucifixion. He had been wondering with all of a sincere heart how ever he might do enough for the Son of God Who had done so much for him when suddenly, supplanting Christ's image, he saw his own body nailed to the Cross and, in the same image, himself looked down from the Cross and felt his weight upon the nails, and the splintered wood against the whole length of his scourged back: and stoically, with infinite love and forgiveness, gazed downward into the eyes of Richard, and of Roman soldiers, and of jeering Jews, and of many people whom Richard had known. It was a solemn and rewarding moment; but almost within the next breath he recognized that he had no such cause or right as Jesus to die upon the Cross: and turning his head, saw Christ's head higher beside his own and a third head, lower, cursing; and knew that he was, instead, the Penitent Thief.

But it was of course out of the question that in a deep country part of Middle Tennessee, in nineteen twenty-three, he could actually manage to have himself nailed to a Cross; and although (if he should have the courage) he could undoubtedly nail his own feet, and even one hand (if someone else would steady the nail), his right hand would still hang free, and it would look pretty foolish beside a real Crucifixion. With any proper humility he would be content merely to be tied up, as the thieves usually were, and to hang during the three hours of Good Friday that Jesus hung on the Cross. Even that would mean a good deal, if only in token; the widow's mite, only it seemed rather more than the widow had managed; and he realized that many others besides himself would be moved, and impressed, and very likely improved, by the good example. It would be impossible of course to get a Cross without removing the image of Jesus from it, that big life-size one out in the vestibule, and that would be irreverent even if it were allowed. Or someone might make one for him but he doubted it. He might make one for himself if he could sneak into Manual Training Shop and get enough private time, only everybody knew he wasn't any good with his hands

and simple as a Cross must be to make, they would just laugh
at any that he would be likely to make. One of the school's
gridiron bedsteads would be convenient for tying to, and very
likely even more uncomfortable to hang against than a Cross,
but he was forced to doubt, as with the nail-holding and the
Cross, that he could manage the whole tying-up by himself,
and as he thought of asking someone else to help him, he felt
extraordinarily shy. As he singled over each of the few whom
in any degree he trusted, or on whose affection he could at all
depend, he became sure that there was not one who would co-
operate in this, or even really understand about it. It would be
necessary instead to anger and deceive people he disliked into
doing it: but that, he felt, was both unlikely and sinful. If he
got them mad they would do what they wanted to him, not what
he wanted them to do, and he could not imagine how to suggest
to them that the one thing he didn't want was to be stripped of his
garments (except for a loincloth) and tied to a bedstead for three
hours. And even if he should manage to, he would be tricking
them into a sin, and that would be a sin of itself. It was easier
just to imagine it as something already done, and as soon as
he forgot about the problems of getting it done it was better, too.

There he hung, the iron bars and edged slats of the bed acutely
painful against flesh and bone alike; but he made no complaint.
Rather, his eyes were fixed steadfastly upon the expiring eyes of
his crucified Lord, and his own suffering was as naught. There
was a steady murmuring of scorn, pity, regard and amazement
beneath him, and now and again a familiar face and voice was
lifted, pleading with him or commanding him to come down.
Father McPhetridge, the Prior; his wide red face reared up and
told him that this was the most outrageous thing that had ever
been done by a boy in this School and that he was to stop it
immediately and come down and take his punishment like a man.
He replied, gently and calmly, his voice all the more effective
because of its quietness after all that indignant roaring, that
"punishment" (he smiled at the word in his suffering) would have
to come at its own good time; he would descend (with their
help) promptly at three o'clock and not before; and would give
himself up to his punishers without making a struggle. Scourge
me, he said; paddle me with the one with holes in it; put me on
bounds all the rest of the year; expel me even; there is nothing
you can do that won't be to the greater glory of God and so I
forgive you. The Prior, abashed, withdrew; Richard saw his whis-

pering among the other monks and the teachers and his face was
redder than ever, and their whispering eyes were on him. The
football coach Braden Bennett, who had so often sneered at his
music lessons; his face was changed, now: though with a scornful
wonder, men see her sore oppressed. He looked straight back into
those bullying eyes, with such quiet fortitude and forgiveness that
the scorn and the wonder deepened, the wonder even more than
the scorn. His mother pled with him to come down; she was even
crying; and he was awfully sorry for her; but he shook his head
slowly and, smiling gently, told her: "No, Mother, I deeply repent
for making you cry, and feel so bad, but mine hour is not yet
come." She collapsed with sobbing and the women of the place
crowded around her; they took her arms and helped her as she
walked away, all bent over. Some day you'll understand, he told
her within himself, and you'll thank me for it; and he knew the
happiness that comes only of returning evil with good. Willard
Rivenburg's deep dark jaw hung open and Richard could overhear
his whisper, to Bennett, "Jesus that kid's got guts." George Fitzgerald, scarcely able to contain his tears, held up a sponge soaked
in vinegar, which Richard forgivingly refused; and Hobe Gillum
and Jimmy Toole and Parmo Gallatin and Keg Head Hodges and
the others looked at him, glum but respectful; even if it was no
more than politeness, he realized, he would never be last again,
when they chose up sides. Through the half-open Chapel door he
could still hear the voice of the Three Hour Sermon, Father Ogle's
voice, and he realized that the service had no more than an hour,
at the outside, to go; but the voice sounded half-hearted and
sailed hollowly around the almost empty Church; nearly everyone
in the community was gathered here in the vestibule, and there
were some even from nearby towns, and suddenly a photographer
climbed on the sandstone font and aimed at him and flashed a
bulb. STRANGE RITES AT MOUNTAIN SCHOOL, he read: and, as blood
broke scalding upon his nape, sank his face into his hands and
prayed, in despair, *O God forgive me! forgive me if you can
stand to!*

For, musing upon his past vanities with affectionate scorn or
even as with a scornful wonder, the scorn, the living vanity, of one
who has put away childish things, and dwelling upon them in remembrance, he had dwelt once more within them (within Thy
Wounds hide me), ensnaring himself afresh. For these later imaginations were not wholly remembrance; some were newly his,

and only now, even in the very hour of Christ's own passion, he had yet again seduced his soul. If others, if any other in the world, should know those absurd imaginations of his heart: by his dread and horror in the mere thought, he knew his contemptible silliness. But God of course knew, and Christ Himself, even now when the Son was suffering and the Father, grieving that He might not take the Cup from Him, was hovering in love and sorrow, yes, engulfed, enchanted in woe though they were, They knew very clearly though, it now occurred to him, his secret was safe with Them. In insupportable self-loathing he squeezed his eyes so tightly shut that they ached, and dug his chin as tightly against his throat as it would lock and in blind vertigo, scarcely knowing his action, struck himself heavily upon his breastbone, groaning within his soul, *the burden of them is intolerable.* With the second blow he realized, in gratitude and in a new flowering of vainglory, that he had been surprised into contrition so true and so deep that beside it every moment of contrition he had ever known before seemed trivial, even false, and for an instant he questioned the validity of every Absolution he had ever been granted. Yet almost before this question could take form, and even while his fist was preparing its third assault against his inordinate heart, this new doubt was supplanted by a recognition that his action was conspicuous and that it must seem to others as affected, as much put on for outward show, as he himself, observing others, had come to feel that various mannerisms in prayer must be. Bringing his fist against his breast in circumspection he opened his eyes, raised his head a little, and without turning his head, glanced narrowly around him through his eyelashes.

Nobody seemed to have noticed anything out of the ordinary although he could not, of course, be sure of those who knelt behind him. He bowed his head again, twisting it a little to the right, lowered his right shoulder and drew it back a little, and observed from nearly closed eyes. He still could not see those who knelt directly behind him but so far as he could see, nobody seemed to have noticed him; then he caught Hobe Gillum's coppery eye, and blushed. He readjusted his head and shoulder and watched Claude Gray, who knelt a little ahead of him and to the right. Claude's head was flung far back and was so twisted in adoration that the point of his left jaw, bright gold in the candlelight, was the most conspicuous and almost the highest part of it. What was more, it was clear that he was praying, not to the Blessed Sacrament, but to the small, shrouded statue of the

Blessed Virgin above the lavabo table; and noticing now for the first time that a little cup of violets stood on the plaster ledge at her feet, Richard was sure who had searched them out among the wet dead leaves to honor that place. He looked at Claude again, particularly at the tilted curly back of the head and at the abandoned angle of the brightened jaw, and thought, He may really mean it, he may not even know it but I bet he does, I bet he knows it makes a picture and I bet he got it from some picture of some saint or other. But if he did really mean it, and no longer knew he was doing it, then it was not fair to blame him.

He was probably thinking about his mother. It seemed a long time ago he had lost his mother to keep on making so much fuss about it but maybe he took things harder than most people. Richard suddenly felt deeply ashamed of himself in case Claude really was grieving and praying for his dead mother, and he began to feel pity for her and for Claude as well, but then he remembered Claude's voice, which sounded more girlish than a girl's even though it had changed, reciting to him the Litany of the Blessed Virgin in impassioned sugary tones; O most clement O most holy O most sweet Virgin Mary; something of that sort and a lot more besides. He had felt uneasy about the whole thing and at the instant that Claude brought such juicy emphasis to the words *mosst sweeett,* with such meticulousness about both t's, and pronouncing *most* like *moused,* Richard had decided that he definitely disliked the whole prayer; and looking at Claude now, he disliked it even more thoroughly, and he decided that even if Claude was genuine now in his praying, he did not trust that kind of praying. He remembered his mother's gossiping about Claude once, his desire that the School should put lace borders on the cottas and his special attentions to the Blessed Virgin, and saying impatiently, "Well what I can't see is, why doesn't he just —go on over to Rome!"

But now remembering the scorn and impatience which had been in her voice, and still watching Claude, with the long hair of the back of his head like a shabby chrysanthemum, tilted about the weak neck, he felt that Claude was pitiful, and that it was careless and cruel to think of him contemptuously, and as shameful to be watching him in this way, so unaware that he was being watched, or that he might look in the least silly, so defenseless, as it would be to peer at him through a keyhole. How do *I* know, he thought; he's probably praying all right, and even if he isn't I've got no right to look at him like this and—

With this, something he could not quite remember, which seemed to be prodding at the edges of his thought, came abruptly clear. He remembered that he had started looking at Claude, and speculating with mistrust about the quality of his praying, because he himself had done something, without affectation, which might easily be misunderstood to be affected. He could not quite understand it but he was in some ignoble way trying to put off onto Claude something that was wrong with himself, or even worse, was assuming that Claude was doing wrongly what he knew he himself had not done wrongly; and worse even than that, he had so wandered and so lost himself in speculating about the weakness of another that he had degraded and lost his own moment of contrition, and had forgotten the very sin for which he was contrite, in committing still another sin of much the same kind. But now, although he could see the first sin, and the moment of contrition, and the second sin, quite clearly, they formed something more like a picture than a feeling, and there were too many things in the picture for him to look at any one of them really closely. He felt shame and a sort of astonishment. He wondered whether he would ever learn, from committing one sin, how not to commit another of the same sort even in the very moment of repenting it; and he felt that it was strange, and terrible, that repentance so deep and so real as he knew that his had been, could be so fleeting. He felt deeply sorry and was filled with self-dislike as he saw what he had done, but he knew that the feeling was of a much shallower kind than that in which, without foreseeing it, he had struck his breast so hard. He thought of Jesus suffering on the Cross, but the deep and truest contrition was not restored; he looked again at Claude's unpromising head, and felt a mysterious sadness, which he could not quite understand, for whatever was imperfect and incompetent: Claude; poor little Dillon Prince, with his square-bobbed tow hair and his pink lashless eyes, forever crying or just over crying or just about to cry; a hen, with a wry neck which could never be straightened, standing as if shyly to herself in one corner of the chicken run, with one wing hunched; his own imperfect and incontinent mind and spirit; and again of Jesus upon the Cross, suffering and dying that all such imperfections might be made whole, yes, even the poor darn hen; and tears came into his eyes, which he relished, but he knew they had nothing to do with the deep contrition he was trying to recapture. Ye who do truly and earnestly repent you of your sins, he whispered almost aloud, and are in love and charity with your neighbors, draw near with faith and take this Holy Sacrament to your comfort, and make your humble confession to Almighty God, devoutly kneeling.

His heart opened. Almighty and everlasting God, he prayed, Maker of all things, Judge of all men (and he saw as in a wheeling rondure the shining of all things, the shadows of all men), we acknowledge and bewail our manifold sins and wickednesses (and they manifolded themselves upon the air between earth and heaven like falling leaves and falling snow) which we from time to time (and over and over, morning and noon and waking in the night) most grievously have committed in thought (the wandering mind, the lascivious image even now flashed before him), word (the words of obscenity and of cursing) and deed (the shame and the violence of the hands) against Thy Divine Majesty (flung upward like so many arrows and so much filth against the dying Son upon His Cross and the invincible Father upon His Throne), provoking most justly Thy wrath and indignation against us (he bowed his head deeply, with eyes closed, and the entire sky hardened into one spear driving downwards upon his bowed neck, yet Christ upon His Cross merely looked into his eyes without either wrath or indignation). We are heartily sorry for these our misdoings. The remembrance of them is grievous unto us (O yes it is surely grievous), the burden of them is (God, forgive me, forgive me, make them intolerable, intolerable), the burden of them is intolerable (it is, Lord, Lord God I want it to be), is intolerable, Have mercy upon us most merciful Father have mercy upon us (and he pressed his clasped hands tightly against his forehead), for Thy Son Our Lord Jesus Christ's sake forgive us all that is past (is past), and grant that we may ever hereafter serve Thee and please Thee in newness of life, to the honor and glory of Thy Name, Amen.

That we may ever hereafter. Ever hereafter. Serve Thee and please Thee. Serve Thee and please Thee in newness of life. Forgive us all that is past. All. Past. Ever hereafter, in newness of life. Serve Thee, and please Thee. To the honor and glory of Thy Name.

He was as peaceful and light, almost as if he had just received Absolution. Keeping his eyes thinly closed, tilting his head quietly back, he could see the tender light of the candles against his eyelids, and he became aware once again of the strong fragrance of all the flowers. Dying, he whispered to himself. Soon now. For me and for all sinners. O sacred Head. He heard on his rose-mild blindness the infinitesimal flickering of the clock like those tiniest of thorns which cannot be taken out of the skin by thousands, by crown of piercing thorn. Opening his eyes just enough to see, looking through their rainbow flickering of little sharpness, sharp flames on the dark, thorn flames in thousands, each a thorn, a little sword, a tongue of fire, standing from pentecostal waxen foreheads; go ye unto all the world, a briar-patch of blessed fires, burning, just audibly crackling; no; the clock. Now pale flowers, round, in thousands, stared flatly among the thousands of sharp flames, as white and lonely on the humming gloom as organstops, gazed at too fixedly during a stupefying sermon, round and bright as wafers, consecrated Hosts, in the tiny burning and prickling of Time. He did not quite conceive of Time except as a power of measure upon the darkness, yet opened his eyes now and saw that it was almost twenty-five, twenty-three and a half, past four. The clock stood on the lowest step of the Altar. Its leather case was inlaid with silver wire almost as fine as hair, which outlined intricate flowers and leaves. It was his mother's and it had been borrowed for use in the Lady Chapel, as it always was for this Thursday watch, because it was the most nearly silent clock on the place. Now that he looked at it he heard it the more clearly, a sound more avid and delicate than that of a kitten at its saucer, and now that he heard nothing else he saw nothing else except the face of the clock, hard, handless, staring white out of a shadow of trembling gold, like the great Host in a monstrance; and when once again he saw the hands, and the numbers, they showed that only two minutes of his watch remained. Could ye not watch with me one hour? Now he remembered the images and emotions into which he had awakened, so acutely, that they were almost his again; but now in some way they had hardened, they stayed at some distance from him, and he began to realize that during this entire half-hour his mind had been wandering: there had been scarcely one moment of prayer or of realization. Hell of a saint I'd make, he said to himself; and added with cold and level weary self-disgust to the tally of the sins he must soon confess, I swore in Lady Chapel in the presence of the Blessed Sacrament. God be merciful unto me a sinner, he whispered in his mind, crossing himself.

Now for the first time he realized that his knees were very sore. The small of his back ached. When he moved, bending his back, shifting his knees, everything whirled hazily for a moment, then, with a kind of sliding or shunting like the falling into plumb of a weighted curtain, came clear and stayed still. I guess that was nearly fainting, he thought, with satisfaction. He searched the deep grooves in his knees along the edge of the board and reestablished them exactly as they had been and bore down on them to make them hurt the more, and he found that it hurt still more to keep his back completely straight and still, than to move it at all. The pain made him feel strong and reverent, and smiling he whispered silently to Jesus, "It's nothing to what You're doing." Our Father who art in Heaven, he began; he knew now that he would stay another watch through.

Now it was half past four, but nobody moved. Nobody wants to be the first, he thought. No they're all praying, he told himself. I'm the only one noticed what time it is. Behind him he heard a sound of stealthy entering and of knees coming quietly to the floor. Now somebody will give up their place, he thought. It ought to be me.

Claude tilted his head to the other side and now Richard noticed the translucent lavender beads in his hands. He heard somebody stir and stand wearily up and he knew by the rustling starch that it was the Deaconess. She was in when I came. Been an hour. Maybe more. Quit keeping tabs, he told himself sharply. None of your business. There was the sound of her going away and the sound of another entering. Pray, he told himself. I ought to give my place. It was nearly thirty-three minutes after. We beseech Thee O Lord pour Thy Grace into our hearts, that—

The sacristy door opened and there was Lee Allen. He looked more grave and tired than before and he avoided Richard's eyes with an aloofness which abashed him. That as we have known the Incarnation of Thy Son Jesus Christ through the message of an Angel: Lee came silently to the middle and genuflected; then from where he stood, shifting the extinguishing cone in exact rhythm, he put out seven shrunken candles to the left and seven to the right. He genuflected again, and leaned the tall snuffer into the corner, and returned, and genuflected; then strode to the Altar in a quiet and mastering way, reached delicately among the interlocked flowers, and uprooted with each hand a smoking seven-branched candlestick. He genuflected once again and tiptoed out, shutting the door to softly with one shoe. Smoke crinkled from each dark candle as he went. There seemed to be scarcely fewer candles than before, there were so many. There would be others to change, five on each side, the rest were still tall enough. Through the message of an Angel, so by His Cross and Passion:

He heard behind him the prudent raising of a window, and for the first time realized how suffocatingly hot it was, and that he was sweating. The sacristy door opened and there was George Fitzgerald. His eyes were softer and brighter with more tiredness than before and his face was white and bright red in patches. He met Richard's eyes quietly and impersonally. He came to the middle and genuflected, and Richard could see that he was looking at all the flowers before he moved. Some still had strength and some were dying, and now he took two vases of those which were dying, unmeshing them with great care from among the others, and genuflected, and tiptoed out, shutting the door to softly with his shoe. Petals flaked away as he went. The living air touched the back of Richard's neck; now it even cooled his forehead; and now, rank on rank, the flames of the candles acknowledged the invading night; more petals fell. Upon the fragrance of fire and wax and fresh and dying flowers there stole the purity of water from a spring. Snaffling it desperately in an inept hand, somebody sneezed. Claude tilted his head back the first way and started his beads all over again. Richard heard the sound of bare feet withdrawing and knew that it must be Hobe and Jimmy. I haven't even said my prayers, he realized. I'm going to stay, he told himself. Give up your place, he told himself. You got no business hogging it. As much business as: you got no business thinking that either: as Claude with his head on one side and those beads. Give up your place. Come back. Kneel on the floor. The same person sneezed, more violently but better stifled. Claude, straightening his head, laid his beads down carefully, got up, stepped to the middle, genuflected, turned, looking like St. Sebastian, and went to the rear of the Chapel. Richard heard his careful sliding-shut of the window; the flames stood straight; Claude returned, and again began his beads at the beginning. Soul of Christ sanctify me, Richard began aimlessly; the sacristy door opened and there was Lee Allen.

Richard shut his eyes. O God forgive me that I can't do it right, he prayed. O God help me do it better now. Make me to love Thee and to know Thy suffering this day. For Jesus' sake Amen. He crossed himself meticulously and got to his feet; he was dizzy and for a moment his knees hurt very badly. He stepped out of the desk genuflected and turned, and all of a sudden he knew he would have to go out at least for a minute or two, he was much too tired to stay. When he turned to genuflect again at the door, Lee was lighting the second of the tall new candles.

The darkness was cool and stale. From where he stood beside the door of the Lady Chapel, looking back across the nave, he saw the spaced badges of blacker darkness where the Stations of the Cross hung veiled. Tall at his right shoulder, a Madonna stood, a blind black monolith. He walked silently toward the middle of the transept, and now he could see the white stops and keys of the organ. He stood at the center, facing the stripped Altar; sure that it ought not to be done, but in an obstinate and loyal reverence, he put down one knee and then both knees before the desolate shrine: until His coming again.

He bent his head deep toward the floor and heard his voice whisper slowly and fearfully within him the words which, he suspected, only a priest may utter without blasphemy: For in the night in which He was betrayed:

His skin crawled.

This is the night in which He is betrayed.

He felt the floor, bitter against his knees, and whispered aloud, "This is the night in which He is betrayed"; and with the whispering it no longer was, and he whispered within himself, He took bread, and brake it, and gave it unto His disciples, saying, Take, eat, this is my Body which is given for you; do this in remembrance of me.

He saw, and was himself, grown and vested, genuflecting, raising the consecrated Host, again genuflecting, while a bowed kneeling boy, who was also himself, shook the three bells.

Likewise after supper He took the cup, and when He had given thanks he blessed it, and gave it unto his disciples, saying, Drink ye all of this, for this is my blood of the New Testament, which is shed for you and for many for the remission of sins. Do this as oft as ye shall drink it, in remembrance of me.

And with the words For this is my Blood of the New Testament, he knelt so deep in burden of blood that no priestly image entered him, and whispered again, Which is shed for you, and for many, for the remission of sins. And slowly one by one, while his hands lifted, the words stood up within his silence.

O Thou Lord God my Saviour: ("my Saviour," he whispered): Look down on this Thy child.

Lord bless (he tried); O Lord lift up (he tried); O Lord forgive Thy child.

He could just see the empty Altar. There were no more words.

Do this as oft as ye shall drink it, in remembrance of me.

No more.

"Look down on this Thy child," he whispered aloud.

Now his knees hurt very badly.

"For Jesus' sake Amen," he whispered, crossing his breastbone with his thumb. He stood up.

If he went into the vestry they would say, What you doing up? They would tell him to get on back to bed. Not mean about it because of the night it was but they would tell him all the same. Because it was the rule. Or maybe they wouldn't but if they did and he didn't go on back to bed it would be even worse than if they hadn't see him. "I told him Father," he heard Lee Allen say in his serious hollow voice. "That's right Father," George Fitzgerald said, nodding soberly. And that was always worse when somebody had told you; Prefects. "What did you stay out for then?" "I dunno Father." "Course you know. Why did you stay out? Why did all of you stay out, Toole? You heard me tell you all to come straight back to bed." Where were they? He was suddenly scared. If they had gone back it would be even worse for him if he didn't go back too. "Where's Richard?" "I dunno Father." "Course you know, you all went together. Where is he?" "Honest Father I dunno. Last I seen him he was still in Lady Chapel." That ought to make it all right. Still in Lady Chapel. He was late but it was because he was praying. Can't whip anybody for that. "You know what the rule is." No. He'd say that to him, not them, him, at Council Meetings; they'd come back in time. "You know what I told you: come right on back to bed." "But I was staying a second watch Father. Ask Lee. Ask George if I wasn't." "I don't care what you were doing. I told you to come straight back to bed and you didn't do any such thing. Now what have you got to say for yourself?" Or no, maybe he would look embarrassed and just mutter something about You see to it you do what you're told, and not punish him. Or no he would maybe look mad when he heard that about the second watch and say, "And you dare to use *that* for an excuse?" And yet the year before he had stayed a second watch and there had not been any trouble. But that year nobody had told him to come right on back to bed. That was the year three of the boys had never even showed up for the watch they signed for but went over to Lost Cove and got some whiskey.

If they'd gone on back he was in trouble already.

Breathing light, and the breathing shaken by his heart, with the greatest possible stealth he approached the vestry door and,

stiffening beside the frame like an Indian scout, spied slope-
wise between the door and the jamb. George was carefully arranging wild azaleas in a Karo bucket. Lee was not there. Hobe
squatted against the wall; Richard could see only his cheek,
brown-orange in the light of the fiery mount of wax, which had
grown much larger. Willard hung out all over the folding-chair;
the quietly snoring head lay back and the blue chin was the highest part of it. Jimmy sat on the floor between his thighs; he looked
very sleepy. Lee Allen came quickly out of the back passage at
the far end and he seemed to look straight at Richard and Richard flinched away and froze, but it was clear by Lee's voice that
he had not actually seen him. "Ought to wake up Burgy and send
these kids to bed," he said. "They aren't doing any harm," George
said. "I don't keer," Lee said, "but I don't want to get in no
trouble either, you know what they told us." George said nothing
for a little while and then he said, "Me neither," and after a while
he said, "I don't want you to get in trouble, count of me, Lee.
You send them out if you want to. Don't let me hinder you."
After thinking, Lee said, "Nobody hindern me." After a little
he said, "Where's Sockertees?" which was one of Richard's nick-
names, and Richard felt his breathing go thin. And Hobe said,
exactly as Richard had fore-heard him, "Last I seen him he was
still in Lady Chapel." "Well he ain't there now," Lee said. "Probly
went on back to bed," George said. "No," he reflected, "we'd
a heard him go out." "Crazy kid," Lee said. Richard tried to be
sure whether this was said in affection or dislike, but so far as
he could see it was neither, just an indifferent statement of fact.
Dislike would almost have been better; and now he knew that
he could not go in, right after Lee's saying that, and that
although he felt very lonely, and suddenly wanted very much to
be in there with them where no fuss was being made about
not going to bed, he wanted still more not to be anywhere near
them or anywhere near anybody. Crazy kid: crazy kid; yet he
could not go away, for they might say more about him. He
could hear George saying "Oh, he's a good kid" or even just
"Oh, he's all right," and it made everything much better, he
could almost have gone in; but George didn't say anything of
the kind, or anything at all, he just seemed to accept it as a fact
everybody knew; and after a little Lee said, "I got to thin out
them candles some if they're goana last through"; and George did
not answer, and Lee said, "I thought there was a whole box

more of them," and George said, "Not that I know of": and Lee did not answer, and George said, "If you thin out the candles some maybe it'll give the flowers a chance, anyhow. I sure do hate to see dead flowers"; and suddenly, frightened because he was spying, Richard shrank as small against the wall as he could, for someone had come out of the Lady Chapel and now he could make out that it was Claude and realized thankfully, He sleeps in St. Joseph's, he'll go out the front. And sure enough Claude came to the middle as if to bow or genuflect and stood there a moment and then tossed his head upward to one side in a peculiar, saucy way, and turned his back on the Altar and walked back up the middle aisle and through the vestibule door; and after a moment Richard could hear the outside door; and then nothing; and after his breathing was quiet again, he crossed the transept without pausing to bow, and went back into the Lady Chapel.

The prayer-desks were all taken: he knelt at the rear on the bare floor and crossed himself, and closed his eyes, and bowed his head. Lord make my mind not to wander, he prayed, successfully driving from his mind Claude's impudent head. This is the last chance, he told himself. By leaning a little he could just see the clock. Already it was nearly quarter of. He felt fury against himself and subdued it, for it was evil. God be merciful unto me a sinner, he prayed, shutting his eyes again.

He waited carefully with his eyes closed but nothing came to him except his emptiness of soul and the pain of his knees and of his back. Hail Mary, he whispered to himself, and went through the prayer twice. He repeated five more Hail Marys rather rapidly and then three very slowly, trying to allow each word its full weight, and still there was nothing, not even through the words Pray for us sinners now and in the hour of our death. What's wrong with me, he wondered. He kept his eyes shut. Perhaps exactly because he had given his knees a rest, they now hurt worse than ever. Or it was because they were now on the flat floor, instead of braced against the edge of a board. The grooves where they had been against the board hurt badly, the bones just below the kneecaps hurt even worse. And within another minute or so, the small of his back ached worse than it had before. He bent over a little, and though that hurt his back in a new way, it also gave it a sort of rest. He let himself slacken down so that his buttocks sat on his heels, and that at least changed the pressure on the bones of his knees. He leaned forward so that his chest almost rested against his knees, and that helped his back. It'll just look like at Adoration, he reflected; and was ashamed of his hypocrisy. All the same, he thought, if it'll help me pray. Hail Mary, he prayed again. But still there was nothing. His heart was empty and his mind was idle, and he could not forget his discomfort.

He opened his eyes and looked around for a kneeling-pad and he saw one, skated against the baseboard, ahead of him and across the Chapel. He would have to get up and go in front of Julian to get it, and Julian was not using one. He hasn't been kneeling as long as I have, he reflected. What of it. He'll think I came in late. Just now. What of it. But the more he thought about it the more clearly he decided he would not go over and get the pad. If I can't say my prayers right, he told himself, why anyhow I can do this. He felt proudly and calmly vindictive against himself. Closely attentive to everything he was doing, he raised himself straight onto his knees and he straightened his spine so that his knees and the small of his back should hurt as much as possible, and he put the heels of his hands together, the fingers extended, edge to edge, tips touching, and the right thumb crossed over the left, as he had been taught when he was learning to be an acolyte. Ordinarily this strange and careful position of the hands embarrassed him, for it seemed sissy. Only a few of the servers kept to it; most of them, like Richard, simply folded their hands, and so did most of the priests; but now it seemed no more sissy than being on your knees in the first place. It was just the right way to hold your hands to pray, that was all. For all the aching in his knees and his back he was now even more clearly aware of his hands in this unaccustomed position, the palps of the fingers touching so lightly and competently, the locked thumbs, the cleanly hollow of shaded light within the palms; his hands felt full of goodness and quiet and they made him think of pictures of Cathedrals.

He tried to breathe so quietly that he could not feel his chest go in and out or even any air moving in his nostrils, and he gazed studiously at the monstrance, visualizing through the veil the spangling sunlike gold and the white center, and upon that center Christ Crucified, Whom he saw first in metal and then in wood and then in flesh; but he began to wonder whether these efforts at visualization were not mere tricks and temptations of emptiness, for still he was empty of prayer and of feeling. Now that he forbade himself images and dwelt within the discipline of his body his knees and his back began to hurt worse than ever and he began to think with quiet and increasing amazement of young men, boys really, hardly older than he was, not much older than George anyway, who knelt like this on Chapel stone the whole night through in prayer and vigil, their weapons and armor blessed and waiting, soberly shining in the lambent gloom, before the Mass and the Communion and before the greatest moment of their lives when their King touched the flat of the sword to the shoulder and the young man stood up and was assisted in putting upon himself the whole armor of God and rode forth into the glittering meadows of daybreak for the first time a knight, a knight errant, seeking whatever wrong God might send him to set right, whatever tests of bravery and chastity the huge world might hold in ambush for him. O but I can do better than this, he exclaimed to himself in self-contempt; and he thought with envy and reverence of the early time which had belonged to those shining young men, and he pressed down with all his strength and weight, first on one knee and then on the other, so that it was hard not to cry out, and he held his back still more rigidly upright, and he was pleased to find that now, by the way he held his hands out, even his arms ached, deep into the shoulders.

But it's so little to do! he thought, imagining the first, living Crucifix; and he did his best to imagine one hand, against splintery wood, and the point of a spike against the center of the open hand, and a great hammer, and the spike being driven through, breaking a bone, tight into the wood so that the head was all buried in the flesh and the splintered bone, and then to be able to say, *Father forgive them for they know not what they do*. And that's just one hand, he reminded himself. How about both hands. And both feet. Specially both feet crossed on each other and one spike through both insteps. How about when they raise up the Cross with you on it and drop it deep into the hole they dug for it! And imagining that moment he felt a tearing spasm of anguish in the center of each palm and with an instant dazzling of amazed delight, remembering pictures of great saints, shouted within himself, *I've got the Wounds!* and even as he caught himself opening his palms and his eyes to peer and see if this were so he realized that once again this night, and even more blasphemously and absurdly than before, he had sinned in the proud imagination of his heart. *O my God*, his heart moaned, *O my God! My God how can You forgive me!* I'll have to confess it, he realized. I can't. Not this. How can I confess *this!*

The thing he had most dreaded to confess before, an impure act which in its elaborateness had seemed merely the more exciting in the doing and which was so nearly unbearable to specify to another, and a priest at that, that he had gravely considered the risk to his soul of merely generalizing it: beside this new enormity —and twice over in one night, and both times in the Presence— beside this, that ugly and humiliating lustfulness seemed almost easy to tell of. But I'll tell it all the same, he told himself grimly. Because if I don't I'm in mortal sin. No I'll tell it because I did it and I hate to so much, and I don't care who it is I have to tell it to either, I won't dodge whoever it turns out to be and wait for another, not even if it's Father McPhetridge. I'll tell the whole thing just the way it happened—way I thought it happened, that is. I'll tell it all right. Because I've got to.

He looked proudly at the monstrance and felt strength and well-being stand up straight inside him, and self-esteem as well; for it began to occur to him that not many people would even know this for the terrible sin it was, or would feel a contrition so deep, or would have the courage truly and fully, in all of its awful shame-fulness, to confess it: and again the strength and the self-esteem fell from him and he was aghast in the knowledge that still again in this pride and complacency he had sinned and must still again confess; and again that in recognizing this newest sin as swiftly as it arose, and in repenting it and determining to confess it as well, he had in a sense balanced the offense and restored his well-being and his self-esteem; and again in that there was evil, and again in the repenting of it there was good and evil as well, until it began to seem as if he were tempted into eternal wrong by rightness itself or even the mere desire for rightness and as if he were trapped between them, good and evil, as if they were mir-rors laid face to face as he had often wished he could see mirrors, truly reflecting and extending each other forever upon the dark-ness their meeting, their facing, created, and he in the dark middle between them, and there was no true good and no true safety in any effort he might ever make to realize or repent a wrong but only a new temptation which his very soul itself seemed powerless to resist; for was not this sense of peace, of strength, of well-being, itself a sin? yet how else could a forgiven or forgiveable soul possibly feel, or a soul in true contrition or self-punishment? I'm a fool to even try, he groaned to himself, and he felt contempt for every moment of well-being he could recall, which had come of the goodness of a thought or word or deed. *Everything* goes wrong, he realized. Everything anyone can ever do for himself goes wrong. Only His Mercy. That's what He died for. That's what He's dying for today. Only His Mercy can be any help. Nothing anyone can do but pray. O God, he prayed, be *merciful* unto *me*, a *sinner*. Let me not feel good when I am good. *If I am good.* Let me just try to be good, don't let me *feel* good. Don't let me even *know* if I'm good. Just let me try. And in this humility, aware that it was of a true and pure kind which was new to him, he felt a flash of relief, well-being, pride: and tightening his shut eyes, cried out in despair within himself, *There it is again! O God make it go away. Make it not mean anything. O God what I can't help, please forgive it.* He wanted to put himself down on his face on the floor. "*All my trust I put in Thee,*" he whispered aloud and, aware that he had whispered aloud, opened his eyes in the fear that he had been noticed. Nobody seemed to have noticed. Now Jimmy and Hobe were kneeling a little ahead of him. He found that he was drenched with sweat and as short of breath as if he had been running. He felt weak and quiet. The burden of them is intolerable. He could feel the words sincerely and quietly now yet at the same time they meant nothing to him. All my trust I put in Thee, he repeated silently. O let me not fail Thee.

Tonight.
This very night.
For in the night in which He was betrayed.
Now fragments of his first moment awake returned but now they were dry and tired like dead leaves, as dry and tired as he was. He tried to realize what it all meant. But all that he could realize was dry and tired like the tired dry fire of the candles.
He came into the world to be with us and save us, and this is what happened. This is what it all came to.
The light shineth in darkness and the darkness comprehended it not.
He came unto His own and His own received Him not.
So there He was just sitting there waiting. Just waiting to die.
Words stirred and stood up inside him which lifted his heart: But as many as received Him, to them gave He power to become the sons of God.

And the Word was made Flesh and dwelt among us:
He closed his eyes and bowed his head.
Flesh.
All for us.
All his suffering for all of us.

He remembered the terrible thing his uncle had said: "Well who *asked* him to die for me? *I* didn't. He needn't try and collect on the debt," he had said, "because there's no debt, far's I'm concerned." Nearly always when he thought of this Richard was shocked almost into awe of such blasphemy; and some few times when some priest or his mother was insisting what we all owe Jesus he had been tempted to wonder, wasn't it maybe really so, for it was a fact; Jesus had done it without anybody asking Him to: but now it seemed neither blasphemous nor persuasive but only empty and idle and cruel and as he thought of it he could see the man of whom it had been said, sitting very quietly on a stool or maybe a bench among the iron-breasted helmeted soldiers while they hit him and spat in his face and mocked him. Nobody could come near him or help him or even speak a word of love or thanks or comfort to him now. He could see him only as if he spied down on what was happening through a cellar window and it would be torture and death to dare to even try to get in, and no use could come of it, even if he did. The way, maybe, Peter had stayed. All of Peter's betraying and cowardliness was over and done with now. Nothing could ever wipe out for him what he had done. He wasn't even crying any more because he couldn't even cry any more. He was just hiding around on the outskirts, spying through the window. He was afraid to show himself and he couldn't stand to go away. He must wish he was dead.

Judas, by now, had he hanged himself? Richard couldn't remember for sure when. But if he hadn't yet, that was all there was left for him to do. That was all he was thinking about all the rest of this night, all that was left of his life. I want to die. O I want to be dead. I can't be dead soon enough to suit me. Judas didn't feel contrition, Father Weiler said, he felt remorse. Probably he couldn't cry like Peter. Just terrible cold remorse, as cold and bitter as the sound of the word. Remorse is very different from contrition; a deadly sin. A mortal sin is a sin that cuts us off from God. With remorse you don't feel sorry like contrition, you feel, well you just feel remorse, that's all.

These were just the dead hours. The hours between. They must be the worst hours of all for Jesus and for everyone who loved Him. No more doubt now. No more praying to God the Father, if this Cup can be taken from me: that's over long ago. It can't. That's all. No more judgment, standing trial, answering fool questions. He's already been sentenced to die. He belongs to the Law. Now just the time between. So tired. No sleep all this night. Waiting, getting Himself ready inside, while they mock and sneer and holler at him, and spit in his face, and crown him with thorns, and put the reed in his hand for a scepter, just waiting through the rest of the long night, just getting ready to die, while the night slowly turns into morning, and it's the last morning of all. To suffer so he will cry out, *My God, my God, why hast Thou forsaken me?* And then die. *It is finished.* And then die. And meekly bowing down His head, He gave up the ghost. And then (Richard could remember in advance) the stunned and strange peacefulness, throughout that afternoon and night and through all the next day, and the quiet, almost secret lighting of the tremendous candle in the beginning of the dusk of Holy Saturday, everything still going as if on tiptoe, and then in the first light of morning, the stillest and most wonderful moment of the year, the quietly spoken and simple Mass: "He is risen." And then the rich midmorning and the blinding blaze of Easter. *'Tis the Spring of Souls today, Christ hath burst His prison, and from three days' sleep in Death, like a Sun hath risen.*

But not yet. That is still not known though at the same time it *is* known. We are all in most solemn sorrow and grief and mourning. We know a secret far inside ourselves but we don't dare tell it, even to ourselves. We don't dare to quite believe it will ever really happen again until it really happens again. Until His coming again. For in the night in which He was betrayed. It has happened over nineteen hundred times now and yet it has never happened before. Not yet. And we don't know if it ever can. Never dreamed it could. Can.

Not yet. Now is just the dead time between and he is waiting. This is his last night and his last daybreak begins soon now. Before this day is over he will be dead.

My Jesus, he whispered, clasping his hands strongly; his throat contracted.

O Savior of the World Who by Thy Cross and Precious Blood hast redee——.

Oh you are dying my dear Lord for me, his soul whispered, wondering, weeping. For *me*, and I can't do anything for you. I can't even comfort you, or speak to you or thank you. O my Lord Jesus I can thank you. I can think about you. I can try to know what it is you are going through for me. For me and for all sinners. I can know that every sin I do big or no matter how little is a thorn or a nail or the blow of the hammer or even just a fly that teases and hurts you in your blood, crawling and tickling and sipping and eating at you in the hot day on the Cross with you unable to brush him away or even to move, and every good thing, or true thankfulness or thought of love must make it anyway a little less terrible to suffer. My Lord I love Thee. My Lord I grieve for Thee. My dear Lord I adore Thee. My poor Lord I wish I could suffer for Thee. My Lord I thank Thee. Lord have mercy upon me. Christ have mercy upon me. Lord have mercy upon me.

He opened his eyes in quiet wonder. It was indeed to him the very day. Not just a day in remembrance, but the day. There stood his consecrated Body, veiled among fire and flowers, but also living, in the flesh, on this very morning, at this very moment, He was waiting; and He was now within His last hours.

He won't see the sun go down today.

He looked at all the lights, spearing, aspiring, among the dying flowers. Knobbled and fluted with their own spillings, the candles stood like sheaves; some, bent by the heat, bowed over like winter saplings. Almost all the flowers hung their exhausted faces. They were so shrunken and disheveled now that he could see clearly among them the many shapes and sizes of the vessels which held them, the professional vases and ewers and jars, and the tumblers and tin cans from the poor cabins out the Mountain. He could just hear the clock. Tonight, he whispered, watching that devastation. That night. This minute. He leaned, and looked at the clock. It was one minute after five. Something troubled him which he had done or had left undone, some failure of the soul or default of the heart which he could not quite remember or was it perhaps foresee; he was empty and idle, in some way he had failed. Yet he was also filled to overflowing with a reverent and marveling peace and thankfulness. My cup runneth over, something whispered within him, yet what he saw in his mind's eye was a dry chalice, an empty Grail. No more I could do, he reflected, if I stayed all night. No more. No use: and he continued merely to look without thought at the emblazoned ruin. "Good-by," something whispered from incalculably deep within him. *O good-by, good-by*, his heart replied. A strange and happy sorrow filled him. *It is finished,* his soul whispered. He looked at the humbled backs ahead of him and prayed: The peace of God which passeth all understanding keep our hearts and minds in the knowledge and love of God, and of His Son Jesus Christ. And the blessing of God Almighty, the Father, the Son and the Holy Ghost, be amongst us and remain with us always.

He opened his eyes; and it was all as it was before. Of course it was. He was light and uneasy and at peace within. There was nothing to do or think or say.

He signed himself carefully with the Cross, got up, genuflected, and left the Chapel; just inside the north door, he took off his shoes. Hobe and Jimmy came up behind him and they took off their shoes too.

III

They walked down the sandstone steps into an air so different from the striving candles and the expiring flowers that they were stopped flatfooted on the gravel. Morning had not yet begun but the night was nearly over. The gravel took all the light there was in the perishing darkness and shed it upward, and in the darkness among the trees below the outbuildings a blossoming dogwood flawed like winter breath. In the untouchable silence such a wave of energy swept upward through their bare feet and their three bodies into the sky that they were shaken as if a ghost had touched them. Sharply and almost silently, Hobe laughed.

They looked at the last tired stars and at the dark windows of their dormitory and they wondered what their punishment would be.

"S——t fahr," Hobe said. "Can't even pray, what the f——k *kin* ye do!"

Maybe, Richard reflected, they wouldn't say anything. Couldn't be a better excuse than praying. In brainless exaltation he flexed the soles of his feet against the ground. What of it if they do, he thought.

Rustily, so far down back of them across the fields they could scarcely hear him, a rooster crowed.

"Let's get the rackets," Richard said.

They took it as naturally as if one of them had said it.

"They'd catch us sure," Jimmy said.

"Hell we keer," Hobe said. "Tan our asses anyhow, now."

Creakily, a little nearer, but very faint, a second rooster answered.

Might not, Richard thought; not *anyhow*. What if they do.

"Let's go to the Sand Cut," Hobe said.

"Freeze yer balls off," Jimmy said.

"Sun-up, time we git thur," Hobe said.

Proud, fierce behind the cook's house, the cry of a third rooster shining sprang, speared, vibrated as gaily and teasingly in the centers of their flesh as a jews-harp.

"Come on," Richard said, and started walking rapidly across the pale gravel.

He was surprised that he had spoken and the more surprised to hear them following. How they do it, he thought, stepping along not quite steadily in silent uneasy elation; all there is to it. He led them down past the cook's house.

Pride, he realized; a mortal sin. How do I confess that?

Through the veering wire net he saw, black in the faintness, how the big rooster darted his vigilant head and shuffled his plumage: in the silence before daylight a priest, vesting himself for Mass. Something heavy struck and the whole body splayed, and chuckled with terror; the coward's wives gabbled along their roost.

Richard felt as if he had been hit in the stomach.

I'm scared of both of them, he reflected, specially Hobe, and they know it whenever they want to.

And bigger than either of them, he forced himself to recognize.

Younger. Big for his age that's why I'm clumsy and soft.

Bigger all the same.

Maybe that makes up for the Pride, he thought, as they walked past the bruising foulness of the backhouse.

Privately, safe ahead of them, he struck his breast.

Nothing makes up for anything. Confess you thought it did.

He tried to imagine how to confess it. I have sinned the sin of Pride and some other sin I don't know the name of. I was proud because when I said let's go to the Sand Cut (and it wasn't even me that thought of it first) they came along just as if one of them had said it and all of a sudden I knew that all you have to do is say something and go ahead yourself without waiting and they'll do it. Then something happened that made me know I was scared of them and I admitted to myself I'm : yellow : and then I thought maybe because I made myself admit that, why then I wouldn't have to confess I was proud before. I thought it made up for it.

He tried to imagine the priests to whom he would confess this. Father McPhetridge, Father Whitman, Father Weiler, Father Ogle, Father Fish. Unless maybe if he got Father Fish but even if you tried to dodge and choose which was probably a sin why you couldn't ever tell for sure who you'd get. The others would just think he was crazy or something. Crazy kid. Or trying to get credit. And maybe he would be.

What you say in Confession they never tell because if they do they go straight to Hell. But whoever you confess to, he knows all the same. And if he knows you honestly are trying hard to be good he gives you credit afterwards too, that you sin if you try to get, he can't help himself. And if he thinks you're just trying to get credit why everytime he looks at you from then on you know what he thinks of you.

If he really thought you were, though, probably he wouldn't give you Absolution.

If you know it's a sin why you've got to confess it, no matter what he thinks.

The ferment of the hogpen, deepest of blacks and heaviest of oils, so stuffed and enriched their nostrils that as one they slowed against the fence and looked in. Small as the light was, on all its edges the chopped muck shone like coal. Jimmy slid his hand inside his overalls against his naked body; becoming aware of what he had done, he thoughtfully withdrew it. Straining to see into the darkness of the shed they could just discern the close-lying egglike forms of the hogs.

"Oink: oink," Hobe grunted, in a voice so deep that Richard was surprised.

Crooomphth, sleeping hog replied.

They crossed the stile and struck into the woods, using their unhardened feet somewhat delicately along the familiar path. It was as thrilling cold and as vague and silent here as leaving a hot morning and stepping into a springhouse, and the smell of dead leaves and decaying wood and of the arising year was as keen as the coldness. A dogwood dilated ahead of them, each separate blossom enlarging like an eye, and swung behind, and deeply retired among the black trees ahead they could see the shining of others in the first light, triumphal and sad, lonesome as nebulae; likewise blind clumps of unawakened laurel; and now as the light became adequate they saw that the floor of the woods was still the leathery color of last year's leaves, meagerly stitched with green. In the deeper distances the woods were neutral as a photograph, as they had been all winter, but nearer by, the trunks of the trees were no longer black. Some were blackish, some were brownish, some were gray and gray green and silver brown and silver green and now the forms and varieties of bark, rugged, mosaic, deeply ribbed and satin sleek, knobbled like lepers and fluted like columns of a temple, became entirely distinct. Some of the twigs looked still as dark and fragile as the middle of winter, many were knobbled and pimpled and swollen as if they were about to break open and bleed, and many were the color of bronze and some were the color of blood; on some there were little buds like the nubbins of young deer and on others new leaves as neatly fledged as the feathering ought to be for the arrows Richard had never been able to make perfectly. They could see a long way into the woods as the morning cleared and everywhere underfoot this leather laid its flat musing waves and everywhere among the retreating trees strayed sober clouds of evergreen and mild clouds of blossom and the dreaming laurels, and everywhere, as deep into the stunned woods as they could see, layer above unwavering layer, the young leaves led like open shale; while, against their walking, apostolically, the trees turned. The path among these winding, dancing trees, new to them since late fall, was supple underfoot, the droning trees against which they laid or slapped their hands felt as alive as the flanks of horses, the air was all one listening joy. While they approached the clearing each held in mind a festal imagination of the plum tree, but it hung black, all crazed elbows, in the widened light. From somewhere, however, the fallen slivers of the ruined house it seemed, they were pursued by the chiding, familiar song of an ambushed bird whose kind they did not know; and at the far side of the clearing Richard stopped short and the others passed him: for here, abject against sharp bark, he found a locust shell, transparent silver breathed with gold, the whole back split, the hard claws, its only remaining strength, so clenched into the bark that it was only with great care and gentleness that he was able to detach the shell without destroying it.

It was as if air had been tightened into subtance; only by touch and sight, not at all by weight, could he know he held it. He held it in his cupped hand and looked at the hunched, cloven back, turned it over with one fingertip and examined the brutally elaborate structure of the legs and the little talons. He tested: they could pierce a finger. He turned it again and held it near his eyes: the eyes looked into his. Yes even the eyes were there, blind silver globes which had so perfectly contained the living eyes: even the small rudimentary face in its convulsed and fierce expression, the face of a human embryo, he could remember the engraving in a book of his grandfather's, a paroxysm of armor, frowning, scowling, glaring, very serious, angry, remote, dead, a devil, older, stranger than devils, as early, ancient of days, primordial, as trilobites. Dinosaurs heaved and strove; a pterodactyl, cold-winged, skated on miasmic air, ferns sprang, to make coal in these very coves, more huge than the grandest chestnuts. Silurian, Mesozoic, Protozoic, Jurassic, all the planet one featureless and smoky marsh, Crowns, Thrones, Dominions, Principalities, Archaeozoic, through all ranks and kingdoms, to the central height, armed in the radiant cruelty of immortal patience, Ages and Angels marched clanging in his soul.

When did he come out? Just now? Just this spring? Or has he stayed all winter. And that would mean all fall and summer before.

I'd have seen him; last fall; last spring.

If he was there all the time and I didn't before, how come I saw him now?

All winter. All year. Or just since the first warm weather. Or just now before I found him.

That whole split back. Bet it doesn't hurt any worse than that to be crucified.

He crossed himself.

He sure did hold on hard.

He tried to imagine gripping hard enough that he broke his back wide open and pulled himself out of each leg and arm and finger and toe so cleanly and completely that the exact shape would be left intact.

With veneration, talon by talon, he re-established the shell in its grip against the rigid bark.

By the time he caught up with Hobe and Jimmy they were almost to the railroad track.

At the far end of the break in the woods along the far side of the track they saw the weathered oak tower and soon, walking more briskly along the ties, the relics of machinery and the dead cones of putty-colored sand and the wrinkled sandstone and, at length, the sullen water itself, untouched in all these cold months. There were black slits along the sides of the tower where planks had fallen during the winter. The water was motionless and almost black. The whole place, familiar as it was, was deadly still, and seemed not at all to welcome them. As they left the

track to round the near end of the Sand Cut there was a scuttling
among the reddened brambles but although they went as fast as
they could on their soft feet and threw rocks where the brambles
twitched with noise they got no glimpse of whatever it was, and
soon the scuttling stopped.

Now that they had stopped walking and stood in the brightened silence of the open light the day began to look practical;
they realized how chilly the air still was, even here out of the
woods, and how bitter the water looked, and they no longer felt
like going in. But none of them was willing to admit this frankly
even to himself, and it was only after they stripped that they
became openly hesitant. They took care not to shiver more visibly
than they could help or to appear to dawdle, either, but they did
all dawdle, and they found that they were looking at each other,
in this unhabitual place and hesitant quietness, with more interest than in the dormitory. Although Jimmy was the smallest of
the three in every other way, his was much the biggest and
during the winter he had grown much more hair than Richard
had realized up to now. Hobe still didn't have much but then he
was said to be part Indian so of course he wouldn't, yet, and
probably never would have a lot. What he did have was dark,
though, and showed up well against his dark skin, whereas
Richard's was so light and there was so little of it that he realized
it could probably not be seen at all, farther away than his own
eyes. He suspected, however, that his was really the biggest, because it looked as if Jimmy had at least half a hard-up. Jimmy
looked comfortable in his supremacy whether it was real or not
(he certainly had more hair, anyhow, there wasn't any getting
around that) and seemed to feel none of the embarrassment
which Richard always felt acutely if he was seen with even a
little bit of a hard-up. He turned partly away, though, in honor
of Good Friday, and for the same reason he and Richard glanced
at each other with even less candor than they would have at any
other time, and Richard the more uneasily crossed and crossed
his hands in front of himself. Only Hobe, of any boy Richard
knew, never concealed his own body or his interest in another,
and even now, Good Friday seemed to mean nothing to him.
He looked at them, and watched them look at him, with a cool-
ness which seemed almost amused. He urinated a few drops onto
his belly and rubbed it in with the palm of his hand, against
cramps. He made no gesture of covering himself and grabbed
his testicles with one hand only at the instant he grabbed his

nose with the other to leap with a spangling splash into the water.

He bounced up with an incredulous strangling yell and began a frenzied dogpaddle and both of them knew the water must be even colder than they had thought, and that there was no longer any chance of holding back. Jimmy went in feet first; Richard dove. The iron water distended enormously just beneath him and for an instant, knowing the brutal shock and the pain to which he had now inescapably committed himself, he felt the fatal exhilaration of a falling dream and had just time to dedicate himself *for Thee!*, in a silent shout as deafening bright as a smiting of cymbals, then plunged into the smashing cold. Still crying *for Thee* within his ringing head, he slanted his hands to dive as deep as he could go and, though his eyes were open, could see nothing of the steep sandstone along which his hands guided him, but only the stifled effulgence of light above. It was so much colder than he had been able to imagine that in the first moment he had felt almost unconscious, but the diver's reflex had locked his breath and now that he searched from ledge to ledge downward along the much colder bottom there sprang throughout his flesh such an ardent and serene energy that he was aware of the entire surface of his body as if it were fire, and every muscle seemed to feel its own exact shape and weight, and he wished that he need never come up and lay against the deepest trench of the bottom, his belly foundering in ooze, his eyes shut, staying his hands on rocks. He lifted his face free of the ooze and cautiously opened his eyes; he could feel, more clearly than be sure he saw, the light which enlarged above him. He turned his head and looked up sidelong; there it was, a pure, heavy slab of still light which by imperceptible degrees shaded downward into most deadly darkness. His chest and his head began to knock, it became harder with every pulse to hold onto the rocks. O Lord let me suffer with Thee this day, he prayed, his lungs about to burst; and took hold more firmly. You got no right, his own voice silently told him, you got no right. No right; but still he fought off his need for air, filling his cheeks with the exhausted air from his lungs and taking it down again in the smallest possible gulps. His head was beating and ringing so fiercely that he could scarcely hear the fragments of his own efforts to dedicate and to reprove himself but blindly, with the last of his strength, held himself down. Then he knew that he had stayed down too long; too deep; he could not possibly reach

the air in time. Good. That's fine. *For Thee!* he groaned. *No right!*
Get out! he shouted silently. But even before he could command
it or fully decide to command it his body was working for him;
his feet braced against a ledge, his knees bent, and he leapt upward through the brightening water with more strength than he
had realized he had left although the water seemed interminably
tall above him and he knew still that he would never reach the
surface in time and cried out to himself, *I didn't have the nerve!*
and, *Anyhow I tried,* meaning at once that he had tried to stay
down too long as an act of devotion and that he had tried to save
himself from the deadliest of sins, and now could see unreach-
ably above him, mocking and steep from attainment as stars, that
wincing celestial ceiling of bland silver which set apart water
and air and toward this straining, striving, aspiring, helpless upon
God's will and pleasure, his finger upward stretched like shrieks,
raised up and grew his rooted need in the millennial leisures of
a tree (*for Thee! O for Thee! Thee, Lord!*); and broke the surface in time, head back, gasping, feebly treading water, watching the streaming bruise-colored clamorous and silent whirling
of the world and taking in air so deeply that his lungs felt as if
they were tearing; and soon the world became stable and all of
the coloring and discoloration cleared and stood up strongly
through the top of the woods across the tracks and he could
realize that except for the remote voices of the two boys and the
still more remote voice of a bird the world itself was delicately
silent and all the noise was within his own head and was rapidly
dying: all that he saw still twitched with his pulse and out of the
woods, beating like a heart, the sun stood up.

His teeth still ached at their roots and although he clenched
them to keep them from chattering his chin trembled like a
rabbit's nose and his breath came out shakily in many small
pieces as of glass or ice. From its surface down to about his
waist, the water seemed surprisingly warm, but from waist to
knees it was grimly cold, and his stony feet trod a mortal bleakness of cold and dark to which he was thankfully sure now that
he would never go down again. Yet except for his feet, which no
longer seemed to belong to him, his body still blazed with pleasure in its existence, and it was no longer urgent and rigid but
almost sleepy. He slid his slick hands along his ribs and his sides
and found that in his sex he was as tightly shrunken as if he
were a baby. I could have died, he realized almost casually.
Here I am! his enchanted body sang. I could be dead right now,

he reflected in sleepy awe. *Here I am!* Now that he had his
breath and was quiet he no longer tried to control the rattling of
his teeth but hung standing in the water, his head so turned from
the others that they might not see the silent unexpected tears
and, drowsily trying to make himself aware of the suffering to
which at this moment Jesus was submitting Himself, crying for
tenderness and thankful wonder, gazed steadily into the beating
sun.

But staying still so long, coldness at length overcame him, and
after swimming as fast as he could twice up and down the length
of the quarry, he stumbled out.

He had all but forgotten them; they were already drying themselves with their shirts. Hobe's body was purplish; Jimmy looked
as if he had been caught in a blue net.

"What you trine to do?" Hobe asked. "Drownd yourself?"

"I was just swimming under water."

"I was damn near ready to dive in after you," Jimmy said,
"when you come up."

"We began to think you was drownded," Hobe said.

"No, I was all right," Richard said. He reached for his shirt.
"*Hey!*" he shouted.

Steering, serenely, his sutured brow, the sum of those several
thrusting curves which seemed not of themselves to exert strength
but merely to drink and send backward through them the energies
of the guiding head they guided, a snake more splendid than
Richard had ever seen before was just achieving a sandstone
ledge and the first heat of the risen sun. In every wheaten scale
and in all his barbaric patterning he was new and clear as gems,
so gallant and sporting against the dun, he dazzled, and seeing
him, Richard was acutely aware how sensitive, proud and tired
he must be in his whole body, for it was clear that he had just
struggled out of his old skin and was with his first return of
strength venturing his new one. His style and brightness, his
princely elegance, the coldness of his eye and the knifelike coldness and sweetness of his continuously altering line, his cold pride
in his new magnificence, were not at the first in the least dismayed, not even by Richard's shout; only the little tongue, to
Richard's almost worshiping delight and awe, sped like a thready
horn of smoke, the eye seemed to meet Richard's and become
colder and still more haughty, and the vitality of his elegance
advanced him still further along the stone: so that for a few
seconds Richard saw perfected before him, royally dangerous

and to be adored and to be feared, all that is alien in nature and in beauty: and stood becharmed. But as the others ran up, within an instant so swift that it was impossible to see just what transpired among those curves of liquid paroxysm, with a chilly rasping against stone which excited Richard as nothing he had ever heard before had excited him, drawing a stripe of coldness down his spine, the snake reversed direction and slipped rapidly between the ankles of briars and beneath fallen leaves, his brilliance a constant betrayal. The others were shouting and Jimmy shoved a stick under the snake and flipped him so expertly that for a couple of seconds he sailed on the air in a convulsion of escape, a fluid hieroglyph, and landed on open rock in a humiliating flash of ivory belly before he righted himself and with oily fleetness made once more for the bushes. But now Hobe reared up a rock so heavy he could lift it only clumsily, high above his reeling head; and Richard, standing just behind him, felt himself reach toward the rock to pull it backwards out of his hands. But even as his own hand lifted forward he became aware of Jimmy's astounded eye on him, and thus became aware of what he was doing and caught himself, realizing that they would never understand why he did it, that they would be angry with him and rightly so and might even be mad enough to jump on him; and becoming thus aware, became aware also that it was not only his habit of gentleness to animals which made him want to spare the snake, but something new in him which he could not understand, about which he was profoundly uneasy. These several kinds of awareness came over him with terrible speed and transfixed him into the slowness of a dream, so that the fraction of a second froze the high rock, the incredulous bystander, the bemused hand, and seemed to last almost interminably, while he strove to stay his hand and to set it free. But it was after all only an instant, and before he could bring himself out of his hesitation, Hobe brought the rock crashing down against rock and against one arc of the veering snake which, angled like a broken whip, continued uselessly to thrust energy through its ruptured body, its eyes terrible, its tongue so busy that its speed made the shadow of a blossom. Jimmy hurried up with his stick and beat at its head but the head was still alert to dodge under his blows. Richard felt for a moment as if he had just finished retching. Then he picked up a small rock and yelling *"Get out of the way,"* squatted beside the snake and pounded at its head. The head lashed about his fist like summer lightning as he pounded and in the darkness of his violence the question darted, over and over, *is he poison? is he poison?* but he cared only for one thing, to put as quick an end as he could to all his terrible, ruined, futile writhing and unkillable defiance, and at length he struck and dazed, and struck and missed, and struck and broke the head which nevertheless lifted senilely, the tongue flittering and the one remaining eye entering his own eye like a needle; and again, and the head lay smashd and shifting among its debris; and again, and it was flattened against the stone, though still the body, even out beyond the earlier wound, lashed, lay resting, trembled, lashed.

As he watched this trembling twitching, desperately wishing that he could so crush the snake that it would never move again, he realized that it would not die until sundown, and even as he realized this he heard Hobe say it and became aware, through something quiet in Hobe's voice and through Jimmy's shyness, that they respected him; that in putting his bare hand within range of that clever head and in killing so recklessly and with such brutality, he had lost their contempt and could belong among them if he wanted to. He looked coldly at his trembling hand: bloody at the knuckles and laced with slime, which seemed to itch and to burn as it dried, it still held the rock.

"Better warsh that stuff off," Hobe said. "Git in your blood: *boy!*"

He still squatted, looking at his hand and wondering. In their good opinion, and in the rugged feeling of the hand itself and its ferocious moisture, he began to feel that he had been brave in a way he had never been brave before and he wanted the hand to clear gradually and naturally, the way the smudge clears from the forehead on Ash Wednesday. He could not be sure, in its pristine skin, what kind of snake this was, and the head was wrecked beyond any hope of determining whether it had the coffin shape, or venomous fangs. But it was not a rattler, nor was it likely a copperhead, nor was it striped like a moccasin, so that he had to doubt whether, after all, it had been poisonous. If it had not been poisonous he had not been brave; and if it had not been poisonous he was sorry he had killed it or even been fool enough to yell so the others would see it and so automatically kill it, for he had for a long while been fascinated by snakes and had felt that the harmless ones ought to be let alone, as few people let them alone. He was aware that Hobe had spoken and that he had given no kind of answer, and this made him uneasy. He wanted very much to taste the slime; but they were watching. He turned up the rock and looked at it: the slime and breakage of the snake caught the whitening sunlight like mica. He slammed the rock into the middle of the water (just about where I dove in, he realized upon reflection) and clambered cautiously down to the edge and thrust his hand into the cold water and up to the elbow, beating quietly in the brilliant cold, and watched it in the water; the veins stood out on his forearm almost like a man. He decided that he would only submerge his hand, not wash it, no matter what Hobe advised. But Hobe said nothing.

They dressed thoughtfully and they had very little to say; now that they were on their way back there wasn't much to think about except the trouble which waited for them. There would have been trouble even if they had come straight back from Chapel, for they had outstayed the watch they had signed for by a long time. But they began to realize now that it would not have been as bad as it was bound to be now; maybe they'd even have been let off. If they had gotten back to bed at any time before daylight it wouldn't have been as bad as it would be now. If they had come in just while the sun was rising it would have been bad but not as bad as this. Now it was broad daylight and brighter every minute, and with every minute longer now that they stayed away they were in for worse trouble. They might be kept on bounds, they might have to pull stumps or clean out the pit of the backhouse, they might be whipped, they might even not be let go on the Easter Monday picnic and they had planned to go clear to Wet Cave which had never yet been fully explored, and find new passages and if possible, a new and secret entrance. There was no telling what, for the worst of it was that they had gone against a strict rule so conspicuously on Good Friday, and by taking advantage of a religious event, and there was no way of imagining how much more serious an offense this might seem to priests than to people. The train came down from Coal City and passed them while they dressed, making a great deal of gallant and vigorous noise, but it only sharpened their realization that by now everybody was up and around and that certain people would be looking for them and watching for them already, so that they hardly even had the heart to look up at the blank baggage car and the empty coach and to wave at the engineer who saluted them.

Richard didn't even look up as the train passed, nor had the thought of punishment very clearly entered his mind; all the

while he dressed, he watched the snake. From the break on back
it lay belly up and the pallor of the belly, and the different structure of the scales, so well designed for crawling, were quietly
sickening to see. He tried to see all that he could see without
looking at the annihilated head, but his eyes kept flicking back
to where it lay, mashed almost like soft metal against the rock,
almost as flat and ragged as the toadfrogs and pennies they used
to put on the tracks in Knoxville, after the streetcar ran over
them. The snake moved very weakly now, but strongly enough
that Richard could not doubt it would keep moving, and blindly
experiencing the agony of death, straight on through the morning
and the Three Hour Service and on through the afternoon until,
at last, as the top rim of the sun sank out of sight, the tip of the
tail would give one last quaver and the snake would lie still
forever.

"Well come on," he was startled to hear Hobe's voice at his
shoulder. He turned to go.

"Aint you takin him?"

It had not occurred to Richard; now that it did, he certainly
did not want him.

"No."

"Hell fahr, you kilt him didn you?"

"I don't want him."

Hobe and Jimmy glanced at each other. "Okay," Hobe said.
He took the snake carefully by the tail. The break in the body
held firm; the head pulled loose from the rock like adhesive tape.
He snapped him like a whip; now most of the head was lost.

"He'll bust in the middle," Jimmy said.

"Hell I keer," Hobe said. But he did not snap the snake again.
Half a snake wouldn't be worth showing.

On the far side of the track they fell into single file for the
woods path, Hobe ahead, swinging the limpid snake at the new
leaves, then Jimmy, then Richard. Without consulting or imitation, all three had put their shoes on when they dressed; they
walked rather quickly, and they did not talk.

In refusing the snake, Richard realized, he had lost a considerable portion of their esteem, though not all of it. He was still
regarded as the hero of this occasion and he knew he was still
one of them in a way he had never been before. He was still
pleased to have been accepted and still pleased with his own
courage, though he was sorry the snake had been killed, and
unhappy and uneasy whenever he caught a glimpse of it ahead.

He began to know how very hungry he was and with his hunger he remembered once again, with surprise and shame that he could have forgotten, what Day this was. It must be on past seven o'clock by now. He would not start carrying the Cross until nine. By now He would just be sitting on the stool or the bench in the garrison room, probably sort of like a locker room, while the soldiers paid Him no attention much but just hogged their breakfasts and maybe threw cornbread at Him, no it wouldn't be cornbread; He just sat there with nothing to eat or drink and some of the worst things were already over by now; He sat in the purple robe holding the reed and the blood was drying on His back from the scourges and the torn wounds were itching and the spit was drying on His face (like my hand is drying), not just spit but the nastiest kind of snot, too, if it happened here they'd spit tobacco juice, and down through the drying spit the blood ran from the Crown of Thorns; how did they push those thorns down around His forehead without hurting their hands? And here I am, he thought, suddenly remembering the absoluteness of emotions during the moments just after he woke up that morning. Here I am. He struck his breastbone and tried to imagine how it would feel to be scourged with a cat-o'-nine-tails with lead tips, and to wear a crown of thorns. Busy with twisted and uneven walking, he could not make it very clear to himself. He closed his eyes and almost immediately stumbled on a root. Jesus falls for the first time, he said to himself. God help me. God forgive me I didn't mean it. He kept his eyes open and took care how he walked.

The woods were full of ordinary sunlight now; the colors were no longer strange and the deep perspectives were no longer mysterious, but pleasant and casual. When they came to the clearing it was full of simple light and the bird was no longer singing. When they had come nearly to the other side of this warm open silence Richard hurried back to the tree on which he had left the locust shell, detached it gently, and with great care, scarcely looking at it, settled it into the breast-pocket of his shirt. They were not far into the woods when he caught up. His trotting and quick breathing, now that he slowed again to a walk, made him aware once more of his sharp hunger. It was going to be a long day without food, without, if he could help it, even rinsing his mouth out with water. I'll help it, he told himself, imagining water in his mouth. I'll not do that, anyhow. He thought again of the thorns, and the spittle, and the patience and courage, and of his maculate hand. The least I can do, he told himself. The *least* I can do! The day lifted ahead of him very long and hard, a huge unshaded hill. The climbing of it would go on in the heavy sun without rest throughout this livelong day and for ever so long as he might be alive and there at the top there was dying: His, his; so hard and so long. It won't be over till sundown, he said to himself. Such a terrible and cold heaviness distended in the pit of his stomach, and his knees became suddenly so weak, that for a few moments he had to lean against a tree, and found it difficult to breathe. He had never before known such heaviness or such cold, crushing sorrow. "*Forgive!*" he whispered, barely able to bring the word out: "*Forgive! O God forgive!*" But the cold and enormous heaviness only increased, and the sadness now seemed more than his soul could endure.

After a little, however, he regained sufficient strength in his knees, and walked again, by now a good way behind the others. But the heaviness stayed, so that he felt as if he were carrying an all but impossible weight in the middle of his body.

By now they could see the first of the buildings through the light-leaved woods; and now the whole of the School stood up before them and the two boys ahead walked more slowly, wondering what lie, if any, might lighten their trouble. But they could not think of any that would do and when Richard overtook them, lingering unhappily at the stile, they were so far beyond hope that they didn't even bother to ask him whether he had any ideas.

Now that he was with them again, the heaviness was somewhat less severe, and he began to wonder what had made him so deeply weak and unhappy, and what kind of trouble they would be in for; now he could clearly foresee Father Whitman's hard sleepless eyes in his first look at them as they would come up from the woods, their hair spiky with incriminating wetness; and much as he dreaded in advance the punishment, which would be a whipping for sure, he told himself, he dreaded even more the first meeting with these eyes, and the first words that would be spoken, though he suspected that these would be tempered to the day. He heard Jimmy say to Hobe that he better get rid of that snake, and he thought that he sure better; and he was neither surprised nor particularly troubled when, a few moments later, Hobe slung the snake in among the hogs. He stood with the other children at the fence and watched with interest while two of the hogs, with snarling squeals, scuffled over the snake, tore it apart at its middle wound and, while the two portions still tingled in the muck, gobbled them down. It occurred to him, with a lancing quailing of horror and pity, that the snake was still alive, and would stay alive in their bellies, however chewed, and mangled, and diffused by acids, until the end of the day; but now, remembering the head, he told himself that the snake was so far gone by now that he must be a way beyond really feeling anything, ever any more (the phrase jumped at him): (Who had said that? His mother. "Daddy was terribly hurt so God has taken him up to Heaven to be with Him and he won't come back to us ever any more.") "Ever any more," he heard his quiet voice repeat within him; and within the next moment he ceased to think of the snake with much pain. When the boys turned from the sty he followed them toward the Main Building carrying, step by step with less difficulty, the diminishing weight in his soul and body, his right hand hanging with a feeling of subtle enlargement at his thigh, his left hand sustaining, in exquisite protectiveness, the bodiless shell which rested against his heart.

EDITORS' ANALYSIS

"The Morning Watch," in length, is a short novel rather than a short story. It might also be described as a kind of expanded sketch of a series of characters during a given moment of time, because it lacks the organized plot we usually associate with a story. Unlike the preceding story, "King Solomon," "The Morning Watch" presents actual religious experience with frank directness: it gives us an infinitely careful elaboration of a particular young boy's intense emotional reaction to the celebration of Good Friday. Our pleasure in reading "The Morning Watch" lies partly in admiration for Agee's skill in rendering the play of his central character's mind with such exactness. It also lies, probably, in a reaction to the tenderness of Agee's telling. He manages to produce an absolute sympathy as we view the young boy's tense religious convictions in partial conflict with his very great need to be accepted in the rough, secular world inhabited by the other boys in the school.

QUESTIONS

1. Comment at length on the effects which Agee is able to obtain by the mere greater length of his story. Point out long passages of detailed description of place, of character's feelings, which would be out of place in a short story, but which are the very life-blood of "The Morning Watch." Discuss the effects on you, as reader, of the much richer use of detail in this short novel.

2. Discuss Richard's attempts to identify with Christ, as he imagines

the actual crucifixion. Do you think Agee gives Richard too great self-knowledge when he realizes that his picture of himself undergoing martyrdom is a result of his need for admiration from his friends, even at the cost of torture? Is this an illustration of the psychologists' claim that a child would rather be beaten than ignored?

3. Comment on Richard's fear for his own masculinity, in terms of his admiration for the school athlete Willard, and his dislike of the school aesthete Claude. Does his fear strike you as normal for a boy of his age?

4. The character Hobe's violent reaction, when a shoe is flung against the wall as he is dressing in the dark, is quite different from Richard's reaction to the same event. Remembering this earlier scene, compare Hobe's reactions to nudity while the boys are undressing for their swim, with those of Richard. Is Hobe less sensitive? Simply better able to deal frankly and easily with the world?

5. Comment fully on Richard's bashing in the snake's head, and his reasons for doing so, and his reactions afterwards. Is this risk he takes, with the snake, like his long stay under the water, his own testing of his manhood? A way of winning the admiration of his friends?

6. Why does Richard feel "ashamed of himself" for having learned French instead of German?

7. Comment on the effectiveness of the first sentence of Section II: "The night smelled like new milk."

8. Comment on the final sentence of the story, as it brings to a focus Richard's new sense of manhood. What purpose is served, symbolically, by each of the related details?